THE KEY
STUDENT STUDY GUIDE

Mathematics 30-1

THE KEY student study guide is designed to help students achieve success in school. The content in each study guide is 100% curriculum aligned and serves as an excellent source of material for review and practice. To create this book, teachers, curriculum specialists, and assessment experts have worked closely to develop the instructional pieces that explain each of the key concepts for the course. The practice questions and sample tests have detailed solutions that show problem-solving methods, highlight concepts that are likely to be tested, and point out potential sources of errors. **THE KEY** is a complete guide to be used by students throughout the school year for reviewing and understanding course content, and to prepare for assessments.

CALGARY PUBLIC LIBRARY

P9-DXK-972

© 2012–2017 by Castle Rock Research Corporation
All rights reserved. No part of this book covered by the copyright
hereon may be reproduced or used in any form or by any means
graphic, electronic, or mechanical, including photocopying, recording,
taping, or information storage and retrieval systems without the express
permission of the publisher.

Rao, Gautam, 1961 –

THE KEY – Mathematics 30-1 Alberta

ISBN: 978-1-77044-408-9

1. Mathematics – Juvenile Literature. I. Title

Published by

Castle Rock Research Corp.

2000 First & Jasper

100065 Jasper Avenue

Edmonton, AB T5J 3B1

10 9 8 7

Publisher
Gautam Rao

Contributors
John Campbell
Victoria Garlitos
Kathleen McLennan
Trina Oommen
Sonya Witzman

Dedicated to the memory of Dr. V. S. Rao

Not for Reproduction

THE KEY—Mathematics 30-1

THE KEY consists of the following sections:

KEY Tips for Being Successful at School gives examples of study and review strategies. It includes information about learning styles, study schedules, and note taking for test preparation.

Class Focus includes a unit on each area of the curriculum. Units are divided into sections, each focusing on one of the specific expectations, or main ideas, that students must learn about in that unit. Examples, definitions, and visuals help to explain each main idea. Practice questions on the main ideas are also included. At the end of each unit is a test on the important ideas covered. The practice questions and unit tests help students identify areas they know and those they need to study more. They can also be used as preparation for tests and quizzes. Most questions are of average difficulty, though some are easy and some are hard. Each unit is prefaced by a **Table of Correlations**, which correlates questions in the unit to the specific curriculum expectations. Answers and solutions are found at the end of each unit.

KEY Strategies for Success on Tests helps students get ready for tests. It shows students different types of questions they might see, word clues to look for when reading them, and hints for answering them.

Practice Tests includes two tests based on the entire course. They are very similar to the format and level of difficulty that students may encounter on final tests. In some regions, these tests may be reprinted versions of official tests, or reflect the same difficulty levels and formats as official versions. This gives students the chance to practice using real-world examples. Answers and complete solutions are provided at the end of the section.

For the complete curriculum document (including specific expectations along with examples and sample problems), visit https://education.alberta.ca/mathematics-10-12/programs-of-study/.

THE KEY Study Guides are available for many courses. Check www.castlerockresearch.com for a complete listing of books available for your area.

For information about any of our resources or services, please call Castle Rock Research at 780.448.9619 or visit our website at http://www.castlerockresearch.com.

At Castle Rock Research, we strive to produce an error-free resource. If you should find an error, please contact us so that future editions can be corrected.

Copyright Protected

NOTES

Not for Reproduction

TABLE OF CONTENTS

Copyright Protected

Key Tips for being Successful at School

Copyright Protected

KEY TIPS FOR BEING SUCCESSFUL AT SCHOOL

KEY FACTORS CONTRIBUTING TO SCHOOL SUCCESS

In addition to learning the content of your courses, there are some other things that you can do to help you do your best at school. You can try some of the following strategies:

- **Keep a positive attitude:** Always reflect on what you can already do and what you already know.

- **Be prepared to learn:** Have the necessary pencils, pens, notebooks, and other required materials for participating in class ready.

- **Complete all of your assignments:** Do your best to finish all of your assignments. Even if you know the material well, practice will reinforce your knowledge. If an assignment or question is difficult for you, work through it as far as you can so that your teacher can see exactly where you are having difficulty.

- **Set small goals for yourself when you are learning new material:** For example, when learning the parts of speech, do not try to learn everything in one night. Work on only one part or section each study session. When you have memorized one particular part of speech and understand it, move on to another one. Continue this process until you have memorized and learned all the parts of speech.

- **Review your classroom work regularly at home:** Review to make sure you understand the material you learned in class.

- **Ask your teacher for help:** Your teacher will help you if you do not understand something or if you are having a difficult time completing your assignments.

- **Get plenty of rest and exercise:** Concentrating in class is hard work. It is important to be well-rested and have time to relax and socialize with your friends. This helps you keep a positive attitude about your schoolwork.

- **Eat healthy meals:** A balanced diet keeps you healthy and gives you the energy you need for studying at school and at home.

Not for Reproduction

HOW TO FIND YOUR LEARNING STYLE

Every student learns differently. The manner in which you learn best is called your learning style. By knowing your learning style, you can increase your success at school. Most students use a combination of learning styles. Do you know what type of learner you are? Read the following descriptions. Which of these common learning styles do you use most often?

- **Linguistic Learner:** You may learn best by saying, hearing, and seeing words. You are probably really good at memorizing things such as dates, places, names, and facts. You may need to write down the steps in a process, a formula, or the actions that lead up to a significant event, and then say them out loud.

- **Spatial Learner:** You may learn best by looking at and working with pictures. You are probably really good at puzzles, imagining things, and reading maps and charts. You may need to use strategies like mind mapping and webbing to organize your information and study notes.

- **Kinesthetic Learner:** You may learn best by touching, moving, and figuring things out using manipulatives. You are probably really good at physical activities and learning through movement. You may need to draw your finger over a diagram to remember it, tap out the steps needed to solve a problem, or feel yourself writing or typing a formula.

Copyright Protected

SCHEDULING STUDY TIME

You should review your class notes regularly to ensure that you have a clear understanding of all the new material you learned. Reviewing your lessons on a regular basis helps you to learn and remember ideas and concepts. It also reduces the quantity of material that you need to study prior to a test. Establishing a study schedule will help you to make the best use of your time.

Regardless of the type of study schedule you use, you may want to consider the following suggestions to maximize your study time and effort:

• Organize your work so that you begin with the most challenging material first.

• Divide the subject's content into small, manageable chunks.

• Alternate regularly between your different subjects and types of study activities in order to maintain your interest and motivation.

• Make a daily list with headings like "Must Do," "Should Do," and "Could Do."

• Begin each study session by quickly reviewing what you studied the day before.

• Maintain your usual routine of eating, sleeping, and exercising to help you concentrate better for extended periods of time.

Not for Reproduction

CREATING STUDY NOTES

MIND-MAPPING OR WEBBING

Use the key words, ideas, or concepts from your reading or class notes to create a mind map or web (a diagram or visual representation of the given information). A mind map or web is sometimes referred to as a knowledge map. Use the following steps to create a mind map or web:

1. Write the key word, concept, theory, or formula in the centre of your page.

2. Write down related facts, ideas, events, and information, and link them to the central concept with lines.

3. Use coloured markers, underlining, or symbols to emphasize things such as relationships, timelines, and important information.

The following examples of a Frayer Model illustrate how this technique can be used to study vocabulary.

Definition	Notes
• Perimeter is the distance around the outside of a polygon.	• Perimeter is measured in linear units (e.g., metres, centimetres, and so on).

Perimeter

Examples	Non-Examples
• The length of a fence around a yard	• The area of grass covering a lawn
• The distance around a circle (circumference)	• The size of a rug lying on a floor

Definition	Notes
• A cube is a solid 3-D object with six faces.	• A cube is different from other shapes because it has six equally-sized square faces, eight vertices, and twelve equal edges.

Cube

Examples	Non-Examples

Copyright Protected

INDEX CARDS

To use index cards while studying, follow these steps:

1. Write a key word or question on one side of an index card.

2. On the reverse side, write the definition of the word, answer to the question, or any other important information that you want to remember.

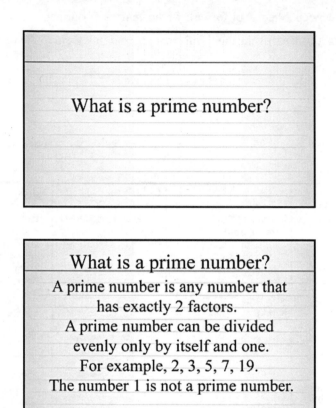

SYMBOLS AND STICKY NOTES—IDENTIFYING IMPORTANT INFORMATION

Use symbols to mark your class notes. The following are some examples:

• An exclamation mark (!) might be used to point out something that must be learned well because it is a very important idea.

• A question mark (?) may highlight something you are not certain about

• A diamond (◊) or asterisk (*) could highlight interesting information that you want to remember.

Sticky notes are useful in the following situations:

• Use sticky notes when you are not allowed to put marks in books.

• Use sticky notes to mark a page in a book that contains an important diagram, formula, explanation, or other information.

• Use sticky notes to mark important facts in research books.

Not for Reproduction

MEMORIZATION TECHNIQUES

- **Association** relates new learning to something you already know. For example, to remember the spelling difference between dessert and desert, recall that the word *sand* has only one *s*. So, because there is sand in a desert, the word *desert* has only one *s*.

- **Mnemonic** devices are sentences that you create to remember a list or group of items. For example, the first letter of each word in the phrase "Every Good Boy Deserves Fudge" helps you to remember the names of the lines on the treble-clef staff (E, G, B, D, and F) in music.

- **Acronyms** are words that are formed from the first letters or parts of the words in a group. For example, RADAR is actually an acronym for Radio Detecting and Ranging, and MASH is an acronym for Mobile Army Surgical Hospital. HOMES helps you to remember the names of the five Great Lakes (Huron, Ontario, Michigan, Erie, and Superior).

- **Visualizing** requires you to use your mind's eye to "see" a chart, list, map, diagram, or sentence as it is in your textbook or notes, on the chalkboard or computer screen, or in a display.

- **Initialisms** are abbreviations that are formed from the first letters or parts of the words in a group. Unlike acronyms, an initialism cannot be pronounced as a word itself. For example, GCF is an initialism for **G**reatest **C**ommon **F**actor.

KEY STRATEGIES FOR REVIEWING

Reviewing textbook material, class notes, and handouts should be an ongoing activity. Spending time reviewing becomes more critical when you are preparing for a test. You may find some of the following review strategies useful when studying during your scheduled study time:

- Before reading a selection, preview it by noting the headings, charts, graphs, and chapter questions.

- Before reviewing a unit, note the headings, charts, graphs, and chapter questions.

- Highlight key concepts, vocabulary, definitions, and formulas.

- Skim the paragraph, and note the key words, phrases, and information.

- Carefully read over each step in a procedure.

- Draw a picture or diagram to help make the concept clearer.

Copyright Protected

KEY STRATEGIES FOR SUCCESS: A CHECKLIST

Reviewing is a huge part of doing well at school and preparing for tests. Here is a checklist for you to keep track of how many suggested strategies for success you are using. Read each question, and put a check mark (✓) in the correct column. Look at the questions where you have checked the "No" column. Think about how you might try using some of these strategies to help you do your best at school.

KEY Strategies for Success	Yes	No
Do you attend school regularly?		
Do you know your personal learning style—how you learn best?		
Do you spend 15 to 30 minutes a day reviewing your notes?		
Do you study in a quiet place at home?		
Do you clearly mark the most important ideas in your study notes?		
Do you use sticky notes to mark texts and research books?		
Do you practise answering multiple-choice and written-response questions?		
Do you ask your teacher for help when you need it?		
Are you maintaining a healthy diet and sleep routine?		
Are you participating in regular physical activity?		

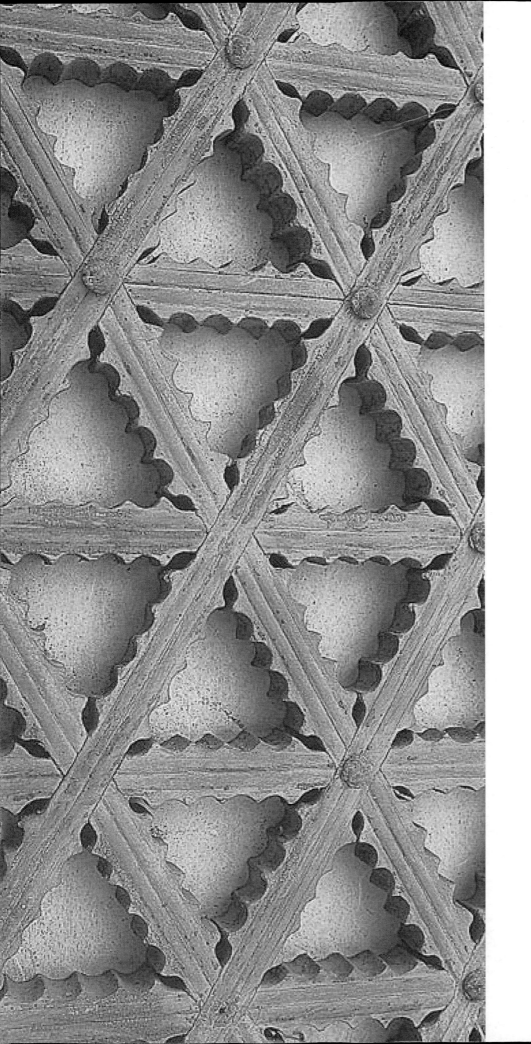

Trigonometry

Copyright Protected

TRIGONOMETRY

Table of Correlations				
Specific Expectation	**Practice Questions**	**Unit Test Questions**	**Practice Test 1**	**Practice Test 2**
It is expected that students will:				
Develop trigonometric reasoning.				
T.1 Demonstrate an understanding of angles in standard position, expressed in degrees and radians.	1, 2, 3, 4, 5, 6, 7, 45	1, 2, 3, 23	1	1
T.2 Develop and apply the equation of the unit circle.	8, 9, 10, 11, 12, 13, 14, 46	4, 5, 6, 7	2, 3	2, 3
T.3 Solve problems, using the six trigonometric ratios for angles expressed in radians and degrees.	15, 16, 17, 18, 19, 20, 21, 47	8, 9, 10, 11, 24	4, 5	4
T.4 Graph and analyze the trigonometric functions sine, cosine and tangent to solve problems.	22, 23, 24, 25, 26, 27, 28, 29, 30, 48	12, 13, 14, 15, 16, 17	6, 7	5, 6, 7
T.5 Solve, algebraically and graphically, first and second degree trigonometric equations with the domain expressed in degrees and radians.	31, 32, 33, 34, 35, 36, 37, 38, 49	18, 19, 20, 21, 25	8, 9, 10	8, 9, 10
T.6 Prove trigonometric identities, using: reciprocal identities; quotient identities; Pythagorean identities; sum or difference identities (restricted to sine, cosine and tangent); and double-angle identities (restricted to sine, cosine and tangent).	39, 40, 41, 42, 43, 44, 50	22, 26	11, 12	11

Not for Reproduction

TRIGONOMETRY

T.1 Demonstrate an understanding of angles in standard position, expressed in degrees and radians.

RADIAN MEASURE

Angles can be measured in degrees or radians. A radian is the angle, θ, at the centre of a circle that subtends an arc, a, equal in length to its radius, r.

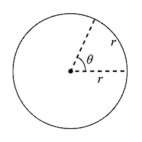

For an angle measuring 2 rad, the corresponding arc length is $2r$.

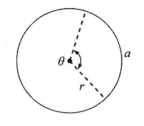

In general, the arc length, a, can be calculated using the equation $a = r\theta$, where θ is measured in radians, and r is the radius.

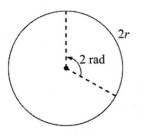

One complete revolution (360°) is equal to 2π rad.

Therefore, $1\,\text{rad} = \dfrac{180°}{\pi}$, and $1° = \dfrac{\pi}{180}\text{rad}$.

These relationships can be used to convert degrees to radians, and vice versa.

Example

Convert 1 rad to degrees.

Solution

To convert to degrees, multiply 1 rad by $\dfrac{180°}{\pi\,\text{rad}}$.

$1\,\text{rad} \times \dfrac{180°}{\pi\,\text{rad}}$

$= \dfrac{180°}{\pi}$

$\approx 57.3°$

Therefore, one radian is approximately 57.3°, which is slightly less than 60°.

COTERMINAL ANGLES

Angles in standard position that share the same terminal arm are called coterminal angles.

For example, all three angles in the following diagram (60°, −300°, and 420°) share the same terminal arm. Therefore, these angles are coterminal.

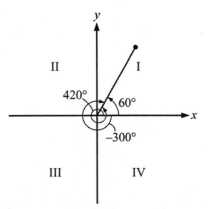

The general formula that gives all coterminal angles of any angle in standard position is $(\theta + 360n)°$, where θ is in degrees, and $n \in I$.

For an angle, θ, measured in radians, the general formula becomes $(\theta + 2\pi n)\,\text{rad}$.

Example

Determine an angle that is coterminal with an angle of $\dfrac{2\pi}{3}$ rad.

Solution

One coterminal angle begins at the initial arm (positive x-axis) and rotates clockwise in the negative direction. Since a complete revolution is 2π rad, the terminal arm will rotate

$$2\pi - \frac{2\pi}{3} = \frac{4\pi}{3}\,\text{rad}\ \text{in the negative direction.}$$

Thus, an angle of $-\dfrac{4\pi}{3}\,\text{rad}$ is coterminal with

$\dfrac{2\pi}{3}$ rad.

Additional coterminal angles are found by adding or subtracting multiples of 2π rad.

Therefore, all angles of the form $\left(\dfrac{2\pi}{3} + 2\pi n\right)\text{rad}$,

where $n \in I$, are coterminal with $\dfrac{2\pi}{3}$ rad.

Practice Questions: 1–7, 45

T.2   Develop and apply the equation of the unit circle.

T.3   Solve problems, using the six trigonometric ratios for angles expressed in radians and degrees.

TRIGONOMETRIC RATIOS OF ANGLES IN STANDARD POSITION

For any angle, θ, in standard position with a point $P(x, y)$ on the terminal arm, a triangle can be formed with the side lengths x (adjacent), y (opposite), and r (hypotenuse).

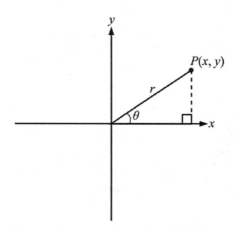

The primary trigonometric ratios and their reciprocals are defined in terms of x, y, and r as follows:

$$\sin\theta = \frac{y}{r} \qquad \csc\theta = \frac{r}{y}$$

$$\cos\theta = \frac{x}{r} \qquad \sec\theta = \frac{r}{x}$$

$$\tan\theta = \frac{y}{x} \qquad \cot = \frac{x}{y}$$

Copyright Protected

Not for Reproduction

When the hypotenuse, r, is equal to 1 unit, the unit circle is formed.

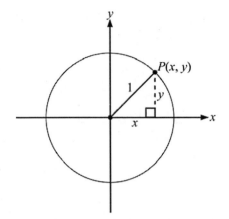

The equation of the unit circle is $x^2 + y^2 = 1$ and is derived by applying the Pythagorean theorem to the right triangle.

In the unit circle, the primary trigonometric ratios and their reciprocals are defined as follows:

$$\sin\theta = \frac{y}{1} = y \qquad \csc\theta = \frac{1}{\sin\theta} = \frac{1}{y}$$

$$\cos\theta = \frac{x}{1} = x \qquad \sec\theta = \frac{1}{\cos\theta} = \frac{1}{x}$$

$$\tan\theta = \frac{y}{x} \qquad \cot\theta = \frac{1}{\tan\theta} = \frac{x}{y}$$

Angles in standard position with a terminal arm of 1 unit are represented on the unit circle.

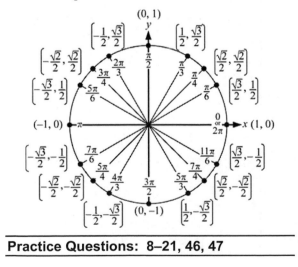

Practice Questions: 8–21, 46, 47

T.4 Graph and analyze the trigonometric functions sine, cosine and tangent to solve problems.

GRAPHS OF TRIGONOMETRIC FUNCTIONS

Trigonometric functions are also referred to as periodic functions. The graphs of periodic functions repeat the same y-value for some consistent change in the domain.

THE GRAPH OF THE SINE FUNCTION

The partial graph of the sine function $y = \sin x$ is illustrated as follows:

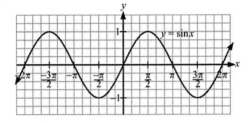

The graph of the function $y = \sin x$, where x is in radians, can be summarized as follows:

- The maximum value is 1, and the minimum value is −1.

- The horizontal midline axis is $y = 0$, and the amplitude is 1.

- The x-intercepts occur when $x = \pi n$ rad, where $n \in I$. The y-intercept is (0, 0).

- The domain is $x \in R$, and the range is $-1 \le y \le 1$.

- The period is 2π rad.

Copyright Protected

THE GRAPH OF THE COSINE FUNCTION

The partial graph of the cosine function $y = \cos x$ is illustrated as follows:

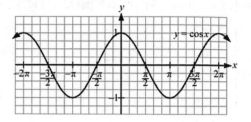

The graph of the function $y = \cos x$, where x is in radians, can be summarized as follows:

- The maximum value is 1, and the minimum value is -1.

- The horizontal midline axis is $y = 0$, and the amplitude is 1.

- The x-intercepts occur when $x = \left(\dfrac{\pi}{2} + \pi n\right)\text{rad}$, where $n \in I$. The y-intercept is (0, 1).

- The domain is $x \in R$, and the range is $-1 \leq y \leq 1$.

- The period is $2\pi \text{ rad}$.

THE GRAPH OF THE TANGENT FUNCTION

The partial graph of the cosine function $y = \tan x$ is illustrated as follows:

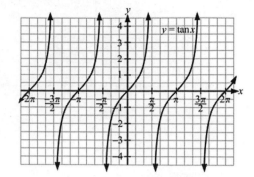

The graph of the function $y = \tan x$, where x is in radians, can be summarized as follows:

- There is no maximum value, minimum value, horizontal midline axis, or amplitude.

- The vertical asymptotes occur when $x = \left(\dfrac{\pi}{2} + \pi n\right)\text{rad}$, where $n \in I$.

- The x-intercepts occur when $x = \pi n \,\text{rad}$, where $n \in I$. The y-intercept is (0, 0).

- The domain is $x \in R$, $x \neq \left(\dfrac{\pi}{2} + \pi n\right)\text{rad}$, where $n \in I$, and the range is $y \in R$.

- The period is $\pi \text{ rad}$.

Not for Reproduction

APPLYING TRANSFORMATIONS TO GRAPHS OF THE SINE FUNCTION AND COSINE FUNCTION

When the graphs of $y = \sin x$ and $y = \cos x$ are transformed to the graphs of

$y = a\sin\left[b(x-c)\right] + d$ and

$y = a\cos\left[b(x-c)\right] + d$, respectively,

the following transformations are applied:

- There is a vertical stretch by a factor of $|a|$.

  If $a < 0$, there is a reflection in the x-axis. The amplitude of the graph is

  $a = \dfrac{maximum - minimum}{2}$.

- There is a horizontal stretch by a factor of $\dfrac{1}{|b|}$.

  If $b < 0$, there is a reflection in the y-axis.

  The period of the graph is $\dfrac{360°}{|b|}$,

  or $\dfrac{2\pi}{|b|}$.

- If $c > 0$, there is a phase shift c units to the right. If $c < 0$, there is a phase shift $|c|$ units to the left.

- If $d > 0$, the translation is d units up. If $d < 0$, the translation is $|d|$ units down.

  The horizontal midline axis is

  $d = \dfrac{maximum + minimum}{2}$.

To sketch the graph of a transformed sine or cosine function, apply stretches and reflections first, followed by translations.

Example

The following transformations are applied in order on the graph of $y = \cos x$:

- Stretched vertically by a factor of 3

- Translated horizontally $\dfrac{\pi}{3}$ rad left

- Translated vertically 2 units up

Determine the amplitude, horizontal midline axis, period, domain, and range of the transformed function.

Solution

Step 1
Determine the amplitude.

Since the graph is stretched vertically by a factor of 3, the value of a is 3. Therefore, the amplitude is 3.

Step 2
Determine the horizontal midline axis.

Since the graph is translated vertically 2 units up, the value of d is 2. Therefore, the equation of the horizontal midline axis is $y = 2$.

Step 3
Determine the period.

Since there is no horizontal stretch, the value of b is 1. Therefore, the period is $\dfrac{2\pi}{|1|} = 2\pi$.

Step 4
Determine the domain and range.

The domain is $x \in R$.

Since the horizontal midline axis is 2, and the amplitude is 3, the maximum value is $2 + 3 = 5$. Similarly, the minimum value is $2 - 3 = -1$. Therefore, the range is $-1 \le y \le 5$.

Copyright Protected

SOLVING REAL-WORLD PROBLEMS INVOLVING TRIGONOMETRIC FUNCTIONS

Numerous real-world problems can be modelled using the sine or cosine functions.

Problems involving graphically represented sinusoidal functions can be solved by interpreting values from the graph.

Example

In a physics lab, a bicycle pedal mechanism is rotated at a constant speed by a small motor. A student then uses a motion sensor to record the vertical height, h, in centimetres, of one pedal above the ground over a time of 2.0 s. The motion of the pedal is shown in the following graph:

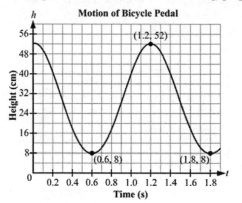

Motion of Bicycle Pedal

a) How long does it take the bicycle wheel to complete one revolution?

Solution

The graph shows a period of 1.2 s (the amount of time until the graph repeats itself). Thus, the time it takes for the wheel to complete one revolution is 1.2 s.

b) How far above the ground is the axle (centre of the wheel) located?

Solution

The axle is located halfway between the lowest point, 8 cm, and the highest point, 52 cm. Therefore, the axle is located $\frac{52+8}{2} = 30\,cm$ above the ground.

Practice Questions: 22–30, 48

T.5 *Solve, algebraically and graphically, first and second degree trigonometric equations with the domain expressed in degrees and radians.*

SOLVING TRIGONOMETRIC EQUATIONS

Solving a trigonometric equation involves finding all the angle measures in a specific domain that satisfy a given equation. Trigonometric equations can be solved algebraically or graphically.

Example

Determine the exact values of θ in the trigonometric equation $\sqrt{3}\tan\theta - 1 = 0$, if $0 \le \theta \le 360°$.

Solution

Method 1: Solve using the unit circle.

Step 1
Isolate $\tan\theta$.
$$\sqrt{3}\tan\theta - 1 = 0$$
$$\tan\theta = \frac{1}{\sqrt{3}}$$

Step 2
Use the unit circle to determine the exact values of θ.

Since $\tan\theta = \frac{y}{x}$, the value of θ corresponds to

angles on the unit circle where the ratio $\frac{y}{x}$ of its

point on the terminal arm is equal to $\frac{1}{\sqrt{3}}$.

Therefore, the values of θ within the domain $0 \le \theta \le 360°$ are 30° and 210°.

Method 2: Solve using the inverse function on a calculator and the CAST rule.

Find the reference angle for $\tan\theta = \frac{1}{\sqrt{3}}$ using the

inverse tangent function on a calculator.

$$\tan\theta = \frac{1}{\sqrt{3}}$$
$$\theta_{ref} = \tan^{-1}\left(\frac{1}{\sqrt{3}}\right)$$
$$\theta_{ref} = 30°$$

Not for Reproduction

According the CAST rule, the tangent function is positive in quadrants I and III. Therefore, the solution in quadrant I is 30°, and the solution in quadrant III is $\theta = 180° + 30° = 210°$.

Method 3: Solve by graphing.

The solutions of the equation $\sqrt{3}\tan\theta - 1 = 0$ are the zeros on its corresponding graph. On a TI-83 or similar calculator, enter the equation as $Y_1 = \sqrt{3}\tan(X) - 1$, and use the zero feature to find the solutions. There are x-intercepts at 30° and 210°.

Second-degree trigonometric equations can be solved using these methods together with factoring and applying the zero product property to each factor.

A general solution is an expression that defines all possible values for θ in an equation. For example, the solutions of the equation $\sin\theta = \frac{1}{2}$ are $\frac{\pi}{6}$ and $\frac{5\pi}{6}$, where $0 < \theta < 2\pi$.
Since the period of the function $y = \sin\theta$ is 2π rad, the set of solutions to the equation $\sin\theta = \frac{1}{2}$ will repeat every 2π rad. Therefore, the general solution is expressed as $\left(\frac{\pi}{6} + 2\pi n\right)$ rad and $\left(\frac{5\pi}{6} + 2\pi n\right)$ rad, where $n \in I$.

Practice Questions: 31–38, 49

T.6   Prove trigonometric identities, using:

- *reciprocal identities*
- *quotient identities*
- *Pythagorean identities*
- *sum or difference identities (restricted to sine, cosine and tangent)*
- *double-angle identities (restricted to sine, cosine and tangent).*

RECIPROCAL, QUOTIENT, AND PYTHAGOREAN IDENTITIES

There are three basic types of trigonometric identities that become the building blocks for creating and examining more complex identities:

1. Reciprocal identities
$$\csc\theta = \frac{1}{\sin\theta}$$
$$\sec\theta = \frac{1}{\cos\theta}$$
$$\cot\theta = \frac{1}{\tan\theta}$$

2. Quotient identities
$$\tan\theta = \frac{\sin\theta}{\cos\theta}$$
$$\cot\theta = \frac{\cos\theta}{\sin\theta}$$

3. Pythagorean identities
$$\sin^2\theta + \cos^2\theta = 1$$
$$1 + \tan^2\theta = \sec^2\theta$$
$$1 + \cot^2\theta = \csc^2\theta$$

The basic trigonometric identities can be used to prove that a trigonometric identity is valid.

Example

Prove the identity $\sec x = \tan x \csc x$.

Solution

Show that LHS = RHS.

Step 1

Apply the reciprocal and quotient identities.

$$\sec x = \tan x \csc x$$

$$\frac{1}{\cos x} = \left(\frac{\sin x}{\cos x}\right)\left(\frac{1}{\sin x}\right)$$

Step 2

Divide out common factors.

$$\frac{1}{\cos x} = \left(\frac{\sin x}{\cos x}\right)\left(\frac{1}{\sin x}\right)$$

$$\frac{1}{\cos x} = \frac{1}{\cos x}$$

Since LHS = RHS, the proof is complete.

SUM, DIFFERENCE, AND DOUBLE-ANGLE IDENTITIES

The sum and difference identities for sine, cosine, and tangent are as follows:

1. $\sin(A + B) = \sin A \cos B + \cos A \sin B$

    $\sin(A - B) = \sin A \cos B - \cos A \sin B$

2. $\cos(A + B) = \cos A \cos B - \sin A \sin B$

    $\cos(A - B) = \cos A \cos B + \sin A \sin B$

3. $\tan(A + B) = \dfrac{\tan A + \tan B}{1 - \tan A \tan B}$

    $\tan(A - B) = \dfrac{\tan A - \tan B}{1 + \tan A \tan B}$

The double-angle identities for sine, cosine, and tangent are as follows:

1. $\sin(2A) = 2 \sin A \cos A$

2. $\cos(2A) = \cos^2 A - \sin^2 A$

3. $\tan(2A) = \dfrac{2 \tan A}{1 - \tan^2 A}$

The sum, difference, and double-angle identities can be used to prove trigonometric identities that contain more than one angle.

Example

Prove the identity $\dfrac{\cos(2x) + 1}{\sin(2x)} = \dfrac{\cos x}{\sin x}$.

Solution

Step 1

Apply the double-angle identity.

$$\frac{\cos(2x) + 1}{\sin(2x)} = \frac{\cos x}{\sin x}$$

$$\frac{\cos^2 x - \sin^2 x + 1}{2 \sin x \cos x} = \frac{\cos x}{\sin x}$$

Step 2

Rearrange terms.

$$\frac{\cos^2 x - \sin^2 x + 1}{2 \sin x \cos x} = \frac{\cos x}{\sin x}$$

$$\frac{\cos^2 x + 1 - \sin^2 x}{2 \sin x \cos x} = \frac{\cos x}{\sin x}$$

Step 3

Apply the Pythagorean identity.

$$\frac{\cos^2 x + \cos^2 x}{2 \sin x \cos x} = \frac{\cos x}{\sin x}$$

$$\frac{2 \cos^2 x}{2 \sin x \cos x} = \frac{\cos x}{\sin x}$$

Step 4

Divide out common factors.

$$\frac{2 \cos^2 x}{2 \sin x \cos x} = \frac{\cos x}{\sin x}$$

$$\frac{\cos x}{\sin x} = \frac{\cos x}{\sin x}$$

Practice Questions: 39–44, 50

Copyright Protected

PRACTICE QUESTIONS—TRIGONOMETRY

1. When 480° is converted into radians, what is its exact value?

   A. $\dfrac{7\pi}{6}$ rad

   B. $\dfrac{8\pi}{6}$ rad

   C. $\dfrac{7\pi}{3}$ rad

   D. $\dfrac{8\pi}{3}$ rad

Use the following information to answer the next question.

An arc, a, subtends an angle in standard position with a measurement of $\dfrac{16\pi}{9}$ rad.

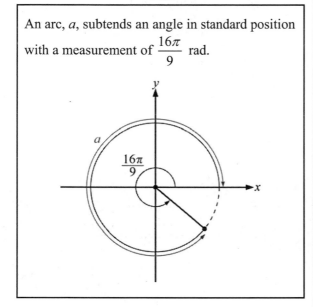

2. If the length of the terminal arm is 12 units, what is the length of a?

   A. 21.33 units

   B. 33.51 units

   C. 38.70 units

   D. 67.02 units

3. Which of following expressions represents the general formula for all angles that are coterminal with an angle $\dfrac{\pi}{8}$ rad, where $n \in I$?

   A. $\left(\dfrac{\pi}{8} + 2n\pi\right)$ rad

   B. $\left(\dfrac{\pi}{8} + \dfrac{\pi n}{2}\right)$ rad

   C. $\left(\dfrac{\pi}{8} + n\pi\right)$ rad

   D. $\left(\dfrac{\pi}{8} + 4\pi\right)$ rad

Use the following information to answer the next question.

In the diagram below, two paths lead from point A to point C. Path 1 follows the arc of a circle that has a radius of 80 m centred at point B. Path 2 follows the line segments $\overline{AB}$ and $\overline{BC}$. The measure of $\angle ABC$ is 100°.

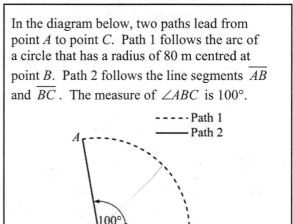

4. The length of path 1 is

   A. greater than the length of path 2 by approximately 20.4 m

   B. greater than the length of path 2 by approximately 640.0 m

   C. less than the length of path 2 by approximately 20.4 m

   D. less than the length of path 2 by approximately 22.2 m

Copyright Protected

Use the following information to answer the next question.

The given diagram illustrates an angle, θ, that is drawn in standard position with its terminal arm in quadrant III.

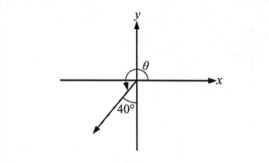

Use the following information to answer the next question.

The given diagram illustrates an angle, θ, that is drawn in standard position with its terminal arm in quadrant II.

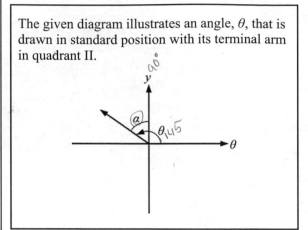

5. Which of the following angles is coterminal with angle θ?

A. $-500°$

B. $-320°$

C. $400°$

D. $590°$

Use the following information to answer the next question.

A student makes a conical filter from a circular piece of paper that has a radius of 24.0 cm. The student cuts out a sector with central angle θ and then tapes the cut edges of the remaining piece together.

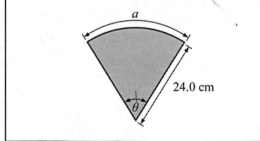

Numerical Response

6. If the student increases angle θ by 0.1 rad, then the arc length, a, of the new cutout sector, correct to the nearest tenth of a centimetre, increases by _____ cm.

Numerical Response

7. If angle measure of $-575°$ is coterminal with angle θ, the measure of angle α is _____°. (Record your answer as a **whole** number.)

8. What is exact value of $\sin\left(\dfrac{5\pi}{4}\right)$?

A. $-\dfrac{\sqrt{2}}{2}$

B. $\dfrac{\sqrt{2}}{2}$

C. $\dfrac{1}{2}$

D. $-\dfrac{1}{2}$

9. Which of the following expressions is equal to the exact value of $\cos\left(\dfrac{5\pi}{4}\right)$?

A. $-\cos(135°)$

B. $-\sin(225°)$

C. $\cos(315°)$

D. $\sin(-45°)$

10. If $\theta = \dfrac{\pi}{6}$ radians and $\cos\theta - k = 0$, then the value of k is

A. -0.17

B. 1.02

C. $\dfrac{1}{2}$

D. $\dfrac{\sqrt{3}}{2}$

11. The exact value of $\csc 750°$ is

A. $\dfrac{1}{2}$ B. 2

C. $\dfrac{\sqrt{3}}{2}$ D. $\dfrac{2}{\sqrt{3}}$

12. What is the exact value of $\sec\left(\dfrac{-20\pi}{3}\right)$?

A. -2 B. 2

C. $\dfrac{\sqrt{2}}{2}$ D. $\dfrac{2}{\sqrt{2}}$

13. The exact value of $\cot\left(\dfrac{7\pi}{4}\right)$ is

A. 1

B. undefined

C. 0

D. -1

Numerical Response

14. If point $P\left(-\dfrac{\sqrt{3}}{2},\ -\dfrac{1}{2}\right)$ lies on the terminal arm of a rotation angle, then the measure of the smallest positive angle, in standard position, to the nearest degree, is _____°. (Record your answer to **one** decimal place.)

15. The point $P\left(\dfrac{-\sqrt{3}}{2},\dfrac{1}{2}\right)$ is on the terminal arm of angle θ, in standard position. The measure of angle θ, where $0<\theta<2\pi$, is

A. $\dfrac{2\pi}{3}$ rad

B. $\dfrac{3\pi}{4}$ rad

C. $\dfrac{5\pi}{6}$ rad

D. $\dfrac{11\pi}{6}$ rad

16. If the terminal arm for an angle θ lies in quadrant III, and $\sin\theta=-\dfrac{\sqrt{7}}{4}$, what is the exact value of $\sec\theta$?

A. $-\dfrac{\sqrt{7}}{4}$

B. $-\dfrac{3}{4}$

C. $\dfrac{4}{\sqrt{7}}$

D. $-\dfrac{4}{3}$

17. If an angle θ in standard position terminates in quadrant II, and $\cos\theta=-\dfrac{1}{4}$, then what are the exact values of $\csc\theta$ and $\cot\theta$, respectively?

A. $\dfrac{\sqrt{15}}{4}$ and $-\dfrac{\sqrt{15}}{15}$

B. $\dfrac{\sqrt{15}}{4}$ and $\dfrac{\sqrt{15}}{15}$

C. $-\dfrac{4\sqrt{15}}{15}$ and $\dfrac{\sqrt{15}}{15}$

D. $\dfrac{4\sqrt{15}}{15}$ and $-\dfrac{\sqrt{15}}{15}$

18. If the terminal arm of angle θ, in standard position, passes through point $(-b, 2b)$, where $b>0$, then the exact values of $\sin\theta$, $\cos\theta$, and $\tan\theta$ are, respectively,

A. $\dfrac{-2}{\sqrt{5}}, \dfrac{1}{\sqrt{5}}$, and 2

B. $\dfrac{2}{\sqrt{5}}, \dfrac{-1}{\sqrt{5}}$, and -2

C. $\dfrac{-1}{\sqrt{5}}, \dfrac{2}{\sqrt{5}}$, and -2

D. $\dfrac{1}{\sqrt{5}}, \dfrac{-2}{\sqrt{5}}$, and 2

Copyright Protected

Use the following information to answer the next question.

The point $P(4, -1)$ is on the terminal arm of an angle in standard position, as shown below.

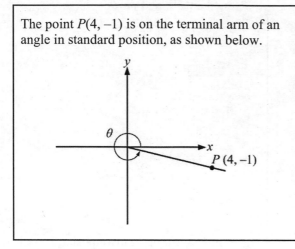

19. The measure of angle θ, correct to the nearest tenth of a radian, is
    A. 0.2 rad
    B. 3.4 rad
    C. 5.8 rad
    D. 6.0 rad

Numerical Response

20. The exact value of $\tan^{-1}\left(\sqrt{3}\right)$ is _____°.
    (Record your answer as a **whole** number.)

Numerical Response

21. The exact value of $\sin^{-1}\left(\dfrac{\sqrt{3}}{2}\right)$ is _____°.
    (Record your answer as a **whole** number.)

Use the following information to answer the next question.

A student examined the graph of $f(x) = \sin x$ and made the following observations.

1. One of the minimum points of the graph occurs at an angle of 1 350°.

2. The function increases between −450° and −270°.

3. An angle where the graph passes through its horizontal midline axis is −620°.

4. The interval between minimum and maximum values is 180°.

22. Which observation about the graph of $f(x) = \sin x$ is **false**?
    A. 1
    B. 2
    C. 3
    D. 4

23. The graph of $y = \sin\theta$ is obtained from the graph of $y = \cos\theta$ by a translation of
    A. π radians to the left
    B. $\dfrac{\pi}{2}$ radians to the left
    C. π radians to the right
    D. $\dfrac{\pi}{2}$ radians to the right

Not for Reproduction

Use the following information to answer the next question.

The partial graph of $f(\theta) = 2\sin^2\theta$ and the partial graph of $g(\theta) = 3\cos\theta$ are shown below.

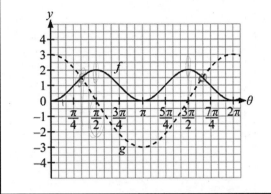

24. Within the domain $0 < \theta < 2\pi$, the interval where $f(\theta) > g(\theta)$ is

A. $0 < \theta < 2\pi$

B. $\dfrac{\pi}{2} < \theta < \dfrac{3\pi}{2}$

C. $\dfrac{\pi}{3} < \theta < \pi$

D. $\dfrac{\pi}{3} < \theta < \dfrac{5\pi}{3}$

25. The period for the graph of the trigonometric function $y = 6\sin\left[8(x-\pi)\right] + 5$ is

A. $\dfrac{\pi}{8}$

B. $\dfrac{\pi}{4}$

C. 4π

D. 8π

Use the following information to answer the next question.

The height of a person above the ground on a ferris wheel is given by the function

$h(t) = 9\sin\left[\dfrac{\pi}{20}(t-10)\right] + 12$, where $h(t)$ is the height in metres of the person t seconds after getting on the ferris wheel.

26. How long does it take the ferris wheel to make one complete revolution?

A. 10 s

B. 20 s

C. 40 s

D. 60 s

Use the following information to answer the next question.

The partial graphs of two sinusoidal functions are shown below on the same grid.

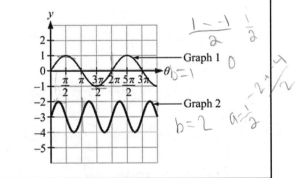

27. The equation of graph 1 is
$y = a\sin b(\theta + c) + d$ for some integers a, b, c, and d. Graph 2 is obtained by changing exactly two parameters in the equation of graph 1. The two parameters that are changed are

A. a and c

B. a and d

C. b and c

D. b and d

Use the following information to answer the next question.

The height, *h*, in metres, of a point on a ferris wheel at time *t*, in seconds, is illustrated in the given graph.

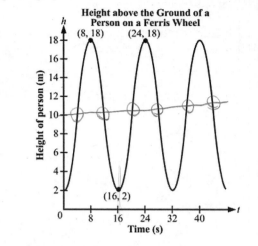

Height above the Ground of a Person on a Ferris Wheel

28. An equation that represents the given graph is

A. $h(t) = 8\cos\left[\dfrac{\pi}{8}(t-8)\right] + 10$

B. $h(t) = 8\sin\left[\dfrac{\pi}{16}(t-4)\right] + 10$

C. $h(t) = 18\sin\left[\dfrac{\pi}{8}(t-4)\right] + 10$

D. $h(t) = 18\cos\left[\dfrac{\pi}{16}(t-8)\right] + 10$

Numerical Response

29. The range of $y = a\sin\theta + b$ is $-1 \le y \le 5$. If *a* is positive, then the values of *a* and *b* are, respectively, _____ and _____.
(Record your answer as a **two-digit** number.)

Use the following information to answer the next question.

A computer-generated partial graph of the air pressure variation of a piano's lowest note is illustrated below. The intercepts shown are at 0, $\dfrac{\pi}{150}$, $\dfrac{\pi}{75}$, and $\dfrac{\pi}{50}$.

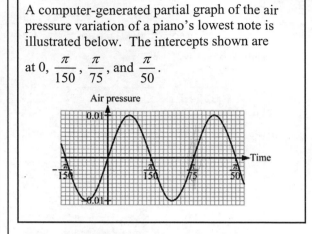

Numerical Response

30. Given that pitch, which is measured in Hertz (Hz), is the reciprocal of the period, the pitch of this note, correct to the nearest tenth, is _____ Hz.
(Record your answer to **one** decimal place.)

31. The three solutions of the equation $f(\theta) = 0$ are 0°, 180°, and 360°. Therefore, the three solutions of the equation $f(\theta - 30°) = 0$ are

A. 0°, 60°, and 120°

B. −30°, 150°, and 330°

C. 30°, 210°, and 390°

D. 0°, 540°, and 1 080°

32. What are the exact solutions to $2\sin^2\theta - 3\sin\theta + 1 = 0$, where $0 \le \theta \le 2\pi$?

A. $\theta = \dfrac{\pi}{3}, \dfrac{\pi}{4}, \dfrac{\pi}{6}$

B. $\theta = \dfrac{\pi}{6}, \dfrac{\pi}{2}, \dfrac{5\pi}{6}$

C. $\theta = \dfrac{\pi}{3}, \dfrac{2\pi}{3}, \dfrac{5\pi}{6}$

D. $\theta = \dfrac{\pi}{6}, \dfrac{5\pi}{6}, \dfrac{7\pi}{6}$

33. When the following pairs of functions are graphed, the pair that could **not** be used to solve the equation $4\sin x - 1 = 0$ is

A. $y = \sin x$ and $y = 1$

B. $y = \sin x$ and $y = \dfrac{1}{4}$

C. $y = 4\sin x$ and $y = 1$

D. $y = 4\sin x - 1$ and $y = 0$

34. If the general solution to the equation $\tan x = -1$ is $x = \dfrac{3\pi}{4} + n\pi$, where $n \in I$, then the general solution to the equation $\tan(3x) = -1$ is

A. $\dfrac{\pi}{4} + \dfrac{n\pi}{3}$, where $n \in I$

B. $\dfrac{\pi}{12} + \dfrac{n\pi}{3}$, where $n \in I$

C. $\dfrac{3\pi}{4} + 3n\pi$, where $n \in I$

D. $\dfrac{\pi}{4} + n\pi$, where $n \in I$

35. The x-intercepts of $f(x) = \sin x$ can be described using $x = a°n$, $n \in I$, where a is equal to

A. 30

B. 45

C. 90

D. 180

36. If $1 + \sin\theta = 2\cos^2\theta$, $0 \le \theta \le 2\pi$, then θ is equal to

A. $\dfrac{\pi}{6}, \dfrac{\pi}{2}, \dfrac{7\pi}{6}$

B. $\dfrac{\pi}{6}, \dfrac{5\pi}{6}, \dfrac{3\pi}{2}$

C. $\dfrac{\pi}{2}, \dfrac{2\pi}{3}, \dfrac{4\pi}{3}$

D. $\dfrac{5\pi}{6}, \dfrac{7\pi}{6}, \dfrac{3\pi}{2}$

Numerical Response

37. The solution of $2\cos\theta + 6 = 8$, where $0° \le \theta < 360°$, is _____°.
(Record your answer as a **whole** number.)

Numerical Response

38. The value of θ that satisfies the equation $5\cos^2\theta - 3\cos\theta = 0$, $0° < \theta < 90°$, correct to the nearest tenth of a degree, is _____°.
(Record your answer to **one** decimal place.)

39. To create an identity for the equation $\dfrac{1 + \cos(2x)}{2} = X$, the value of X would need to be

A. $\sin^2 x$ **B.** $\cos^2 x$

C. $2\sin x$ **D.** $2\cos x$

Use the following information to answer the next question.

In attempting to prove an identity in which the left-hand side of the equation is $\dfrac{1 + \sin x}{1 - \sin x}$, a student performed the following steps:

Step 1
$\dfrac{(1 + \sin x)(1 + \sin x)}{(1 - \sin x)(1 + \sin x)}$

Step 2
$\dfrac{1 + 2\sin x + \sin^2 x}{\cos^2 x}$

Step 3
$\dfrac{1}{\cos^2 x} + \dfrac{2\sin x}{\cos^2 x} + \dfrac{\sin^2 x}{\cos^2 x}$

Step 4
$\sec^2 x + 2\csc x \tan x + \tan^2 x$

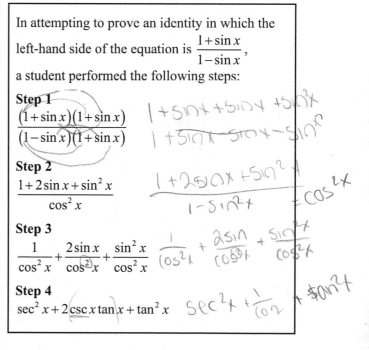

40. The student's first error was made in step

A. 1   **B.** 2

C. 3   **D.** 4

Copyright Protected

Use the following information to answer the next question.

Talia's teacher asked her to prove the identity $\tan A + \cot A = \csc A \sec A$.

41. Which of the following expressions should Talia arrive at to prove the given identity?

A. $\dfrac{\sin A}{\sin A \cos A}$

B. $\dfrac{1}{\sin A \cos A}$

C. $\dfrac{\cos A}{\sin A \cos A}$

D. $\dfrac{1}{\sec A \cos A}$

42. The expression $\sin\theta + (\cot\theta)(\cos\theta)$ is equivalent to

A. 1

B. $\csc\theta$

C. $\sec\theta$

D. $\cot^2\theta$

43. If $\sec\theta = \dfrac{11}{6}$ and θ is an angle in quadrant I, what is the exact value of $\tan(2\theta)$?

A. $-\dfrac{24\sqrt{85}}{49}$

B. $-\dfrac{12\sqrt{85}}{49}$

C. $\dfrac{12\sqrt{85}}{49}$

D. $\dfrac{24\sqrt{85}}{49}$

Use the following information to answer the next question.

Charles wants to verify the identity $\csc x \tan x = \sec x$.

Numerical Response

44. When verifying that the given identity is true for $x = \dfrac{\pi}{6}$ rad, the LHS of the equation, to the nearest hundredth, will equal _____. (Record your answer to **two** decimal places.)

Use the following information to answer the next question.

An angle, θ, in standard position, subtends an arc with a length of 88 units.

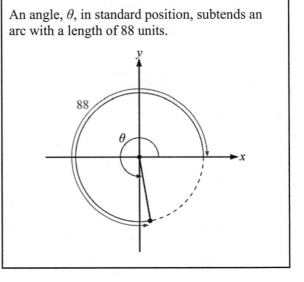

Written Response

45. If the length of the terminal arm is 18 units, calculate the measure of angle θ to nearest hundredth of a radian.

Not for Reproduction

Written Response

46. What is the exact value of the expression

$$\tan 30° + \left(\frac{\tan 60°}{\tan 45°} \right)?$$

Written Response

47. If θ is in quadrant IV, and $\sec\theta = \dfrac{\sqrt{26}}{5}$,

what is the exact value of $\tan\theta$?

Written Response

48. Determine the amplitude, period, phase shift, domain, and range for the function

$$y = -\frac{2}{5}\sin\left[-3(x+15°)\right] + 4.$$

Written Response

49. What is the solution to the equation

$$\sqrt{3}\tan^2\theta + \tan\theta = 0 \text{, where } 0 \le \theta \le 2\pi ?$$

Written Response

50. If $\sin\theta = \dfrac{4}{5}$ and $\cos\theta = -\dfrac{3}{5}$, what is the

exact value of $\sin\left(\dfrac{\pi}{2} + \theta\right)?$

Copyright Protected

ANSWERS AND SOLUTIONS—PRACTICE QUESTIONS

1. D	11. B	21. 60	31. C	41. B
2. D	12. A	22. C	32. B	42. B
3. A	13. D	23. D	33. A	43. B
4. C	14. 210	24. D	34. A	44. 1.15
5. D	15. C	25. B	35. D	45. WR
6. 2.4	16. D	26. C	36. B	46. WR
7. 55	17. D	27. D	37. 0	47. WR
8. A	18. B	28. A	38. 53.1	48. WR
9. D	19. D	29. 32	39. B	49. WR
10. D	20. 60	30. 23.9	40. D	50. WR

1. D

To convert from degrees to radians, multiply the degree measure by $\dfrac{\pi \, \text{rad}}{180°}$.

$480° \times \dfrac{\pi \, \text{rad}}{180°}$

$= \dfrac{480\pi}{180} \text{rad}$

$= \dfrac{8\pi}{3} \text{ rad}$

When 480° is converted into radians, its exact value is $\dfrac{8\pi}{3}$ rad .

2. D

The length of the terminal arm is equal to the radius of the circle. Calculate the arc length using the arc length formula, $a = r\theta$.

$a = r\theta$

$a = (12)\left(\dfrac{16\pi}{9}\right)$

$a \approx 67.02$

The arc length is about 67.02 units.

3. A

All angles in the form $(\theta + 2\pi n)\,\text{rad}$ will be coterminal with θ, where θ is in radians, and $n \in I$.

Therefore, angles coterminal with $\dfrac{\pi}{8}$ rad are

$\left(\dfrac{\pi}{8} + 2\pi n\right)\text{rad}$, where $n \in I$.

4. C

It is given that $r = AB$, $AB = BC = 80$ m, and $\angle ABC = 100°$. Compare the length of path 1 with path 2.

Step 1
Convert the angle 100° to radians.

$100° \times \dfrac{\pi \, \text{rad}}{180°}$

$= \dfrac{100\pi}{180} \text{rad}$

$= \dfrac{5\pi}{9} \text{ rad}$

Step 2
Calculate the length of path 1 using the arc length formula, $a = r\theta$.

$a = r\theta$

$a = (80)\left(\dfrac{5\pi}{9}\right)$

$a = 139.626... $ m

Step 3
Calculate length of path 2.

$AB + BC$

$= 80 + 80$

$= 160 \, \text{m}$

Not for Reproduction

Step 4
Subtract the length of path 1 from the length of path 2.

path 2 − path 1
$= 160 - 139.626\ldots$
≈ 20.4 m

Therefore, the length of path 1 is approximately 20.4 m less than the length of path 2.

5. D

Step 1
Determine the measure of θ.

The angle between the terminal arm and the x-axis is $90° - 40° = 50°$. Therefore, the measure of θ is $180° + 50° = 230°$.

Step 2
Determine the general formula of all angles coterminal with 230°.

All angles in the form $(\theta + 360n)°$ are coterminal with angle θ, where θ is in degrees, and $n \in I$. Thus, the angle 230° is coterminal with all angles in the form $(230 + 360n)°$, $n \in I$.

Step 3
Determine which one of the given angle measurements is conterminal with 230°.
If $n = 1$, an angle that is coterminal with 230° can be calculated as follows:
$230° + 360°(1) = 230° + 360° = 590°$

6. 2.4

Step 1
Substitute 24 for r into the equation $a = r\theta$.
$a = r\theta$
$a = 24\theta$

Step 2
Since θ is increased by 0.1 rad, substitute $\theta + 0.1$ for θ into the equation $24\theta = a$.
$24\theta = a$
$24(\theta + 0.1) = a$
$24\theta + 2.4 = a$

Therefore, a increases by 2.4 cm.

7. 55

Step 1
Determine the measure of θ.

All angles in the form $(\theta + 360n)°$ are coterminal with angle θ, where $n \in I$.

An angle of measure −575° is coterminal with angle θ, and angle θ terminates in quadrant II. Thus, the measure of angle θ can be determined by substituting −575° for θ and 2 for n in the expression $(\theta + 360n)°$.

$(\theta + 360n)°$
$= (-575 + 360(2))°$
$= -575° + 720°$
$= 145°$

Step 2
Determine the measure of angle α.

Since the measure of angle θ is 145°, the measure of angle α is $145° - 90° = 55°$.

8. A

The angle $\dfrac{5\pi}{4}$ terminates in quadrant III and corresponds to the point $\left(-\dfrac{\sqrt{2}}{2}, -\dfrac{\sqrt{2}}{2}\right)$ on the unit circle. Since the sine ratio is the y-coordinate of the point, the exact value of $\sin\left(\dfrac{5\pi}{4}\right)$ is $-\dfrac{\sqrt{2}}{2}$.

9. D

Step 1
Convert $\dfrac{5\pi}{4}$ to degrees.

$\dfrac{5\pi}{4}\text{rad} \times \dfrac{180°}{\pi\,\text{rad}}$
$= \dfrac{900°}{4}$
$= 225°$

Therefore, $\cos\left(\dfrac{5\pi}{4}\right) = \cos 225°$.

Step 2
Evaluate $\cos 225°$ using the unit circle.

The angle 225° terminates in quadrant III and corresponds to the point $\left(-\dfrac{\sqrt{2}}{2}, -\dfrac{\sqrt{2}}{2}\right)$ on the unit circle. Since the cosine ratio is the x-coordinate of the point, the exact value of $\cos 225°$ is $-\dfrac{\sqrt{2}}{2}$.

Step 3

Evaluate the given expressions.

$$-\cos\left(135°\right) = -\left(\dfrac{-\sqrt{2}}{2}\right) = \dfrac{\sqrt{2}}{2}$$

$$\cos\left(315°\right) = \dfrac{\sqrt{2}}{2}$$

$$-\sin\left(225°\right) = -\left(\dfrac{-\sqrt{2}}{2}\right) = \dfrac{\sqrt{2}}{2}$$

$$\sin\left(-45°\right) = \sin\left(315°\right) = -\dfrac{\sqrt{2}}{2}$$

The value $-\dfrac{\sqrt{2}}{2}$ is equivalent to $\cos\left(225°\right)$.

Therefore, the exact value of $\cos\left(\dfrac{5\pi}{4}\right)$ is the same as $\sin(-45°)$.

10. D

Step 1

Substitute $\dfrac{\pi}{6}$ for θ in the equation.

$$\cos\left(\dfrac{\pi}{6}\right) - k = 0$$

$$\cos\left(\dfrac{\pi}{6}\right) = k$$

Step 2

Evaluate $\cos\left(\dfrac{\pi}{6}\right)$.

According to the unit circle, the value of $\cos\left(\dfrac{\pi}{6}\right)$ is $\dfrac{\sqrt{3}}{2}$. Therefore, the value of k is $\dfrac{\sqrt{3}}{2}$.

11. B

The angle 750° terminates in quadrant I, and the reference angle is 30°. On the unit circle, $\csc\theta = \dfrac{1}{y}$, and the angle 750° corresponds to the point $\left(\dfrac{\sqrt{3}}{2}, \dfrac{1}{2}\right)$. Therefore, the exact value of $\csc 750°$ is $\dfrac{1}{\frac{1}{2}} = 2$.

12. A

The angle $\dfrac{-20\pi}{3}$ is coterminal with $\dfrac{4\pi}{3}$.

On the unit circle, $\sec\theta = \dfrac{1}{x}$, and the angle $\dfrac{-20\pi}{3}$ corresponds to the point $\left(-\dfrac{1}{2}, -\dfrac{\sqrt{3}}{2}\right)$. Therefore, the exact value of $\sec\left(\dfrac{-20\pi}{3}\right)$ is $\dfrac{1}{-\frac{1}{2}} = -2$.

13. D

On the unit circle, $\cot\theta = \dfrac{x}{y}$, and the angle $\dfrac{7\pi}{4}$ corresponds to the point $\left(\dfrac{\sqrt{2}}{2}, -\dfrac{\sqrt{2}}{2}\right)$. Therefore, the exact value of $\cot\left(\dfrac{7\pi}{4}\right)$ is determined as follows:

$$\cot\left(\dfrac{7\pi}{4}\right)$$

$$= \dfrac{\frac{\sqrt{2}}{2}}{-\frac{\sqrt{2}}{2}}$$

$$= -1$$

14. 210

According to the unit circle, point $P\left(-\dfrac{\sqrt{3}}{2}, -\dfrac{1}{2}\right)$ is in quadrant III on the terminal arm of a positive rotation angle of 210°.

Copyright Protected

Not for Reproduction

15. C

According to the unit circle, point $P\left(-\dfrac{\sqrt{3}}{2}, \dfrac{1}{2}\right)$ is in quadrant II on the terminal arm of a positive rotation angle of $\dfrac{5\pi}{6}$ rad.

16. D

Since $\sin\theta = \dfrac{y}{r}$, and it is given that $\sin\theta = -\dfrac{\sqrt{7}}{4}$, possible values for y and r are $y = -\sqrt{7}$ and $r = 4$.

Step 1
Determine the value of x using the Pythagorean theorem.
$$x^2 + y^2 = r^2$$
$$x^2 + \left(-\sqrt{7}\right)^2 = \left(4\right)^2$$
$$x^2 + 7 = 16$$
$$x^2 = 9$$
$$x = \pm 3$$

Because θ is in quadrant III, x must be negative. Therefore, $x = -3$.

Step 2
Determine the exact value of $\sec\theta$.
$$\sec\theta = \dfrac{r}{x}$$
$$\sec\theta = -\dfrac{4}{3}$$

17. D

Since $\cos\theta = \dfrac{x}{r}$, and it is given that $\cos\theta = -\dfrac{1}{4}$, possible values for x and r are $x = -1$ and $r = 4$.

Step 1
Determine the value of y using the Pythagorean theorem.
$$x^2 + y^2 = r^2$$
$$\left(-1\right)^2 + y^2 = \left(4\right)^2$$
$$1 + y^2 = 16$$
$$y^2 = 15$$
$$y = \pm\sqrt{15}$$

Since θ is in quadrant II, y must be positive. Therefore, $y = \sqrt{15}$.

Step 2
Determine the exact value of $\csc\theta$.
$$\csc\theta = \dfrac{r}{y}$$
$$\csc\theta = \dfrac{4}{\sqrt{15}}$$
$$\csc\theta = \dfrac{4\sqrt{15}}{15}$$

Step 3
Determine the exact value of $\cot\theta$.
$$\cot\theta = \dfrac{x}{y}$$
$$\cot\theta = \dfrac{-1}{\sqrt{15}}$$
$$\cot\theta = -\dfrac{\sqrt{15}}{15}$$

18. B

The point $(-b, 2b)$ must be in quadrant II, and $\tan\theta = \dfrac{y}{x} = \dfrac{2b}{-b} = -2$.

It is given that $\left(-b\right)^2 + \left(2b\right)^2 = r^2$.
$$b^2 + 4b^2 = r^2$$
$$5b^2 = r^2$$
$$\sqrt{5}b = r$$

Find the exact value of $\sin\theta$ and $\cos\theta$
$$\sin\theta = \dfrac{y}{r} = \dfrac{2b}{\sqrt{5}b} = \dfrac{2}{\sqrt{5}}$$
$$\cos\theta = \dfrac{x}{r} = \dfrac{-b}{\sqrt{5}b} = \dfrac{-1}{\sqrt{5}}$$

19. D

The coordinates of point P in the given diagram are $x = 4$ and $y = -1$. Substitute these values into $\tan\theta = \dfrac{y}{x}$, and determine the value of θ.

$$\tan\theta = \dfrac{y}{x}$$
$$\tan\theta = \dfrac{-1}{4}$$
$$\theta = \tan^{-1}\left(-\dfrac{1}{4}\right)$$
$$\theta_{\text{ref}} \approx -0.24 \text{ rad}$$

Since angle θ_{ref} is in quadrant IV, and θ is positive, solve for θ by adding -0.24 rad to 2π rad.

$\theta = 2\pi \text{ rad} + (-0.25) \text{ rad}$

$\theta \approx 6.0 \text{ rad}$

20. 60

From the unit circle, the terminal arm of the angle $60°$ is the point in quadrant I with coordinates $\left(\dfrac{1}{2}, \dfrac{\sqrt{3}}{2}\right)$. Since the tangent is equal to the ratio $\dfrac{y}{x}$, and $\dfrac{\left(\dfrac{\sqrt{3}}{2}\right)}{\left(\dfrac{1}{2}\right)} = \sqrt{3}$, the value of $\tan^{-1}\left(\sqrt{3}\right)$ is $60°$. Alternatively, inputting $\tan^{-1}\left(\sqrt{3}\right)$ into a calculator in degree mode will generate an answer of $60°$.

21. 60

The terminal arm of the angle $60°$ meets the unit circle at the point, in quadrant I, with coordinates $\left(\dfrac{1}{2}, \dfrac{\sqrt{3}}{2}\right)$. Since the y-coordinate is equal to the sine of the angle, the value of $\sin^{-1}\left(\dfrac{\sqrt{3}}{2}\right) = 60°$.

Alternatively, inputting $\sin^{-1}\left(\dfrac{\sqrt{3}}{2}\right)$ on a calculator in degree mode will generate an answer of $60°$.

22. C

Observation 1 is true.

Minimum points occur at angles of $-90°$, $270°$, $630°$, ... or $(-90 + 360n)°$, $n \in I$.

When $n = 4$, $\theta = (-90 + 4(360))° = 1\,350°$.

Thus, there is a minimum point at $1\,350°$.

Observation 2 is true.

The sine function increases for intervals $(-90 + n360)° < x < (90 + n360)°$, $n \in I$.

When $n = -1$, $(-90 - 360)° < x < (90 - 360)°$, or $-450° < x < -270°$.

Observation 3 is false.

The angles occurring on the horizontal midline axis, $y = 0$, are the x-intercepts. The x-intercepts occur when $x = 180°n$, $n \in I$. Thus, solve for n when $x = -620°$.

$x = 180°n$

$-620° = 180°n$

$\dfrac{-620°}{180°} = n$

$n = -3.444...$

Since n does not equal an integer, $-620°$ does not lie on the horizontal axis of the graph of $f(x) = \sin x$.

Observation 4 is true.

The period is $360°$ for $f(x) = \sin x$, which indicates the interval between successive maximum or minimum values. Therefore, the interval between minimum and maximum values would be $\dfrac{360°}{2} = 180°$.

23. D

The graphs of $y = \sin\theta$ and $y = \cos\theta$ are shown.

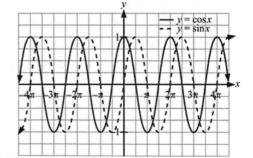

The first maximum of the graph of $y = \sin x$ is $\left(\dfrac{\pi}{2}, 1\right)$. The closest maximum on the graph of $y = \cos x$ to the point $\left(\dfrac{\pi}{2}, 1\right)$ is $(0, 1)$ on the right. Therefore, the graph of $y = \sin x$ is obtained from the graph of $y = \cos x$ by a phase shift $\left|\dfrac{\pi}{2} - 0\right| = \dfrac{\pi}{2}$ rad to the right.

Not for Reproduction

24. D

The interval where $f(\theta) > g(\theta)$ is where the graph of f is above the graph of g. Each square on the grid represents a horizontal distance of $\dfrac{\pi}{\left(\dfrac{4}{3}\right)}$, or $\dfrac{\pi}{12}$, rad.

Step 1
Determine the first point of intersection between $f(\theta)$ and $g(\theta)$.

The graphs of f and g intersect $\dfrac{\pi}{12}$ rad to the right of $\dfrac{\pi}{4}$ rad.

$$\dfrac{\pi}{4} + \dfrac{\pi}{12}$$
$$= \dfrac{3\pi}{12} + \dfrac{1\pi}{12}$$
$$= \dfrac{4\pi}{12}$$
$$= \dfrac{\pi}{3}$$

Step 2
Determine the second point of intersection between $f(\theta)$ and $g(\theta)$.

The graphs of f and g intersect $\dfrac{2\pi}{12}$ rad to the right of $\dfrac{\pi}{4}$ rad.

$$\dfrac{3\pi}{2} + \dfrac{2\pi}{12}$$
$$= \dfrac{18\pi}{12} + \dfrac{2\pi}{12}$$
$$= \dfrac{20\pi}{12}$$
$$= \dfrac{5\pi}{3}$$

The graph of f is above the graph of g between the points of intersections. The required interval is $\dfrac{\pi}{3} < \theta < \dfrac{5\pi}{3}$.

25. B

Step 1
Determine the value of b.

The periodic function $y = 6\sin\left[8(x - \pi)\right] + 5$ is in the form $y = a\sin\left[b(x - c)\right] + d$. In the function $y = 6\sin\left[8(x - \pi)\right] + 5$, the value of b is 8.

Step 2
Calculate the period of the function $y = 6\sin\left[8(x - \pi)\right] + 5$ using the formula $\text{period} = \dfrac{2\pi}{|b|}$.

$$\text{period} = \dfrac{2\pi}{|b|}$$
$$\text{period} = \dfrac{2\pi}{8}$$
$$\text{period} = \dfrac{\pi}{4}$$

26. C

Step 1
Determine the value of b.

The periodic function $h(t) = 9\sin\left[\dfrac{\pi}{20}(t - 10)\right] + 12$ is in the form $y = a\cos\left[b(x - c)\right] + d$.

Therefore, the value of b is $\dfrac{\pi}{20}$.

Step 2
Substitute the value of b into the period formula, and solve.

$$\text{period} = \dfrac{2\pi}{|b|}$$
$$\text{period} = \dfrac{2\pi}{\left(\dfrac{\pi}{20}\right)}$$
$$\text{period} = 2\pi\left(\dfrac{20}{\pi}\right)$$
$$\text{period} = 40$$

Therefore, it will take 40 s for the ferris wheel to complete one revolution.

27. D

Compare graph 2 with graph 1 to determine which parameters have changed on graph 1 to obtain graph 2.

Graphs 1 and 2 both have an amplitude of 1; therefore, there is no change in parameter a. The period of graph 1 is 2π, and the period of graph 2 is π. Therefore, there is a change in parameter b. There is no phase shift, so there is no change in parameter c. Graph 2 is obtained from the graph 1 by a vertical translation 3 units down. Therefore, there is a change in parameter d.

Therefore, graph 2 is obtained from graph 1 by changing the parameters b and d.

28. A

Step 1
Determine the maximum and minimum values.

In the given graph, the maximum value is 18, and the minimum value is 2.

Step 2
Determine the amplitude, a.

Apply the amplitude formula.

$$amplitude = \frac{maximum - minimum}{2}$$
$$amplitude = \frac{18 - 2}{2}$$
$$amplitude = \frac{16}{2}$$
$$amplitude = 8$$

Step 3
Determine the value of b.

From the graph, the period is 16 s. Apply the formula $period = \dfrac{2\pi}{|b|}$ to determine the value of b.

$$period = \frac{2\pi}{|b|}$$
$$16 = \frac{2\pi}{|b|}$$
$$|b| = \frac{2\pi}{16}$$
$$b = \frac{\pi}{8}$$

Step 4
Determine the phase shift, c.

The first maximum (18) occurs when $x = 8$. Therefore, the phase shift is 8 for the cosine function and 4 for the sine function.

An equation that represents the given graph is

$h(t) = 8\cos\left[\dfrac{\pi}{8}(t-8)\right] + 10$. For the sine function,

the equation would be $h(t) = 8\sin\left[\dfrac{\pi}{8}(t-4)\right] + 10$.

29. 32

From the range $-1 \leq y \leq 5$, the maximum value is 5, and the minimum value is -1.

Step 1
Determine the value of a.

The value of a is the amplitude. Apply the amplitude formula.

$$amplitude = \frac{maximum - minimum}{2}$$
$$amplitude = \frac{5 - (-1)}{2}$$
$$amplitude = 3$$

Therefore, the value of a is 3.

Step 2
Determine the value of b.

The value of b is the horizontal midline axis. Apply the horizontal midline axis formula.

$$y = \frac{maximum + minimum}{2}$$
$$y = \frac{5 + (-1)}{2}$$
$$y = 2$$

Therefore, the value of b is 2.

Therefore, $a = 3$, and $b = 2$.

Copyright Protected

30. 23.9

From the graph, the period of the function is $\dfrac{\pi}{75}$.

Therefore, the pitch of the note is calculated as follows:

$$\text{pitch} = \dfrac{1}{\text{period}}$$

$$\text{pitch} = \dfrac{1}{\dfrac{\pi}{75}}$$

$$\text{pitch} = \dfrac{75}{\pi}$$

$$\text{pitch} \approx 23.9 \text{ Hz}$$

31. C

The equation $f(\theta - 30°) = 0$ is obtained from $f(\theta) = 0$ by a phase shift of 30° to the right.

Thus, the solutions 0°, 180°, and 360° are also phase shifted 30° to the right, giving new solutions of 30°, 210°, and 390°.

32. B

Step 1
Factor the trigonometric equation, and apply the zero product property to each of the factors.

$$2\sin^2\theta - 3\sin\theta + 1 = 0$$
$$(2\sin\theta - 1)(\sin\theta - 1) = 0$$

$$
\begin{array}{ll}
2\sin\theta - 1 = 0 & \sin\theta - 1 = 0 \\
2\sin\theta = 1 & \sin\theta = 1 \\
\sin\theta = \dfrac{1}{2} &
\end{array}
$$

Step 2
Determine the values of θ using the unit circle.

Since $\sin\theta = y$, the values of θ are angles on the unit circle where the y-coordinate of its point on the unit circle is equal to $\dfrac{1}{2}$ or 1. Therefore, when $\sin\theta = \dfrac{1}{2}$, the values of θ are $\dfrac{\pi}{6}$ and $\dfrac{5\pi}{6}$.

When $\sin\theta = 1$, the value of θ is $\dfrac{\pi}{2}$.

Therefore, the solutions are $\theta = \dfrac{\pi}{6}, \dfrac{\pi}{2}$, and $\dfrac{5\pi}{6}$.

33. A

The equation $4\sin x - 1 = 0$ can be solved by graphing two functions and finding their points of intersections. One solution is to change the form of the equation to $y = 4\sin x$ and $y = 1$.

The pair $y = \sin x$ and $y = 1$ has $y = 1$ but also $y = \sin x$, which is not the same as $y = 4\sin x$ and $y = 1$. The other pairs of functions would give correct solutions.

34. A

If x is a solution of $\tan x = -1$, then $\dfrac{x}{3}$ is a solution of $\tan(3x) = -1$.

Divide the general solution of $\tan x = -1$ by 3.

$$x = \dfrac{3\pi}{4} + n\pi$$

$$\dfrac{x}{3} = \dfrac{\dfrac{3\pi}{4} + n\pi}{3}$$

$$\dfrac{x}{3} = \dfrac{\left(\dfrac{3\pi}{4}\right)}{3} + \dfrac{n\pi}{3}$$

$$\dfrac{x}{3} = \dfrac{\pi}{4} + \dfrac{n\pi}{3}$$

Therefore, the general solution of $\tan(3x) = -1$ is

$\dfrac{\pi}{4} + \dfrac{n\pi}{3}$, where $n \in I$.

35. D

The x-intercepts of $f(x) = \sin x$ are multiples of 180°. As such, the x-intercepts can be described by $x = 180°n$, where $n \in I$. Therefore, the value of a is 180.

36. B

Step 1
Apply the identity $\sin^2\theta + \cos^2\theta = 1$.

Let $\cos^2\theta = 1 - \sin^2\theta$, and simplify.

$$1 + \sin\theta = 2(1 - \sin^2\theta)$$
$$1 + \sin\theta = 2 - 2\sin^2\theta$$

Copyright Protected

Step 2

Bring all terms to one side, and solve for $\sin\theta$ by factoring.

$$1+\sin\theta = 2-2\sin^2\theta$$
$$2\sin^2\theta+\sin\theta-1=0$$
$$(2\sin\theta-1)(\sin\theta+1)=0$$

$$2\sin\theta-1=0 \qquad \sin\theta+1=0$$
$$2\sin\theta=1 \qquad\quad\; \sin\theta=-1$$
$$\sin\theta=\frac{1}{2}$$

Step 3

Determine the values of θ within the domain $0\le\theta\le 2\pi$.

Using the unit circle, the values of θ in the equation $\sin\theta=\frac{1}{2}$ are $\frac{\pi}{6}$ and $\frac{5\pi}{6}$. The value of θ in the equation $\sin\theta=-1$ is $\frac{3\pi}{2}$.

Therefore, $\theta=\frac{\pi}{6}$, $\frac{5\pi}{6}$, and $\frac{3\pi}{2}$.

37. 0

Step 1

Isolate $\cos\theta$.
$$2\cos\theta+6=8$$
$$2\cos\theta=2$$
$$\cos\theta=1$$

Step 2

Determine the value of θ.
$$\theta=\cos^{-1}(1)$$
$$\theta=0°$$

Within the domain $0°\le\theta<360°$, the value of θ is 0°.

38. 53.1

Step 1

Factor the equation, and apply the zero product property rule to each factor.
$$5\cos^2\theta-3\cos\theta=0$$
$$\cos\theta(5\cos\theta-3)=0$$

$$\cos\theta=0 \qquad 5\cos\theta-3=0$$
$$\qquad\qquad\quad 5\cos\theta=3$$
$$\qquad\qquad\quad \cos\theta=\frac{3}{5}$$

Step 2

Solve for θ.

Using the unit circle, the value of θ in the equation $\cos\theta=0$ is 90°. Using the inverse cosine function on a calculator, the value of θ in the equation $\cos\theta=\frac{3}{5}$ is $\cos^{-1}\left(\frac{3}{5}\right)\approx 53.1°$.

Step 3

Determine which values of θ fit the given domain $0°<\theta<90°$.

The given domain is $0°<\theta<90°$. Therefore, the value of θ that satisfies the equation is $\theta\approx 53.1°$.

39. B

Simplify the LHS to determine the expression that represents X.

Step 1

Apply the double-angle identity.
$$\frac{1+\cos(2x)}{2}=X$$
$$\frac{1+\left(\cos^2 x-\sin^2 x\right)}{2}=X$$
$$\frac{1+\cos^2 x-\sin^2 x}{2}=X$$

Step 2

Rearrange the terms in the numerator.
$$\frac{1+\cos^2 x-\sin^2 x}{2}=X$$
$$\frac{1-\sin^2 x+\cos^2 x}{2}=X$$

Step 3

Apply the Pythagorean identity.
$$\frac{1-\sin^2 x+\cos^2 x}{2}=X$$
$$\frac{\cos^2 x+\cos^2 x}{2}=X$$
$$\frac{2\cos^2 x}{2}=X$$
$$\cos^2 x=X$$

Therefore, to create an identity for the given equation, X would need to be $\cos^2 x$.

Not for Reproduction

40. D

In step 1, the student multiplied the numerator and the denominator by $1 + \sin x$.

$$\frac{1 + \sin x}{1 - \sin x}$$
$$= \frac{(1 + \sin x)(1 + \sin x)}{(1 - \sin x)(1 + \sin x)}$$

The student did not make any errors in step 1.

In step 2, the student expanded the numerator and denominator.

$$\frac{(1 + \sin x)(1 + \sin x)}{(1 - \sin x)(1 + \sin x)}$$
$$= \frac{1 + 2\sin x + \sin^2 x}{1 - \sin^2 x}$$

Then, the student applied the Pythagorean identity to the denominator.

$$\frac{1 + 2\sin x + \sin^2 x}{1 - \sin^2 x}$$
$$= \frac{1 + 2\sin x + \sin^2 x}{\cos^2 x}$$

The student did not make any errors in step 2.

In step 3, the student divided each term in the numerator by the denominator.

$$\frac{1 + 2\sin x + \sin^2 x}{\cos^2 x}$$
$$= \frac{1}{\cos^2 x} + \frac{2\sin x}{\cos^2 x} + \frac{\sin^2 x}{\cos^2 x}$$

The student did not make any errors in step 3.

In step 4, the student applied the reciprocal and quotient identities.

$$\frac{1}{\cos^2 x} + \frac{2\sin x}{\cos^2 x} + \frac{\sin^2 x}{\cos^2 x}$$
$$= \frac{1}{\cos^2 x} + 2 \times \frac{1}{\cos x} \times \frac{\sin x}{\cos x} + \frac{\sin^2 x}{\cos^2 x}$$
$$= \sec^2 x + 2\sec x \tan x + \tan^2 x$$

The student's first error occurs in step 4.

The student incorrectly replaced $\dfrac{1}{\cos x}$ with $\csc x$ instead of $\sec x$.

41. B

Step 1
Apply the quotient identities.
$$\tan A + \cot A = \csc A \sec A$$
$$\frac{\sin A}{\cos A} + \frac{\cos A}{\sin A} = \csc A \sec A$$

Step 2
Apply the reciprocal identities.
$$\frac{\sin A}{\cos A} + \frac{\cos A}{\sin A}$$
$$= \csc A \sec A$$
$$= \frac{1}{\sin A}\left(\frac{1}{\cos A}\right)$$
$$= \frac{1}{\sin A \cos A}$$

Step 3
Express the RHS as a single fraction.
$$\frac{\sin A}{\cos A} + \frac{\cos A}{\sin A} = \frac{1}{\sin A \cos A}$$
$$\frac{\sin^2 A}{\cos A \sin A} + \frac{\cos^2 A}{\cos A \sin A} = \frac{1}{\sin A \cos A}$$
$$\frac{\sin^2 A + \cos^2 A}{\cos A \sin A} = \frac{1}{\sin A \cos A}$$

Step 4
Apply the Pythagorean identity.
$$\frac{\sin^2 A + \cos^2 A}{\cos A \sin A} = \frac{1}{\sin A \cos A}$$
$$\frac{1}{\cos A \sin A} = \frac{1}{\sin A \cos A}$$
$$\frac{1}{\sin A \cos A} = \frac{1}{\sin A \cos A}$$

Therefore, Talia should arrive at expression $\dfrac{1}{\sin A \cos A}$ to prove the identity.

42. B

Step 1
Apply the quotient identity.
$$\sin \theta + (\cot \theta)(\cos \theta)$$
$$= \sin \theta + \left(\frac{\cos \theta}{\sin \theta}\right)(\cos \theta)$$
$$= \sin \theta + \frac{\cos^2 \theta}{\sin \theta}$$

Step 2

Write as a single fraction.

$$\sin\theta+\frac{\cos^2\theta}{\sin\theta}$$
$$=\frac{\sin^2\theta}{\sin\theta}+\frac{\cos^2\theta}{\sin\theta}$$
$$=\frac{\sin^2\theta+\cos^2\theta}{\sin\theta}$$

Step 3

Apply the Pythagorean identity.

$$\frac{\sin^2\theta+\cos^2\theta}{\sin\theta}$$
$$=\frac{1}{\sin\theta}$$

Step 4

Apply the reciprocal identity.

$$\frac{1}{\sin\theta}$$
$$=\csc\theta$$

43. B

Step 1

Find the value of $\tan\theta$.

Recall the Pythagorean identity, $1+\tan^2\theta=\sec^2\theta$. Substitute $\frac{11}{6}$ for $\sec\theta$, and solve for $\tan\theta$.

$$1+\tan^2\theta=\sec^2\theta$$
$$\tan^2\theta=\sec^2\theta-1$$
$$\tan^2\theta=\left(\frac{11}{6}\right)^2-1$$
$$\tan^2\theta=\frac{121}{36}-1$$
$$\tan^2\theta=\frac{85}{36}$$
$$\tan\theta=\pm\sqrt{\frac{85}{36}}$$
$$\tan\theta=\frac{\pm\sqrt{85}}{6}$$

Since θ is an angle in quadrant I, $\tan\theta$ is positive.

Therefore, $\tan\theta=\frac{\sqrt{85}}{6}$.

Step 2

Find the exact value of $\tan(2\theta)$.

Apply the identity double-angle identity $\tan(2\theta)=\frac{2\tan\theta}{1-\tan^2\theta}$.

Substitute $\frac{\sqrt{85}}{6}$ for $\tan\theta$, and solve for $\tan(2\theta)$.

$$\tan(2\theta)=\frac{2\tan\theta}{1-\tan^2\theta}$$
$$\tan(2\theta)=\frac{2\left(\frac{\sqrt{85}}{6}\right)}{1-\left(\frac{\sqrt{85}}{6}\right)^2}$$
$$\tan(2\theta)=\frac{\frac{\sqrt{85}}{3}}{1-\left(\frac{85}{36}\right)}$$
$$\tan(2\theta)=\frac{\frac{\sqrt{85}}{3}}{-\frac{49}{36}}$$
$$\tan(2\theta)=\left(\frac{\sqrt{85}}{3}\right)\left(-\frac{36}{49}\right)$$
$$\tan(2\theta)=-\frac{36\sqrt{85}}{147}$$
$$\tan(2\theta)=-\frac{12\sqrt{85}}{49}$$

Therefore, $\tan(2\theta)=-\frac{12\sqrt{85}}{49}$.

44. 1.15

Substitute $\frac{\pi}{6}$ for x, and evaluate each side of the equation.

$$\csc x\tan x=\sec x$$
$$\csc\left(\frac{\pi}{6}\right)\tan\left(\frac{\pi}{6}\right)=\sec\left(\frac{\pi}{6}\right)$$
$$2\left(\frac{1}{\sqrt{3}}\right)=\frac{2}{\sqrt{3}}$$
$$\frac{2}{\sqrt{3}}=\frac{2}{\sqrt{3}}$$
$$1.15\approx1.15$$

To the nearest hundredth, the LHS of the equation is 1.15.

Copyright Protected

Not for Reproduction

45. **WR**

Calculate the measure of θ using the arc length formula, $a = r\theta$.

Let $r = 18$, $a = 88$, and solve for θ.

$$a = r\theta$$
$$88 = (18)\theta$$
$$\frac{88}{18} = \theta$$
$$4.88 \approx \theta$$

Therefore, the measure of θ is 4.88 rad.

46. **WR**

Step 1
Determine the exact value of $\tan 30°$ by using the special triangle and primary trigonometric ratio.

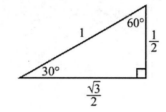

$$\tan \theta = \frac{\text{opposite}}{\text{adjacent}}$$
$$\tan 30° = \frac{\frac{1}{2}}{\frac{\sqrt{3}}{2}}$$
$$\tan 30° = \frac{1}{\sqrt{3}}$$

Step 2
Determine the exact value of $\tan 60°$ by using the special triangle and primary trigonometric ratio.

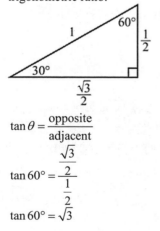

$$\tan \theta = \frac{\text{opposite}}{\text{adjacent}}$$
$$\tan 60° = \frac{\frac{\sqrt{3}}{2}}{\frac{1}{2}}$$
$$\tan 60° = \sqrt{3}$$

Step 3
Determine the exact value of $\tan 45°$ by using the special triangle and primary trigonometric ratio.

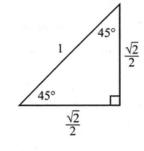

$$\tan \theta = \frac{\text{opposite}}{\text{adjacent}}$$
$$\tan 45° = \frac{\frac{\sqrt{2}}{2}}{\frac{\sqrt{2}}{2}}$$
$$\tan 45° = 1$$

Step 4

Evaluate the given expression.

$$\tan 30° + \frac{\tan 60°}{\tan 45°}$$
$$= \frac{1}{\sqrt{3}} + \frac{\sqrt{3}}{1}$$
$$= \frac{1}{\sqrt{3}} + \frac{3}{\sqrt{3}}$$
$$= \frac{4}{\sqrt{3}}$$
$$= \frac{4\sqrt{3}}{3}$$

Copyright Protected

47. **WR**

Since $\sec\theta=\dfrac{\sqrt{26}}{5}$, possible values are $x=5$ and $r=\sqrt{26}$.

Apply the Pythagorean theorem to find the value of y.

$$x^2+y^2=r^2$$
$$\left(5\right)^2+y^2=\left(\sqrt{26}\right)^2$$
$$25+y^2=26$$
$$y^2=1$$
$$y=\pm1$$

Since θ is in quadrant IV, y must be negative.

Thus, $\tan\theta=-\dfrac{1}{5}$.

48. **WR**

Compare the given sine function,

$y=-\dfrac{2}{5}\sin\left[-3\left(x+15°\right)\right]+4$ to the general sine

function, $y=a\sin\left[b\left(x-c\right)\right]+d$.

Step 1
Determine the amplitude.

The value of a is $-\dfrac{2}{5}$. Therefore, the amplitude

is $\left|-\dfrac{2}{5}\right|=\dfrac{2}{5}$.

Step 2
Determine the period.

The value of b is -3. Apply the formula

$\text{period}=\dfrac{360°}{|b|}$ to find the period.

$$\text{period}=\dfrac{360°}{|k|}$$
$$\text{period}=\dfrac{360°}{|-3|}$$
$$\text{period}=120°$$

Step 3
Determine the phase shift.

The value of c is $-15°$. Therefore, the phase shift is $15°$ to the left.

Step 4
Determine the domain.

The domain is $x\in\mathrm{R}$.

Step 5
Determine the range.

The range of a sine function

$y=a\sin\left[b\left(x-c\right)\right]+d$ is given by

$\left(-|a|+d\right)\le y\le\left(|a|+d\right)$.

The value of a is $-\dfrac{2}{5}$, and the value of d is 4.

$$\left(-|a|+c\right)\le y\le\left(|a|+c\right)$$
$$\left(-\left|-\dfrac{2}{5}\right|+4\right)\le y\le\left(\left|-\dfrac{2}{5}\right|+4\right)$$
$$\left(-\dfrac{2}{5}+4\right)\le y\le\left(\dfrac{2}{5}+4\right)$$
$$\dfrac{18}{5}\le y\le\dfrac{22}{5}$$

The range is $\dfrac{18}{5}\le y\le\dfrac{22}{5}$.

49. **WR**

Step 1
Factor, and apply the zero product property to each factor.

$$\sqrt{3}\tan^2\theta+\tan\theta=0$$
$$\tan\theta\left(\sqrt{3}\tan\theta+1\right)=0$$
$$\tan\theta=0 \quad \sqrt{3}\tan\theta+1=0$$
$$\sqrt{3}\tan\theta=-1$$
$$\tan\theta=-\dfrac{1}{\sqrt{3}}$$

Step 2
Determine the solution to the equation $\tan\theta=0$, where $0\le\theta\le2\pi$.

The values of θ for which $\tan\theta=0$ are 0 and π.

Not for Reproduction

Step 3
Determine the solution to the equation

$\tan\theta = -\dfrac{1}{\sqrt{3}}$, where $0 \le \theta \le 2\pi$.

According to the unit circle, the exact values of θ
in the equation $\tan\theta = -\dfrac{1}{\sqrt{3}}$ are $\dfrac{5\pi}{6}$

and $\dfrac{11\pi}{6}$.

Therefore, the solutions the equation

$\sqrt{3}\tan^2\theta + \tan\theta = 0$ are $\theta = 0, \dfrac{5\pi}{6}, \pi$, and $\dfrac{11\pi}{6}$.

50. **WR**

Step 1
Apply the identity
$\sin(A+B) = \sin A\cos B + \cos A\sin B$.

Since $\sin\left(\dfrac{\pi}{2} + \theta\right)$, it follows that $A = \dfrac{\pi}{2}$ and

$B = \theta$. Therefore, the expression can be rewritten

as $\sin\left(\dfrac{\pi}{2} + \theta\right) = \sin\left(\dfrac{\pi}{2}\right)\cos\theta + \cos\left(\dfrac{\pi}{2}\right)\sin\theta$.

Step 2
Evaluate.

Replace $\cos\theta$ with $-\dfrac{3}{5}$ and $\sin\theta$ with $\dfrac{4}{5}$.

$\sin\left(\dfrac{\pi}{2} + \theta\right)$

$= \sin\left(\dfrac{\pi}{2}\right)\left(-\dfrac{3}{5}\right) + \cos\left(\dfrac{\pi}{2}\right)\left(\dfrac{4}{5}\right)$

$= 1\left(-\dfrac{3}{5}\right) + 0\left(\dfrac{4}{5}\right)$

$= -\dfrac{3}{5}$

The exact value of $\sin\left(\dfrac{\pi}{2} + \theta\right)$ is $-\dfrac{3}{5}$.

UNIT TEST—TRIGONOMETRY

Use the following information to answer the next question.

A triangle is shown.

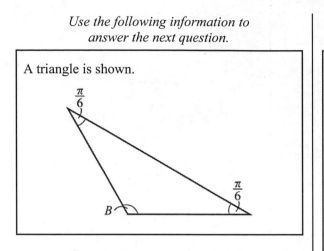

1. If $\angle B$ is sketched in standard position on the Cartesian plane, in which quadrant will it terminate?

   A. I   **B.** II

   C. III   **D.** IV

Use the following information to answer the next question.

The given diagram illustrates an angle, θ, drawn in standard position with its terminal arm in quadrant II.

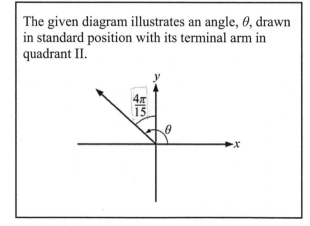

2. Which of the following angles is coterminal with angle θ?

   A. $-\dfrac{34\pi}{15}$ **B.** $-\dfrac{49\pi}{15}$

   C. $-\dfrac{67\pi}{30}$ **D.** $-\dfrac{97\pi}{30}$

Use the following information to answer the next question.

Two points, A and B, are on Earth's equator, and point C is at the centre of Earth. The measure of $\angle ACB$ is 74°, as shown below.

3. If the circumference of Earth at the equator is approximately 40 070 km, then the shortest arc length from point A to point B, correct to the nearest kilometre, is

   A. 31 026 km

   B. 16 474 km

   C. 8 237 km

   D. 4 938 km

4. The exact value of $\cos\left(\dfrac{5\pi}{3}\right) - \cos\pi$ is $\dfrac{A}{B}$, where A and B represent integers. If $A \geq 0$ and $B > 0$, then the minimum value of A is

   A. 0

   B. 1

   C. 2

   D. 3

Copyright Protected

5. The exact value of

   $\tan\left(\dfrac{3\pi}{4}\right) - \tan\left(\dfrac{7\pi}{4}\right) + \tan\pi$ is

   A. 2

   B. 0

   C. –2

   D. undefined

6. If the exact value of $\csc 570°$ is $\dfrac{A}{B}$, where

   A and B are integers and $B > 0$, then the value of A is

   A. –2

   B. –1

   C. 0

   D. 1

7. What is the value of the expression

   $\cos 330° \sin\left(\dfrac{4\pi}{3}\right) + \cot\left(\dfrac{\pi}{2}\right)\sec 120°$?

   A. $-\dfrac{3}{4}$

   B. $-\dfrac{1}{2}$

   C. 0

   D. 1

   Use the following information to answer the next question.

   Angle θ is in standard position with its terminal arm in quadrant II. The terminal arm has a length of $\sqrt{29}$ and contains point $P(x, 5)$.

   ---

8. What is the value of $\cot\theta$?

   A. $-\dfrac{5}{2}$ B. $-\dfrac{2}{5}$

   C. $\dfrac{2}{5}$ D. $\dfrac{5}{2}$

9. If $\tan\theta = \dfrac{4}{3}$ and $\sin\theta < 0$, then the value of

   $(\sin\theta - \cos\theta)^2$ is

   A. $\dfrac{1}{25}$

   B. $\dfrac{16}{25}$

   C. $\dfrac{24}{25}$

   D. $\dfrac{49}{25}$

10. What is the exact value of

    $\cos^{-1}\left(\dfrac{1}{2}\right) - \cos^{-1}\left(-\dfrac{\sqrt{2}}{2}\right)$?

    A. $\dfrac{7\pi}{12}$

    B. $\dfrac{13\pi}{12}$

    C. $-\dfrac{5\pi}{12}$

    D. $-\dfrac{7\pi}{12}$

11. If $\sin\theta = 0.8$ and $\dfrac{\pi}{2} < \theta < \pi$, then $\tan\theta$ is

    A. $-\dfrac{4}{5}$

    B. $-\dfrac{4}{3}$

    C. $-\dfrac{3}{5}$

    D. $-\dfrac{3}{4}$

12. The period of the function
$f(\theta) = 2\sin(5\theta - 3)$ is

A. $\dfrac{\pi}{5}$

B. $\dfrac{2\pi}{5}$

C. 5π

D. 10π

Use the following information to answer the next question.

The two sets of numbers shown on the graph below represent the highest and lowest temperatures over 12 months at Waterton National Park in southern Alberta.

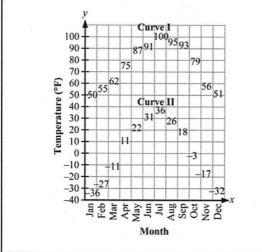

13. Each of these sets of numbers can be modelled by a sinusoidal curve of the form $y = a\sin[b(t-c)] + d$. The two parameters in the equation representing curve I that would change the most in value in the equation representing curve II are

A. a and b

B. b and c

C. c and d

D. a and d

14. Which of the following statements does **not** describe the graph of $f(\theta) = -3\sin\left(\theta - \dfrac{\pi}{2}\right)$?

A. The amplitude is 3.

B. The period is 2π.

C. The graph of $f(\theta) = -3\sin\left(\theta - \dfrac{\pi}{2}\right)$ is the same as the graph of $f(\theta) = -3\sin(\theta)$ with a phase shift of $\dfrac{\pi}{2}$ to the right.

D. The graph of $f(\theta) = -3\sin\left(\theta - \dfrac{\pi}{2}\right)$ is the same as the graph of $f(\theta) = \sin\left(\theta - \dfrac{\pi}{2}\right)$ with a vertical translation of 3 units down.

Use the following information to answer the next question.

A student is investigating the effects of changing the values of the parameters a, b, c, and d in the equation $y = a\sin[b(\theta + c)] + d$. The graph of each of the following functions is plotted:

$$f(\theta) = \sin\theta$$
$$g(\theta) = 2\sin\theta$$
$$h(\theta) = \sin 2\theta$$
$$k(\theta) = \sin(\theta + 2)$$
$$l(\theta) = \sin\theta + 2$$

15. The equation whose graph will have the same θ-intercepts as the graph of $y = f(\theta)$ is

A. $y = g(\theta)$

B. $y = h(\theta)$

C. $y = k(\theta)$

D. $y = l(\theta)$

Copyright Protected

Not for Reproduction

Use the following information to answer the next question.

The height of a particular tide at time t, in hours, is given by the function $h(t) = 3\sin\left(\dfrac{\pi}{14}t\right) + 5$.

16. How long does the tide take to reach its first maximum height?

A. 7 h

B. 8 h

C. 9 h

D. 10 h

Use the following information to answer the next question.

The partial graph of the function $f(\theta) = a\sin(\theta + c) + d$ is shown below.

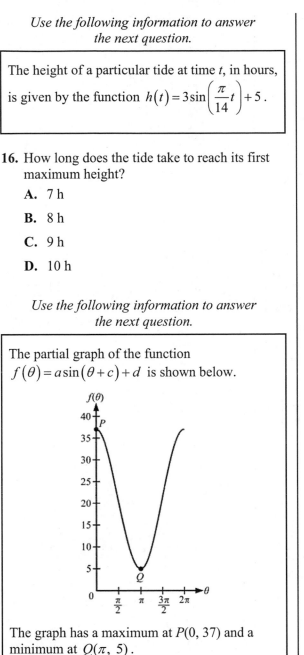

The graph has a maximum at $P(0, 37)$ and a minimum at $Q(\pi, 5)$.

Numerical Response

17. Based on the information above, the value of d, correct to the nearest **whole** number, is _____.

18. What are the exact values of θ for the equation $2\sin\theta = \sin\theta$, where $0° \le \theta < 360°$?

A. 90° and 180°

B. 0° and 30°

C. 90° and 270°

D. 0° and 180°

19. What is the approximate solution to the equation $2\sin^2\theta + \tan^2\theta - 1 = 0$, if $0 \le \theta \le 90°$?

A. 23.8°

B. 29.2°

C. 32.8°

D. 47.2°

20. The horizontal line $y = 2$ intersects the graph of $y = 2\sin^2\theta + 3\sin\theta$ at two points in the interval $0 \le \theta \le \pi$. The θ values of the points of intersection can be found by solving

A. $2\sin^2\theta + 3\sin\theta = 2$

B. $2\sin^2\theta + 3\sin\theta = -2$

C. $2\sin^2\theta + 3\sin\theta = 0$

D. $2\sin^2\theta = 0$ and $3\sin\theta = 0$

21. If $2\sin\theta\cos\theta - \cos\theta = 0$, $0 \le \theta < 2\pi$, then the values of θ are

A. $0, \dfrac{\pi}{3}, \pi$, and $\dfrac{5\pi}{3}$

B. $0, \dfrac{\pi}{3}, \dfrac{5\pi}{6}$, and $\dfrac{3\pi}{2}$

C. $\dfrac{\pi}{6}, \dfrac{\pi}{2}, \pi$, and $\dfrac{5\pi}{3}$

D. $\dfrac{\pi}{6}, \dfrac{\pi}{2}, \dfrac{5\pi}{6}$ and $\dfrac{3\pi}{2}$

22. A student was asked to determine an expression for $\cos(2x)$, given $\cos x = k$. He began with $\cos(2x) = \cos(x + x)$ and determined that an expression for $\cos(2x)$, in terms of k, is

A. -1

B. $2k$

C. $2k - 1$

D. $2k^2 - 1$

Use the following information to answer the next question.

Terry is flying a gas-powered model airplane on a circular path that subtends an angle of $\dfrac{3\pi}{4}$ rad. The distance from the centre of the circular path to the airplane is 15 m.

Written Response

23. **a)** Sketch the path of the plane in standard position if the centre of the circular path is the origin.

b) To the nearest hundredth, what distance is travelled by the plane?

Written Response

24. If $\tan\theta = -\dfrac{5}{2}$ and $\dfrac{\pi}{2} \le \theta \le \pi$, what are the exact values of $\sin\theta$ and $\cos\theta$?

Copyright Protected

Not for Reproduction

Written Response

25. Determine the solution to the equation
$2\sin^2\theta + 2\sin\theta - \sqrt{3}\sin\theta - \sqrt{3} = 0$,
if $0 \le \theta \le 360°$.

Written Response

26. If $\sin\theta = -\dfrac{2}{3}$ and $\cos\theta = \dfrac{4}{3}$, what is the exact value of $\cos(\pi + \theta)$?

Copyright Protected

ANSWERS AND SOLUTIONS—UNIT TEST

1. B	7. A	13. D	19. C	25. WR
2. D	8. B	14. D	20. A	26. WR
3. C	9. A	15. A	21. D	
4. D	10. C	16. A	22. D	
5. B	11. B	17. 21	23. WR	
6. A	12. B	18. D	24. WR	

1. B

Step 1

Determine the value of $\angle B$.

Since the sum of the angles is equal to π (180°),

subtract the two $\dfrac{\pi}{6}$ angles from π.

$$\angle B = \pi - \frac{\pi}{6} - \frac{\pi}{6}$$
$$\angle B = \frac{6\pi}{6} - \frac{\pi}{6} - \frac{\pi}{6}$$
$$\angle B = \frac{4\pi}{6}$$
$$\angle B = \frac{2\pi}{3}$$

Step 2

Determine the quadrant in which the

angle $\dfrac{2\pi}{3}$ rad terminates.

Since π is half a revolution, $\dfrac{2\pi}{3}$ rad is $\dfrac{2}{3}$ of half

a revolution. This sketch shows an angle

of $\dfrac{2\pi}{3}$ rad in standard position.

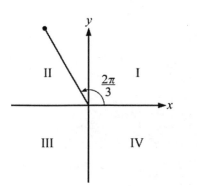

Therefore, $\angle B$ (or $\dfrac{2\pi}{3}$ rad) terminates in

quadrant II.

2. D

Step 1

Determine the measure of angle θ.

Since θ is quadrant II, add $\dfrac{\pi}{2}$ to $\dfrac{4\pi}{15}$.

$$\frac{4\pi}{15} + \frac{\pi}{2}$$
$$= \frac{8\pi}{30} + \frac{15\pi}{30}$$
$$= \frac{23\pi}{30} \text{ rad}$$

Step 2

Determine which of the given angles is coterminal
with angle θ.

For any angle, θ, measured in radians, all angles
of the form $(\theta + 2\pi n)$ rad, where $n \in I$, will be
coterminal with angle θ.

To find an angle coterminal with $\dfrac{23\pi}{30}$, let $n = -2$

and $\theta = \dfrac{23\pi}{30}$.

$$(\theta + 2\pi n)$$
$$= \frac{23\pi}{30} + 2\pi(-2)$$
$$= \frac{23\pi}{30} - 4\pi$$
$$= \frac{23\pi}{30} - \frac{120}{30}\pi$$
$$= -\frac{97\pi}{30} \text{ rad}$$

Not for Reproduction

3. C

Step 1

Set up a ratio that compares the angles and arc lengths.

$$\frac{74°}{360°} = \frac{a}{40\ 070}$$

Step 2

Solve for a.

$$\frac{74°}{360°} = \frac{a}{40\ 070}$$
$$74 \times 40\ 070 = 360 \times a$$
$$\frac{74 \times 40\ 070}{360} = a$$
$$8\ 327\ \text{km} \approx a$$

4. D

Step 1

Determine the exact value of $\cos\left(\dfrac{5\pi}{3}\right)$.

According to the unit circle, the point on the terminal arm of the angle $\dfrac{5\pi}{3}$ rad is $\left(\dfrac{1}{2}, -\dfrac{\sqrt{3}}{2}\right)$.

Since $\cos\theta = x$ on the unit circle, and the x-coordinate of the ordered pair $\left(\dfrac{1}{2}, -\dfrac{\sqrt{3}}{2}\right)$ is $\dfrac{1}{2}$,

it follows that $\cos\left(\dfrac{5\pi}{3}\right) = \dfrac{1}{2}$.

Step 2

Determine the exact value of $\cos\pi$.

Referring to the unit circle, the point on the terminal arm of the angle π rad is $(-1, 0)$. Since $\cos\theta = x$ on the unit circle, and the x-coordinate of the ordered pair $(-1, 0)$ is -1, it follows that $\cos\pi = -1$.

Step 3

Evaluate the given expression by substituting $\dfrac{1}{2}$ for $\cos\left(\dfrac{5\pi}{3}\right)$ and -1 for $\cos(\pi)$.

$$\cos\left(\frac{5\pi}{3}\right) - \cos\pi$$
$$= \frac{1}{2} - (-1)$$
$$= \frac{1}{2} + 1$$
$$= \frac{3}{2}$$

Step 4

Determine the value of A.

It is given that $\cos\left(\dfrac{5\pi}{3}\right) - \cos\pi = \dfrac{A}{B}$, and it has been determined that $\cos\left(\dfrac{5\pi}{3}\right) - \cos\pi = \dfrac{3}{2}$.

It then follows that the minimum value of A is 3.

5. B

According to the unit circle, the value of $\tan\left(\dfrac{3\pi}{4}\right)$ and $\tan\left(\dfrac{7\pi}{4}\right)$ is -1, and the value of $\tan\pi$ is 0.

Substitute the known values into the expression, and simplify.

$$\tan\left(\frac{3\pi}{4}\right) - \tan\left(\frac{7\pi}{4}\right) + \tan(\pi)$$
$$= -1 - (-1) - 0$$
$$= 0$$

The exact value of $\tan\left(\dfrac{3\pi}{4}\right) - \tan\left(\dfrac{7\pi}{4}\right) + \tan(\pi)$ is 0.

Copyright Protected

6. **A**

Step 1
Determine the exact value of csc570°.

The angle 570° is coterminal with 210°. On the unit circle, $\csc\theta = \dfrac{1}{y}$, and the point on the terminal arm of 210° is $\left(-\dfrac{\sqrt{3}}{2}, -\dfrac{1}{2}\right)$. Therefore, the exact value of csc570° is $\dfrac{1}{\left(-\dfrac{1}{2}\right)} = -2$

Step 2
Determine the value of A.

It is given that $\csc 570° = \dfrac{A}{B}$, $B > 0$, and it has been determined that $\csc 570° = -2 = -\dfrac{2}{1}$.
Therefore, $A = -2$.

7. **A**

Step 1
Evaluate the expression $\cos 330° \sin\left(\dfrac{4\pi}{3}\right)$.

According to the unit circle, $\cos 330° = \dfrac{\sqrt{3}}{2}$, and $\sin\left(\dfrac{4\pi}{3}\right) = -\dfrac{\sqrt{3}}{2}$. Therefore, the expression is evaluated as follows:
$$\cos 330° \sin\left(\dfrac{4\pi}{3}\right)$$
$$= \left(\dfrac{\sqrt{3}}{2}\right)\left(-\dfrac{\sqrt{3}}{2}\right)$$
$$= -\dfrac{3}{4}$$

Step 2
Evaluate the expression $\cot\left(\dfrac{\pi}{2}\right)\sec 120°$.

According to the unit circle, $\cot\left(\dfrac{\pi}{2}\right) = 0$, and $\sec 120° = \dfrac{1}{-\dfrac{1}{2}} = -2$. Therefore, the expression is evaluated as follows:
$$\cot\left(\dfrac{\pi}{2}\right)\sec 120°$$
$$= (0)(-2)$$
$$= 0$$

Step 3
Evaluate the expression $\cos 330° \sin\left(\dfrac{4\pi}{3}\right) + \cot\left(\dfrac{\pi}{2}\right)\sec 120°$.
$$\cos 330° \sin\left(\dfrac{4\pi}{3}\right) + \cot\left(\dfrac{\pi}{2}\right)\sec 120°$$
$$= -\dfrac{3}{4} + 0$$
$$= -\dfrac{3}{4}$$

8. **B**

Step 1
Sketch a diagram.

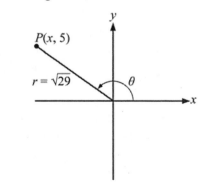

The terminal arm for angle θ lies in the second quadrant, $r = \sqrt{29}$, and $y = 5$.

Not for Reproduction

Step 2

Determine the exact value of $\cot\theta = \dfrac{x}{y}$.

The cotangent ratio is $\cot\theta = \dfrac{x}{y}$. Since the values of y and r are given, apply the Pythagorean theorem to determine the value of x.

$$r = x^2 + y^2$$
$$\left(\sqrt{29}\right)^2 = x^2 + 5^2$$
$$29 = x^2 + 25$$
$$4 = x^2$$
$$\pm 2 = x$$

Since θ is an angle terminating in quadrant II, x must be -2. Therefore, $\cot\theta = -\dfrac{2}{5}$.

9. A

Step 1
Identify the quadrant in which angle θ terminates.

Since the tangent ratio is positive and the sine ratio is negative, angle θ terminates in quadrant III.

Step 2
Determine the value of r using the Pythagorean theorem.

Possible values for x and y in quadrant III are $y = -4$ and $x = -3$.
$$r^2 = x^2 + y^2$$
$$r^2 = (-3)^2 + (-4)^2$$
$$r^2 = 9 + 16$$
$$r^2 = 25$$
$$r = \sqrt{25}$$
$$r = 5$$

Step 3
Determine the values of $\sin\theta$ and $\cos\theta$.

Let $x = -3$, $y = -4$, and $r = 5$.
$$\sin\theta = \frac{y}{r} = -\frac{4}{5}$$
$$\cos\theta = \frac{x}{r} = -\frac{3}{5}$$

Step 4
Evaluate $\left(\sin\theta - \cos\theta\right)^2$.

$$\left(\sin\theta - \cos\theta\right)^2$$
$$= \left(\left(-\frac{4}{5}\right) - \left(-\frac{3}{5}\right)\right)^2$$
$$= \left(-\frac{4}{5} + \frac{3}{5}\right)^2$$
$$= \left(-\frac{1}{5}\right)^2$$
$$= \frac{1}{25}$$

10. C

Step 1

Determine the exact values of the two inverse cosines.

According to the unit circle, the terminal arm of the angle $\dfrac{\pi}{3}$ has the point in quadrant I with coordinates $\left(\dfrac{1}{2}, \dfrac{\sqrt{3}}{2}\right)$. Since the x-coordinate is equal to the cosine of the angle, the value of $\cos^{-1}\left(\dfrac{1}{2}\right) = \dfrac{\pi}{3}$. Likewise, the terminal arm of the angle $\dfrac{3\pi}{4}$ has the point in quadrant II with coordinates $\left(-\dfrac{\sqrt{2}}{2}, \dfrac{\sqrt{2}}{2}\right)$, so the value of $\cos^{-1}\left(-\dfrac{\sqrt{2}}{2}\right) = \dfrac{3\pi}{4}$.

Step 2
Determine the exact value of the given expression.
$$\cos^{-1}\left(\frac{1}{2}\right) - \cos^{-1}\left(-\frac{\sqrt{2}}{2}\right)$$
$$= \frac{\pi}{3} - \frac{3\pi}{4}$$
$$= \frac{4\pi}{12} - \frac{9\pi}{12}$$
$$= -\frac{5\pi}{12}$$

Copyright Protected

11. B

If $\sin \theta = 0.8$ and $\dfrac{\pi}{2} < \theta < \pi$, then θ is in quadrant

II. Rewrite the equation $\sin \theta = 0.8$ as $\sin \theta = \dfrac{8}{10}$.

Therefore, $y = 8$ and $r = 10$.

Apply the Pythagorean theorem to find the value of x.

$x^2 + y^2 = r^2$

$x^2 + 8^2 = 10^2$

$x^2 + 64 = 100$

$x^2 = 36$

$x = \pm 6$

Since θ is in quadrant II, then x is –6.

Therefore, the exact value of $\tan \theta$ is $-\dfrac{8}{6}$,

or $-\dfrac{4}{3}$.

12. B

In the general sine function

$y = a \sin\left[b(\theta - c)\right] + d$, the period is $\dfrac{2\pi}{|b|}$.

Step 1

Write the function $f(\theta) = 2\sin(5\theta - 3)$ in the

form $y = a\sin\left[b(\theta - c)\right] + d$.

$f(\theta) = 2\sin(5\theta - 3)$

$f(\theta) = 2\sin\left[5\left(\theta - \dfrac{3}{5}\right)\right]$

Step 2

Determine the period of the function.

The value of b is 5. Therefore, the period of the

function is $\dfrac{2\pi}{5}$.

13. D

The two curves differ in amplitude and each have a different horizontal midline axis. Amplitude is affected by parameter a, and the horizontal midline axis is affected by d. Therefore, the two parameters in curve I that would change the most to obtain curve II are a and d.

14. D

Step 1

Determine the amplitude.

The value of a is –3. Therefore, the amplitude is $|-3| = 3$.

Statement **A** is true.

Step 2

Determine the period.

The value of b is 1. Therefore, the period is

$\dfrac{2\pi}{|1|} = 2\pi$.

Statement **B** is true.

Step 3

Determine the phase shift.

The value of c is $\dfrac{\pi}{2}$, which means there is a phase

shift $\dfrac{\pi}{2}$ units to the right.

Statement **C** is true.

Step 4

Determine the vertical translation.

The value of d is 0, which means there is no vertical translation.

Statement **D** is false.

15. A

When parameter a alone is changed (that is, when only the amplitude is changed), there will be no change in the θ-intercepts. Changing the parameters b, c, or d will have an effect on the θ-intercepts. Therefore, the θ-intercepts of $g(\theta) = 2\sin \theta$ will be the same as those of $f(\theta) = \sin \theta$ because only parameter a is changed.

Not for Reproduction

16. A

Step 1
Determine the values of a and d.

In the given function $h(t) = 3\sin\left(\dfrac{\pi}{14}t\right) + 5$, $a = 3$,

and $d = 5$.

Step 2
Determine the maximum height.

The maximum height is given by $|a| + d$.

$|a| + d$
$= |3| + 5$
$= 3 + 5$
$= 8$

Step 3

Let $h(t) = 8$ in the function $h(t) = 3\sin\left(\dfrac{\pi}{14}t\right) + 5$.

$h(t) = 3\sin\left(\dfrac{\pi}{14}t\right) + 5$

$8 = 3\sin\left(\dfrac{\pi}{14}t\right) + 5$

Step 4
Solve for t.

$8 = 3\sin\left(\dfrac{\pi}{14}t\right) + 5$

$3 = 3\sin\left(\dfrac{\pi}{14}t\right)$

$1 = \sin\left(\dfrac{\pi}{14}t\right)$

$\sin^{-1}(1) = \dfrac{\pi}{14}t$

$\dfrac{\pi}{2} = \dfrac{\pi}{14}t$

$\dfrac{14\pi}{2\pi} = t$

$7 = t$

Therefore, the tide takes 7 h to reach its maximum height (8 m).

17. 21

The value of d is equal to the horizontal midline axis. The horizontal midline axis is determined

using the formula $y = \dfrac{\text{maximum} + \text{minimum}}{2}$

Step 1
Determine the maximum and minimum values.

From the given graph, the maximum value of $f(\theta)$ is 37, and the minimum value is 5.

Step 2
Calculate the value of d.

$y = \dfrac{\text{maximum} + \text{minimum}}{2}$

$y = \dfrac{37 + 5}{2}$

$y = \dfrac{42}{2}$

$y = 21$

Therefore, the value of d is 21.

18. D

Step 1
Bring all terms with to one side, and solve for θ.

$2\sin\theta = \sin\theta$

$2\sin\theta - \sin\theta = 0$

$\sin\theta = 0$

Step 2
Determine the value of θ, where $0° \leq \theta < 360°$.

According to the unit circle, the values of θ in the equation $\sin\theta = 0$ are 0° and 180°.

Copyright Protected

19. C

The solutions of a trigonometric equation are the zeros of the corresponding trigonometric function and the x-intercepts on the graph of the trigonometric function.

Step 1
Graph the related function using a TI-83 or similar calculator.

Enter the equation as $Y_1 = 2\sin(X)^2 + \tan(X)^2 - 1$, and press $\boxed{\text{GRAPH}}$. Ensure your calculator is in degree mode. An appropriate window setting is $x{:}[0, 90, 45]$ and $y{:}[-3, 3, 1]$.

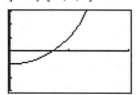

Step 2
Determine the x-intercept of the graph.

Find the x-intercept of the graph using the zero feature on the calculator.

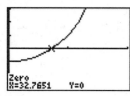

Therefore, the solution of θ is approximately 32.8°.

20. A

Given that the horizontal line $y = 2$ intersects the graph of $y = 2\sin^2\theta + 3\sin\theta$ at two points, the values of θ can be solved using the equation $2\sin^2\theta + 3\sin\theta = 2$.

21. D

Step 1
Factor the equation, and apply the zero product property to each factor.
$$2\sin\theta\cos\theta - \cos\theta = 0$$
$$\cos\theta(2\sin\theta - 1) = 0$$
$$\cos\theta = 0 \qquad 2\sin\theta - 1 = 0$$
$$2\sin\theta = 1$$
$$\sin\theta = \frac{1}{2}$$

Step 2
Determine the values of θ where $0 \le \theta \le 2\pi$.

According to the unit circle, the values of θ in the equation $\cos\theta = 0$ are $\dfrac{\pi}{2}$ and $\dfrac{3\pi}{2}$. The values of θ in the equation $\sin\theta = \dfrac{1}{2}$ are $\dfrac{\pi}{6}$ and $\dfrac{5\pi}{6}$.

Therefore, the values of θ that satisfy the equation $2\sin\theta\cos\theta - \cos\theta = 0$ are $\theta = \dfrac{\pi}{6}, \dfrac{\pi}{2}, \dfrac{5\pi}{6}$, and $\dfrac{3\pi}{2}$.

22. D

Step 1
Apply the sum formula for cosine.
$$\cos(2x) = \cos(x + x)$$
$$\cos(2x) = \cos x \cos x - \sin x \sin x$$
$$\cos(2x) = \cos^2 x - \sin^2 x$$

Step 2
Apply the Pythagorean identity $\cos^2 x + \sin^2 x = 1$.

Substitute $1 - \cos^2 x$ for $\sin^2 x$, and simplify.
$$\cos(2x) = \cos^2 x - \sin^2 x$$
$$\cos(2x) = \cos^2 x - (1 - \cos^2 x)$$
$$\cos(2x) = \cos^2 x - 1 + \cos^2 x$$
$$\cos(2x) = 2\cos^2 x - 1$$

Step 3
Let $\cos x = k$ in the equation $\cos(2x) = 2\cos^2 x - 1$, and simplify.
$$\cos(2x) = 2\cos^2 x - 1$$
$$\cos(2x) = 2(k)^2 - 1$$
$$\cos(2x) = 2k^2 - 1$$

23. WR

a) The angle $\dfrac{3\pi}{4}$ rad terminates in quadrant II, and the length of its terminal arm is 15 m. The path of the airplane is represented by the solid black curve in the given diagram.

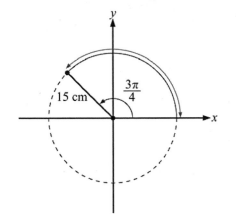

b) Calculate the distance using the arc length formula, $a = r\theta$.

Let $r = 15$ and $\dfrac{3\pi}{4}$ rad.

$a = r\theta$

$a = (15)\left(\dfrac{3\pi}{4}\right)$

$a \approx 35.34$

Therefore, the distance travelled by the plane is 35.34 m.

24. WR

Since $\tan\theta = \dfrac{y}{x}$ and $\dfrac{\pi}{2} \le \theta \le \pi$, angle θ is in quadrant II, and possible values for x and y are -2 and 5, respectively.

Step 1
Determine the value of r.

Apply the Pythagorean theorem to determine the value of r.
$r^2 = x^2 + y^2$
$r^2 = (-2)^2 + (5)^2$
$r^2 = 4 + 25$
$r^2 = 29$
$r = \sqrt{29}$

Step 2
Determine the exact values of $\sin\theta$ and $\cos\theta$.

$\sin\theta = \dfrac{y}{r} \qquad\qquad \cos\theta = \dfrac{x}{r}$

$\sin\theta = \dfrac{5}{\sqrt{29}} \qquad\quad \cos\theta = \dfrac{-2}{\sqrt{29}}$

$\qquad\qquad\qquad\qquad \cos\theta = -\dfrac{2}{\sqrt{29}}$

25. WR

Step 1

Factor the equation by grouping, and apply the zero product property to each factor.
$$2\sin^2\theta + 2\sin\theta - \sqrt{3}\sin\theta - \sqrt{3} = 0$$
$$\left(2\sin^2\theta + 2\sin\theta\right) + \left(-\sqrt{3}\sin\theta - \sqrt{3}\right) = 0$$
$$2\sin\theta(\sin\theta + 1) - \sqrt{3}(\sin\theta + 1) = 0$$
$$(\sin\theta + 1)(2\sin\theta - \sqrt{3}) = 0$$

$\sin\theta + 1 = 0 \qquad\qquad 2\sin\theta - \sqrt{3} = 0$
$\sin\theta = -1 \qquad\qquad\quad 2\sin\theta = \sqrt{3}$
$\qquad\qquad\qquad\qquad\qquad \sin\theta = \dfrac{\sqrt{3}}{2}$

Step 2
Determine the solution to the equation $\sin\theta - -1$.

Within the domain $0° \le \theta \le 360°$, the value of θ in the equation $\sin\theta = -1$ is 270°.

Step 3
Determine the general solution for the equation $\sin\theta = \dfrac{\sqrt{3}}{2}$.

Within the domain $0° \le \theta \le 360°$, the values of θ in the equation $\sin\theta = \dfrac{\sqrt{3}}{2}$ are 60° and 120°.

Step 4
State the solution for the equation $2\sin^2\theta + 2\sin\theta - \sqrt{3}\sin\theta - \sqrt{3} = 0$.

The solutions to the equation are 60°, 120°, and 270°.

26. **WR**

Step 1
Apply the identity
$\cos(A+B) = \cos A \cos B - \sin A \sin B$.

Since $\cos(\pi + \theta)$, it follows that $A = \pi$ and $B = \theta$. Therefore, the expression can be rewritten as
$\cos(\pi + \theta) = \cos \pi \cos \theta - \sin \pi \sin \theta$.

Step 2
Evaluate.

Replace $\cos \theta$ with $\dfrac{4}{3}$ and $\sin \theta$ with $-\dfrac{2}{3}$.

$\cos(\pi + \theta)$
$= \cos \pi \cos \theta - \sin \pi \sin \theta$
$= \cos \pi \left(\dfrac{4}{3}\right) - \sin \pi \left(-\dfrac{2}{3}\right)$
$= (-1)\left(\dfrac{4}{3}\right) - (0)\left(-\dfrac{2}{3}\right)$
$= -\dfrac{4}{3}$

The exact value of $\cos(\pi + \theta)$ is $-\dfrac{4}{3}$.

Copyright Protected

Copyright Protected

RELATIONS AND FUNCTIONS

Table of Correlations				
Specific Expectation	**Practice Questions**	**Unit Test Questions**	**Practice Test 1**	**Practice Test 2**
It is expected that students will:				
Develop algebraic and graphical reasoning through the study of relations.				
RF.1 Demonstrate an understanding of operations on, and compositions of, functions.	1, 2, 3, 4, 5, 6	1, 35	13, 14	12, 13
RF.2 Demonstrate an understanding of the effects of horizontal and vertical translations on the graphs of functions and their related equations.	7, 8, 9, 10, 70	2, 3, 4	15	14
RF.3 Demonstrate an understanding of the effects of horizontal and vertical stretches on the graphs of functions and their related equations.	11, 12, 13, 14, 15	5, 6	16	15
RF.4 Apply translations and stretches to the graphs and equations of functions.	16, 17, 18, 19, 20	7, 8, 9	17	16
RF.5 Demonstrate an understanding of the effects of reflections on the graphs of functions and their related equations, including reflections through the: x-axis; y-axis; and line y = x.	21, 22, 23, 24	10, 11, 33	18	17, 18
RF.6 Demonstrate an understanding of inverses of relations.	25, 26, 27, 28, 29, 30	12, 13	19, 20	19
RF.7 Demonstrate an understanding of logarithms.	31, 32, 33, 34	15, 16	21, 22	20
RF.8 Demonstrate an understanding of the product, quotient and power laws of logarithms.	35, 36, 37, 38, 39, 40, 41	18	23, 24	21
RF.9 Graph and analyze exponential and logarithmic functions.	42, 43, 44, 45, 46, 47, 71	17, 19, 20, 21	25	22, 23
RF.10 Solve problems that involve exponential and logarithmic equations.	48, 49, 50, 51, 52, 53, 72	14, 22, 23, 24, 34	26	24, 25
RF.11 Demonstrate an understanding of factoring polynomials of degree greater than 2 (limited to polynomials of degree ≤ 5 with integral coefficients).	54, 55, 56, 57, 73	25, 26, 27	27	26
RF.12 Graph and analyze polynomial functions (limited to polynomial functions of degree ≤ 5).	58, 59, 60, 61	36	28, 29	27
RF.13 Graph and analyze radical functions (limited to functions involving one radical).	62, 63, 64, 65	28, 29, 37	30	28, 29
RF.14 Graph and analyze rational functions (limited to numerators and denominators that are monomials, binomials or trinomials).	66, 67, 68, 69	30, 31, 32	31	30

Not for Reproduction

RELATIONS AND FUNCTIONS

RF.1 Demonstrate an understanding of operations on, and compositions of, functions.

OPERATIONS ON FUNCTIONS

Functions can be combined using the four arithmetic operations: addition, subtraction, multiplication, and division. For example, the quadratic function $f(x) = 2x^3 + 3x$ can be considered the sum of $y = 2x^3$ and $y = 3x$.

The composition of two functions involves using one function as the input of another. A composite function is represented with the notation $f(g(x))$ or $f \circ g$. The notation $f(g(x))$ or $f \circ g$ means that every x-variable in $f(x)$ is replaced with the function $g(x)$.

Example

Determine an expression for $f(g(x))$ if $f(x) = 2x + 3$ and $g(x) = x - 7$.

Solution

Step 1
Replace x in $f(x)$ with $g(x)$.
$$f(x) = 2x + 3$$
$$f(g(x)) = 2(x-7) + 3$$

Step 2
Simplify.
$$f(g(x)) = 2(x-7) + 3$$
$$f(g(x)) = 2x - 14 + 3$$
$$f(g(x)) = 2x - 11$$

Therefore, $f(g(x)) = 2x - 11$.

When evaluating a composition of functions $f(g(x))$ for a specific value of x, calculate the value of the inner function, and use that result as input for the outer function.

For example, to determine the value of $f(g(-2))$, first calculate the value of $g(-2)$, and then use the result to calculate $f(g(-2))$.

Related Questions: 1–6

RF.2 Demonstrate an understanding of the effects of horizontal and vertical translations on the graphs of functions and their related equations.

RF.3 Demonstrate an understanding of the effects of horizontal and vertical stretches on the graphs of functions and their related equations.

RF.4 Apply translations and stretches to the graphs and equations of functions.

APPLYING TRANSLATIONS AND STRETCHES

A translation involves moving the graph of a function either horizontally, vertically, or both horizontally and vertically. A stretch involves making the graph of a function either narrower or wider.

When the graph of a function $y = f(x)$ is transformed to the graph of $y - k = af[b(x-h)]$, the following transformations occur:

- A vertical stretch about the x-axis by a factor of $|a|$

- A horizontal stretch about the y-axis by a factor of $\dfrac{1}{|b|}$

- If $h > 0$, there is a horizontal translation h units right. If $h < 0$, there is a translation $|h|$ units left.

- If $k > 0$, there is a vertical translation k units up. If $k < 0$, there is a translation $|k|$ units down.

The order in which transformations are performed affects the final transformed function.

When graphing the function $y - k = af\left[b(x-h)\right]$, stretches with respect to one or both of the axes are performed first, followed by any vertical and horizontal translations.

Related Questions: 7–20, 70

RF.5   Demonstrate an understanding of the effects of reflections on the graphs of functions and their related equations, including reflections through the:
- *x-axis*
- *y-axis*
- *line y = x*

REFLECTIONS OF FUNCTIONS

A reflection flips an original graph either horizontally, vertically, or diagonally.

The following reflections can occur on the graph of $y = f(x)$:

- A reflection in the *x*-axis occurs when *y* is replaced with –*y* in the equation $y = f(x)$, resulting in the graph of $y = -f(x)$.

- A reflection in the *y*-axis occurs when *x* is replaced with –*x* in the equation $y = f(x)$, resulting in the graph of $y = f(-x)$.

- A reflection in the line *y* = *x* occurs when *x* and *y* are interchanged in the equation $y = f(x)$ and then solved for *y*, resulting in the graph of $x = f(y)$ or $y = f^{-1}(x)$.

Related Questions: 21–24

RF.6   Demonstrate an understanding of inverses of relations.

THE INVERSE OF A RELATION

The inverse of a relation is obtained by interchanging the *x*- and *y*-values in the ordered pairs of the relation. As a result, the domain of the inverse is the range of the original relation, and the range of the inverse is the domain of the original relation.

To determine the equation of an inverse relation, interchange the *x*- and *y*-variables in the original relation, and then solve for *y*. The function notation for the inverse of a function is $f^{-1}(x)$. Note that the inverse relation of a function is not always a function. Therefore, the notation $f^{-1}(x)$ can be used only when the inverse is a function.

Example

Determine the inverse of $f(x) = 2x + 3$.

Solution

Step 1
Replace $f(x)$ with *y*.
$$y = 2x + 3$$

Step 2
Interchange *x* and *y*.
$$y = 2x + 3$$
$$x = 2y + 3$$

Step 3
Solve for *y*.
$$x = 2y + 3$$
$$x - 3 = 2y$$
$$\frac{x-3}{2} = y$$

Since the inverse is a function, the inverse can be expressed as $f^{-1}(x) = \dfrac{x-3}{2}$.

Copyright Protected

Not for Reproduction

When $f(x) = 2x + 3$ and $f^{-1}(x) = \dfrac{x-3}{2}$ are graphed on the same axes, the graph of $f^{-1}(x)$ is a reflection of $f(x)$ in the line $y = x$.

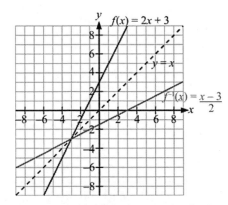

In general, the graph of an inverse is obtained by reflecting the graph of the original relation in the line $y = x$. Every ordered pair (x, y) on the graph of a function will become (y, x) on the graph of its inverse.

Related Questions: 25–30

RF.7   *Demonstrate an understanding of logarithms.*

RF.8   *Demonstrate an understanding of the product, quotient and power laws of logarithms.*

DEFINING LOGARITHMS

A logarithmic expression is of the form $\log_b a$, where b is called the base, and $b > 0$ and $b \neq 1$. The value of $\log_b a$ is defined as the number x that makes the statement $b^x = a$ true.
For example, $\log_3 27$ is defined as the number x that makes the statement $3^x = 27$ true.
Thus, $\log_3 27 = 3$ because $3^3 = 27$.

From the definition of a logarithm, it follows that an exponential equation can be converted to a logarithmic equation by applying the property that if $a = b^c$, then $c = \log_b a$. The base, b, must be greater than 0 and not equal to 1 ($b > 0$ and $b \neq 1$). This is consistent with avoiding negative bases in exponential functions.

THE LAWS OF LOGARITHMS

The laws of logarithms can be combined to simplify and evaluate expressions where the individual logarithms all have the same base.

The logarithmic laws are as follows:

- The product law of logarithms is
  $\log_b (xy) = \log_b x + \log_b y$.

- The quotient law of logarithms is
  $\log_b \left(\dfrac{x}{y}\right) = \log_b x - \log_b y$.

- The power law of logarithms is
  $\log_b x^n = n \log_b x$.

A useful relationship connecting logarithmic expressions with different bases is the change of base formula $\log_b a = \dfrac{\log_c a}{\log_c b}$, where $c > 0$ and $c \neq 1$. Once applied, it allows work to be done in base c instead of base b.

Example

Express $3\log_2 x + 9\log_8 (5x)$ as a single simplified logarithm in the form of $\log_2 a$.

Solution
Step 1
Express $\log_8 (5x)$ with a base of 2.

Apply the change of base formula.
$3\log_2 x + 9\log_8 (5x)$
$= 3\log_2 x + 9\left[\dfrac{\log_2 (5x)}{\log_2 8}\right]$

Step 2
Evaluate $\log_2 8$.
$3\log_2 x + 9\left[\dfrac{\log_2 (5x)}{\log_2 8}\right]$
$= 3\log_2 x + 9\left[\dfrac{\log_2 (5x)}{3}\right]$
$= 3\log_2 x + 3\log_2 (5x)$

Copyright Protected

Step 3

Factor out 3, and apply the product law of logarithms.

$3\log_2 x + 3\log_2 (5x)$
$= 3\left(\log_2 x + \log_2 (5x)\right)$
$= 3\log_2 \left(x(5x)\right)$
$= 3\log_2 \left(5x^2\right)$

Step 4

Apply the power law of logarithms to express $3\log_2 \left(5x^2\right)$ in the form $\log_2 a$.

$3\log_2 \left(5x^2\right)$
$= \log_2 \left(5x^2\right)^3$
$= \log_2 \left(125x^6\right)$

Related Questions: 31–41

RF.9   Graph and analyze exponential and logarithmic functions.

THE GRAPHS OF EXPONENTIAL AND LOGARITHMIC FUNCTIONS

An exponential function is of the form $y = b^x$, where b is a base greater than 0, and x is the exponent. The characteristics of the graph of an exponential function $y = b^x$, where $b > 0$, can be summarized as follows:

- If $b > 1$, the graph of the function shows exponential growth.
- If $0 < b < 1$, the graph of the function shows exponential decay.
- The horizontal asymptote is $y = 0$, or simply the x-axis.
- The domain is $x \in R$, and the range is $y > 0$.
- The y-intercept is (0, 1), and there are no x-intercepts since the x-axis is an asymptote.

The graphs of $y = 2^x$, $y = 3^x$, and $y = \left(\dfrac{1}{2}\right)^x$ are shown.

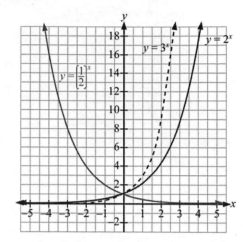

You can sketch the graph of an exponential function by applying transformations to graph of $y = b^x$, where $b > 0$.

The inverse of an exponential function $y = b^x$, where $b > 0$, is referred to as a logarithmic function and is expressed as $y = \log_b x$, where $b > 0$. The characteristics of the graph of a logarithmic function $y = \log_b x$, where $b > 0$ and $b \neq 1$, can be summarized in the following points:

- The graph of $y = \log_b x$ is the inverse graph of the function $y = b^x$.

- If $b > 1$, the graph of the function is increasing.

- If $0 < b < 1$, the graph of the function is decreasing.

- The vertical asymptote is $x = 0$, or simply the y-axis.

- The domain is $x > 0$, and the range is $y \in R$.

- The x-intercept is (1, 0), and there are no y-intercepts since the y-axis is an asymptote.

Not for Reproduction

The graphs of $y = \log_2 x$ and its inverse, $y = 2^x$, are shown.

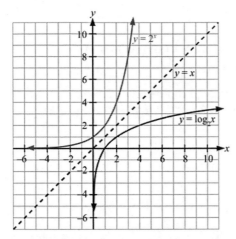

One method used to sketch the graph of logarithmic function is to first sketch its inverse function and then reflect it in the line $y = x$. Another method is to apply transformations to the graph of $y = \log_b x$, where $b > 0$ and $b \neq 1$.

Related Questions: 42–47, 71

RF.10 Solve problems that involve exponential and logarithmic equations.

SOLVING PROBLEMS WITH EXPONENTIAL EQUATIONS

A method of solving an exponential equation in which the bases are powers of the same number is based on the property that if $b^x = b^y$, where $b \neq 1$ or $b \neq 0$, then $x = y$.

For example, in the equation $27^{x-2} = 81^{x+1}$, the bases 27 and 81 are both powers of 3.

The equation can be rewritten as $\left(3^3\right)^{x-2} = \left(3^4\right)^{x+1}$ and solved as follows:

$$\left(3^3\right)^{x-2} = \left(3^4\right)^{x+1}$$
$$3^{3x-6} = 3^{4x+4}$$
$$3x - 6 = 4x + 4$$
$$-x = 10$$
$$x = -10$$

When exponential equations have bases that are not powers of one another, an approximate solution can be obtained by taking the logarithm of each side of the equation in a common base. For example, in the equation $5^{2x} = 110$, the bases 5 and 110 are not powers of the same base. Therefore, take the logarithm of both sides, and solve for x.

$$5^{2x} = 110$$
$$\log 5^{2x} = \log 110$$
$$2x \log 5 = \log 110$$
$$x = \frac{\log 110}{2 \log 5}$$
$$x \approx 1.46$$

An exponential function can be used to model a situation in which a quantity is increasing or decreasing at an exponential rate. A general formula that defines a quantity either growing or decaying exponentially is given by the equation

$N_t = N_0 \times R^{\frac{t}{p}}$, which uses the following variables:

- N_t—the quantity at time t.

- N_0—the initial size or value (when $t = 0$).

- R—the growth rate. Exponential growth occurs when $R > 1$, and exponential decay occurs when $0 < R < 1$.

- t—the elapsed time.

- p—the period of time that it takes the quantity to grow or decay by a factor of R.

SOLVING PROBLEMS WITH LOGARITHMIC EQUATIONS

A logarithmic equation can be solved by converting it to an exponential equation or by using appropriate logarithmic laws. It is important to check for extraneous solutions. Only logarithms of positive numbers exist, so any solution values that result in the logarithm of a negative number or 0 must be eliminated.

Example

Solve for x in the equation $\log_4(3x+10) = \log_2 7$.

Solution

Step 1

Bring all terms to one side of the equation.

$\log_4(3x+10) - \log_2 7 = 0$

Step 2

Express $\log_2 7$ with a base of 4.

Apply the change of base formula.

$\log_4(3x+10) - \dfrac{\log_4 7}{\log_4 2} = 0$

Step 3

Evaluate $\log_4 2$.

$\log_4(3x+10) - \dfrac{\log_4 7}{\dfrac{1}{2}} = 0$

$\log_4(3x+10) - 2\log_4 7 = 0$

Step 4

Apply the power law of logarithms.

$\log_4(3x+10) - \log_4(7^2) = 0$

Step 5

Apply the quotient law of logarithms.

$\log_4\left(\dfrac{3x+10}{7^2}\right) = 0$

Step 6

Convert the logarithmic equation to exponential form, and solve for x.

$4^0 = \dfrac{3x+10}{7^2}$

$1 = \dfrac{3x+10}{49}$

$49 = 3x+10$

$39 = 3x$

$x = 13$

When $x = 13$, $3x + 10 > 0$. Therefore, the solution $x = 13$ is verified.

Related Questions: 48–53, 72

RF.11 Demonstrate an understanding of factoring polynomials of degree greater than 2 (limited to polynomials of degree ≤ 5 with integral coefficients).

DIVIDING A POLYNOMIAL BY A BINOMIAL

A polynomial can be divided by a binomial of the form $(x - a)$ using two methods: long division and synthetic division.

Polynomial long division is similar to the long division of real numbers. For example, the long division of $P(x) = x^3 - 5x^2 + 3x + 9$ by $(x - 3)$ can be shown as follows:

$$
\begin{array}{r}
x^2 - 2x - 3 \\
x-3 \overline{) x^3 - 5x^2 + 3x + 9} \\
\underline{x^3 - 3x^2} \\
-2x^2 + 3x \\
\underline{-2x^2 + 6x} \\
-3x + 9 \\
\underline{-3x + 9} \\
0
\end{array}
$$

The quotient is $x^2 - 2x - 3$, and the remainder is 0.

Synthetic division is another method of dividing a polynomial by binomial without having to contend with variables. Synthetic division uses only the coefficients of the terms in the polynomial and the root of the binomial. The coefficients must be written in descending order by degree of its term. Any missing powers can be represented by 0.

Copyright Protected

Not for Reproduction

Example

Divide $P(x) = x^3 - 5x^2 + 3x + 9$ by $(x-3)$ using synthetic division.

Solution

Step 1

Write the root of $(x-3)$ and the coefficients of $P(x)$ in decreasing order by degree as shown in the given configuration.

$$3 \underline{|1 \quad -5 \quad 3 \quad 9}$$

Step 2

Bring down the first coefficient of the $P(x)$ below the division line.

$$3 \underline{|1 \quad -5 \quad 3 \quad 9}$$
$$\downarrow$$
$$1$$

Step 3

Multiply the first coefficient by the root of the binomial, and write the product below the second coefficient in the dividend.

$$3 \underline{|1 \quad -5 \quad 3 \quad 9}$$
$$\downarrow \quad 3$$
$$1$$

Step 4

Add the two values in the second column to get the second number in the bottom row.

$$3 \underline{|1 \quad -5 \quad 3 \quad 9}$$
$$\downarrow \quad 3$$
$$1 \quad -2$$

Step 5

Continue to multiply the root of the binomial by the newest number in the last row, and write the answer in the next spot in the second row. Add to get the next number in the last row.

$$3 \underline{|1 \quad -5 \quad 3 \quad 9}$$
$$\downarrow \quad 3 \quad -6 \quad -9$$
$$1 \quad -2 \quad -3 \quad 0$$

Step 6

Determine the quotient. The numbers in the last row correspond to the coefficients of the quotient, and the last number is the remainder. The degree of the quotient is 1 less than the degree of the polynomial.

Therefore, the quotient is read from the last line as $x^2 - 2x - 3$ with a remainder of 0.

THE REMAINDER THEOREM AND THE FACTOR THEOREM

THE REMAINDER THEOREM

The remainder theorem provides a method to find the remainder when a polynomial is divided by a binomial. The remainder theorem states that when a polynomial function $P(x)$ is divided by a binomial of the form $(x-a)$, the remainder is equal to $P(a)$.

Example

Without using division, determine the remainder when $P(x) = x^3 - 4x^2 + 5x + 1$ is divided by $(x-1)$.

Solution

When $P(x) = x^3 - 4x^2 + 5x + 1$ is divided by $(x-1)$, the remainder is $P(1)$.

Determine the value of $P(1)$.
$$P(1) = (1)^3 - 4(1)^2 + 5(1) + 1$$
$$P(1) = 1 - 4 + 5 + 1$$
$$P(1) = 3$$

The remainder is 3.

THE FACTOR THEOREM

The factor theorem is a special case of the remainder theorem. The factor theorem states that if a is substituted for x in the polynomial $P(x)$ and the resulting function value is 0, then $(x-a)$ is a factor of $P(x)$. In other words, if $P(a) = 0$, then $(x-a)$ is a factor of $P(x)$.

Polynomials of higher degree can be factored using the factor theorem and then some type of division (long or synthetic).

Copyright Protected

Example

Completely factor $P(x) = x^3 + 7x^2 - 10x - 16$, if $P(2) = 0$.

Solution

According to the factor theorem, since $P(2) = 0$, $(x - 2)$ is a factor of $P(x)$.

Find another factor of $P(x)$ by dividing it by $(x - 2)$.

Use synthetic division.

$$
\begin{array}{r|rrr}
2 & 1 & 7 & -10 & -16 \\
  & \downarrow & 2 & 18 & 16 \\
\hline
  & 1 & 9 & 8 & 0
\end{array}
$$

Another factor is $(x^2 + 9x + 8)$. The factor $(x^2 + 9x + 8)$ is a quadratic trinomial and can be factored as $(x + 1)(x + 8)$.

Therefore, the complete factorization is $P(x) = (x - 2)(x + 1)(x + 8)$.

Related Questions: 54–57, 73

RF.12   Graph and analyze polynomial functions (limited to polynomial functions of degree ≤ 5).

GRAPHS OF POLYNOMIAL FUNCTIONS

The general form of a polynomial function is $f(x) = a_n x^n + a_{n-1} x^{n-1} + a_{n-2} x^{n-2} + \ldots + a_2 x^2 + a_1 x + a_0$, where $a_n \neq 0$. The degree of the polynomial is a positive whole number and is given by the value of n. The value of a_n is the leading coefficient. The constant term is a_0 and represents the y-intercept on the graph of the function.

The factored form of a polynomial is $f(x) = a(x - r_1)(x - r_2)(x - r_3)\ldots(x - r_n)$, the numbers r_1, r_2, r_3, $\ldots r_n$ are the zeros, and the leading coefficient is a. The repeated zeros of the corresponding function are referred to in terms of their multiplicity. For example, in $f(x) = (x - 2)^3$, the multiplicity of the zero 2 is 3.

The following characteristics from the completely factored form of a polynomial function,

$$f(x) = a(x - r_1)(x - r_2)(x - r_3)\ldots(x - r_n),$$

can be used to sketch the graph of $f(x)$:

- r_1, r_2, r_3, $\ldots r_n$ are the x-intercepts on the graph of $f(x)$.

- The multiplicities of the zeros determine the behaviour of the graph at the x-intercepts.

- The degree of a polynomial function is equal to the sum of the multiplicities of its zeros.

- The end behaviour of the graph is determined by the degree and the leading coefficient, a.

- The y-intercept of the polynomial occurs when $x = 0$.

For example, the graph of $f(x) = x^4 - 5x^3$ is shown. The degree of $f(x)$ is 4, and the leading coefficient is 1. The factored form of the polynomial is $f(x) = x^3(x - 5)$. The zeros are 0 and 5 and have multiplicities of 3 and 1, respectively. Therefore, the graph crosses the x-axis at $x = 5$ and is tangent to and crosses the x-axis at $x = 0$. The constant is 0, which implies that the y-intercept is 0.

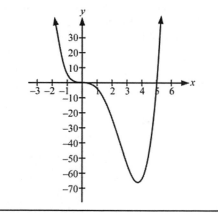

Related Questions: 58–61

Not for Reproduction

RF.13   Graph and analyze radical functions (limited to functions involving one radical).

GRAPHS OF RADICAL FUNCTIONS

The graph of the most basic radical function, $y = \sqrt{x}$, is shown.

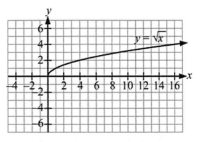

Since the square root of a negative number is not a real number, the domain of $y = \sqrt{x}$ is $x \geq 0$, and the range is $y \geq 0$. The x- and y-intercepts are located at (0, 0).

You can graph radical functions by applying transformations on the graph of $y = \sqrt{x}$.

For example, the graph of $y = 2\sqrt{(x+4)}$ is obtained from the graph of $y = \sqrt{x}$ by a vertical stretch factor of 2 and a translation 4 units left.

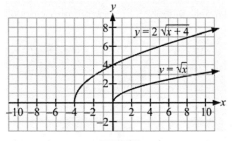

The domain of $y = 2\sqrt{(x+4)}$ is $x \geq -4$, and the range is $y \geq 0$. The x-intercept is located at (–4, 0), and the y-intercept is located at (0, 4).

Related Questions: 62–65

RF.14   Graph and analyze rational functions (limited to numerators and denominators that are monomials, binomials or trinomials).

GRAPHS OF RATIONAL FUNCTIONS

A rational function is a function in the form $f(x) = \dfrac{P(x)}{Q(x)}$, where $P(x)$ and $Q(x)$ are polynomial functions, and $Q(x) \neq 0$.

Any non-permissible value of $f(x)$ will produce either a vertical asymptote or a hole on the graph. The holes are determined from the factored form of a rational function. The horizontal asymptote is determined from the degree of the numerator and the denominator. The graph can intersect or touch a horizontal asymptote but not a vertical asymptote.

Follow these general steps to sketch the graph of the rational function $y = \dfrac{P(x)}{Q(x)}$:

1. Factor the numerator and denominator of the function to identify the vertical asymptotes and holes.

2. If a horizontal asymptote exists, determine if the graph will intersect or touch the horizontal asymptote.

3. Determine the x- and y-intercepts.

4. Show the graph increasing as x approaches the vertical asymptotes.

5. Show the graph decreasing as x approaches the vertical asymptotes.

6. If a horizontal asymptote exists, show the graph approaching the horizontal asymptote.

7. If any holes exist, place an empty point on the graph where the hole exists.

For example, the graph of $f(x) = \dfrac{x^2 + x}{x^2 - 2x - 3}$ is shown. The factored form of the rational function is $f(x) = \dfrac{x(x+1)}{(x+1)(x-3)}$. Therefore, $f(x)$ has a vertical asymptote at $x = 3$, a hole in the graph where $x = 1$, and a horizontal asymptote at $y = 1$.

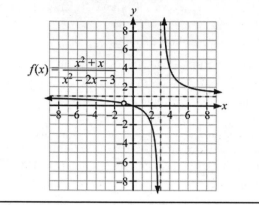

$f(x) = \dfrac{x^2 + x}{x^2 - 2x - 3}$

Related Questions: 66–69

Copyright Protected

Not for Reproduction

PRACTICE QUESTIONS—RELATIONS AND FUNCTIONS

1. If $h(x) = 2x - 6$, $g(x) = x^2 - 9$, and $f(x) = h(x)g(x)$, then $f(x)$, in simplified expanded form, is

    A. $4x^2 - 24x + 36$

    B. $2x^3 - 24x^2 + 54$

    C. $x^4 - 6x^3 - 18x^2 + 81$

    D. $2x^3 - 6x^2 - 18x + 54$

Use the following information to answer the next question.

> A function is given by $f(x) = \dfrac{g(x)}{h(x)}$, where
>
> $g(x) = x^2 - 25$, $h(x) = x + 5$, and $h(x) \neq 0$.

2. The simplified form of $f(x)$ is

    A. $x + 5, x \neq 5$

    B. $x - 5, x \neq 5$

    C. $x - 5, x \neq -5$

    D. $x + 5\ x \neq -5$

Use the following information to answer the next question.

> When the functions $g(x) = x^2 - 2x + 1$ and $h(x) = x^2 + 3x - 4$ are given, a third function, $f(x)$, is defined as $f(x) = g(x) - h(x)$.

3. The simplified form of $f(x)$ is

    A. $x - 3$

    B. $5x - 5$

    C. $-5x + 5$

    D. $-5x - 3$

4. If $f(x) = (x - 1)$ and $g(x) = (x - 2)^2$, then $g(f(x))$, expressed in general form, is

    A. $x^2 + 2x + 1$

    B. $x^2 - 2x + 1$

    C. $x^2 - 6x + 9$

    D. $x^2 + 6x + 9$

5. If $f(x) = \dfrac{1}{2}x^2 - 10$, then the value of $f(f(-6))$ is

    A. 6

    B. 8

    C. 22

    D. 64

Numerical Response

6. If $g(f(x)) = 4$, where $f(x) = 3x - 7$ and $g(x) = 5 - 2x$, then x, correct to the nearest **tenth**, is equal to _____.

7. The graph of $y = x^3$ was transformed to the graph of $y = (x - 3)^3 + 4$. Which of the following statements describes the transformation?

    A. The graph of $y = x^3$ has been translated 4 units to the right and 3 units upward.

    B. The graph of $y = x^3$ has been translated 3 units to the left and 4 units downward.

    C. The point (x, y) on the graph $y = x^3$ has been translated to point $(x + 3, y + 4)$.

    D. The point (x, y) on the graph $y = x^3$ has been translated to point $(x - 3, y - 4)$.

8. What are the coordinates of the point on the graph of $y = f(x)$ that corresponds to the point (5, 4) on the graph of $y = f(x+6)$?

A. $(-1, 4)$

B. $(5, -2)$

C. $(5, 10)$

D. $(11, 4)$

Use the following information to answer the next question.

The partial graph of the function $y = f(x)$ is shown below. The range of function f is $f(x) \geq -11$.

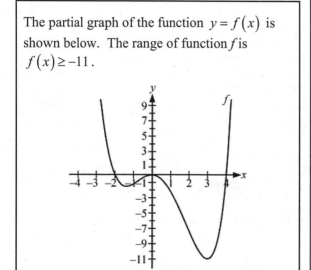

9. If function f is transformed to a new function $g(x) = f(x-3)+2$, then the range of function g will be

A. $g(x) \geq -11$

B. $g(x) \geq -9$

C. $g(x) \geq -8$

D. $g(x) \geq 0$

10. Given the graph of $y = f(x)$, the graph of $y+1 = f(x)-4$ can be drawn by translating the graph of $y = f(x)$ vertically

A. down by 4 units

B. down by 5 units

C. up by 4 units

D. up by 5 units

11. If y is replaced by $\frac{1}{2}y$ in the equation $y = f(x)$, then the graph of $y = f(x)$ will be stretched

A. horizontally about the y-axis by a factor of $\frac{1}{2}$

B. horizontally about the y-axis by a factor of 2

C. vertically about the x-axis by a factor of $\frac{1}{2}$

D. vertically about the x-axis by a factor of 2

12. The graph of $y = f(x)$ contains the point $(-3, 9)$. What corresponding point is on the graph of $y = f\left(\frac{1}{3}x\right)$?

A. $(-1, 9)$

B. $(-3, 3)$

C. $(-3, 27)$

D. $(-9, 9)$

Copyright Protected

Not for Reproduction

The graph of a quadratic function $y = f(x)$ is shown.

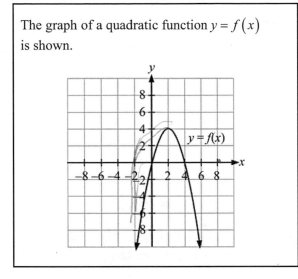

13. The graph of $y = f\left(\dfrac{1}{2}x\right)$ will have

    A. a different domain, but the same range as the graph of $y = f(x)$

    B. a different domain and a different range than the graph of $y = f(x)$

    C. the same domain and the same range as the graph of $y = f(x)$

    D. the same domain but a different range than the graph of $y = f(x)$

The graph of a quadratic function $y = f(x)$ is shown.

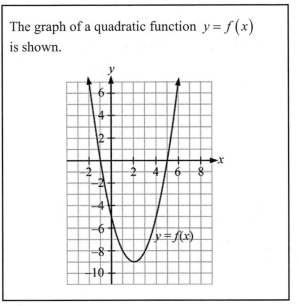

14. If the graph of $y = f(x)$ has integral zeros and is vertically stretched about the *x*-axis by a factor of $\dfrac{1}{5}$, the *x*-intercepts of the transformed graph will be located at the ordered pairs

    A. $\left(-\dfrac{1}{5}, 0\right)$ and $(25, 0)$

    B. $\left(-\dfrac{1}{5}, 0\right)$ and $(1, 0)$

    C. $(-5, 0)$ and $(25, 0)$

    D. $(-1, 0)$ and $(5, 0)$

Use the following information to answer the next question.

The graph of $y = 8x^2 + 3$ is stretched horizontally about the y-axis by a factor of 4 and stretched vertically about the x-axis by a factor of 2.

15. The equation of the transformed graph is

   A. $y = \dfrac{1}{4}x^2 + \dfrac{3}{2}$

   B. $y = x^2 + 6$

   C. $y = 64x^2 + \dfrac{3}{2}$

   D. $y = 256x^2 + 6$

Use the following information to answer the next question.

In the given order, these transformations are applied to the graph of $y = \dfrac{1}{x}$:

- Stretched vertically about the x-axis by a factor of 3
- Reflected in the x-axis
- Translated 4 units right and 2 units down

16. Which of the following equations represents the transformed function?

   A. $y = \dfrac{2x + 5}{x + 4}$

   B. $y = \dfrac{-2x + 5}{x - 4}$

   C. $y = \dfrac{6x + 23}{3x + 12}$

   D. $y = \dfrac{6x - 23}{-3x + 12}$

17. If the point $(2, -8)$ is on the graph of $y = f(x)$, then what is the corresponding point on the graph of $y = f\left(\dfrac{1}{4}x - 1\right)$?

   A. $(9, -8)$

   B. $(12, -8)$

   C. $\left(\dfrac{3}{2}, -8\right)$

   D. $\left(\dfrac{9}{2}, -8\right)$

Use the following information to answer the next question.

The graph of the function $y = f(x)$ is stretched horizontally about the y-axis by a factor of $\dfrac{1}{4}$, stretched vertically about the x-axis by a factor of 3, reflected in the x-axis, translated 5 units to the left, and translated 2 units down.

18. If the transformations are done in the given order, then the equation of the transformed function is

   A. $y = -3f(4x + 20) - 2$

   B. $y = 3f(-4x + 20) - 2$

   C. $y = 3f\left(-\dfrac{1}{4}x + 20\right) - 2$

   D. $y = -3f\left(\dfrac{1}{4}x + 20\right) - 2$

Not for Reproduction

19. Which of the following sets of transformations to the graph of $y = x^2$ will result in the equation $y = 9(x - 7)^2$ for the transformed graph?

A. A vertical stretch about the *x*-axis by a factor of 9 and then a horizontal translation of 7 units left

B. A vertical stretch about the *x*-axis by a factor of 9 and then a horizontal translation of 7 units right

C. A horizontal stretch about the *y*-axis by a factor of 9 and then a horizontal translation of 7 units left

D. A horizontal stretch about the *y*-axis by a factor of 9 and then a horizontal translation of 7 units right

Use the following information to answer the next question.

The graph of a function, $y = f(x)$, is stretched horizontally about the *y*-axis by a factor of 4 and translated 3 units down.

Numerical Response

20. If the point (–4, 2) on the graph of $y = f(x)$ corresponds to the point (*p*, *q*) on the transformed graph, then the value of $|p + q|$ is _____.

Use the following information to answer the next question.

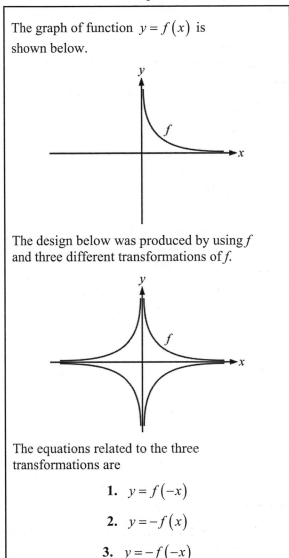

The graph of function $y = f(x)$ is shown below.

The design below was produced by using *f* and three different transformations of *f*.

The equations related to the three transformations are

1. $y = f(-x)$

2. $y = -f(x)$

3. $y = -f(-x)$

Numerical Response

21. The equation that produced the portion of the design found in
quadrant II is equation number _____
quadrant III is equation number _____
quadrant IV is equation number _____
(Record your answer as a **three-digit** number.)

Copyright Protected

22. If the graph of $y = f(x)$ contains the point $(3, -5)$, then the graph of $y = f(-x)$ will contain the point

A. $(-5, 3)$

B. $(-3, 5)$

C. $(-3, -5)$

D. $(3, 5)$

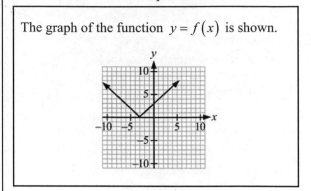

Use the following information to answer the next question.

The graph $y = f(x)$ contains the point $(-2, 7)$. The graph of $y = f(x)$ is then reflected across the line $y = x$. The point $(-2, 7)$ corresponds to point A on the transformed graph.

23. What are the coordinates of point A?

A. $(2, -7)$

B. $(7, -2)$

C. $\left(-\dfrac{1}{2}, \dfrac{1}{7}\right)$

D. $\left(\dfrac{1}{7}, -\dfrac{1}{2}\right)$

Use the following information to answer the next question.

The graph of the function $y = f(x)$ is shown.

24. Which of the following sketches illustrates the graph of $y = f(-x)$?

A.

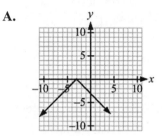

B.

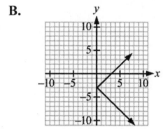

C.

D.

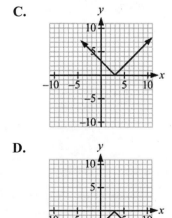

Not for Reproduction

25. If $f(x) = x^2 - 4$, where x is an integer and $0 \le x \le 3$, then which of the following sets of ordered pairs could define $f^{-1}(x)$?

A. $\left\{ \left(-\dfrac{1}{4}, 0\right), \left(-\dfrac{1}{3}, 0\right), (0, 2), \left(\dfrac{1}{5}, 3\right) \right\}$

B. $\{(-4, 0), (-3, 1), (0, 2), (5, 3)\}$

C. $\left\{ \left(\dfrac{1}{4}, 0\right), \left(\dfrac{1}{3}, 0\right), (0, 2), \left(-\dfrac{1}{5}, 3\right) \right\}$

D. $\{(4, 0), (3, 1), (0, 2), (-5, 3)\}$

Use the following information to answer the next question.

> Function A is defined by
> $\{(-2, 0), (0, 3), (2, 0), (4, 6), (6, 8)\}$.

26. What is the inverse of function A?

A. $\{(0, -2), (3, 0), (0, 2), (6, 4), (8, 6)\}$

B. $\{(8, 6), (6, 4), (0, -2), (0, 2), (3, 0)\}$

C. $\{(0, -2), (3, 0), (2, 2), (6, 4), (8, 6)\}$

D. $\{(6, 4), (4, 6), (0, 2), (0, 3), (-2, 0)\}$

27. What is the inverse of $y = 2 - \sqrt{x}$, where $x \ge 0$ and $y \le 2$?

A. $y = x^2 - 4$, where $x \ge 0$ and $y \le 2$

B. $y = x^2 - 4$, where $x \le 2$ and $y \ge 0$

C. $y = x^2 - 4x + 4$, where $x \ge 0$ and $y \le 2$

D. $y = x^2 - 4x + 4$, where $x \le 2$ and $y \ge 0$

28. If $f(x) = \dfrac{6}{x - 7}$, then $f^{-1}(x)$ is equal to

A. $7 - \dfrac{6}{x}$

B. $\dfrac{6 - 7x}{x}$

C. $\dfrac{7x + 6}{x}$

D. $\dfrac{6x + 7}{x}$

29. The inverse of the quadratic function $f(x) = \dfrac{1}{2}(x + 6)^2 - 5$ is

A. $y = \pm\sqrt{2x + 5} - 6$

B. $y = \pm\sqrt{2x + 10} - 6$

C. $y = \pm 2\sqrt{x + 5} - 6$

D. $y = \pm 2\sqrt{x - 6} + 5$

Copyright Protected

Use the following information to answer the next question.

The graph of the function $y = f(x)$ is shown.

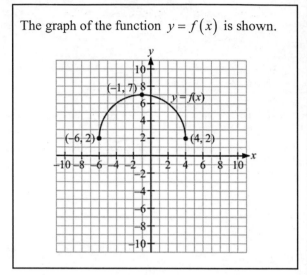

30. Which of the following statements about the given function and its inverse, $y = F(x)$, is **false**?

A. If the domain of $f(x)$ is restricted to $x \geq -1$, then the inverse, F, is a function.

B. If the domain of $f(x)$ is restricted to $x \leq -1$, then the inverse, F, is a function.

C. If the domain of $f(x)$ is restricted to $x \geq 2$, then the inverse, F, is a function.

D. If the domain of $f(x)$ is restricted to $x \leq 2$, then the inverse, F, is a function.

31. The x-intercept of the graph of $y = \log_b x$, where $b > 0$ and $b \neq 1$, is

A. 0

B. 1

C. undefined

D. dependent on the value of b

32. A logarithmic form of the equation $81^{\frac{3}{4}} = 27$ is

A. $\log_{27}\left(\dfrac{3}{4}\right) = 81$

B. $\log_{\frac{3}{4}}(27) = 81$

C. $\log_{27}(81) = \dfrac{3}{4}$

D. $\log_{81}(27) = \dfrac{3}{4}$

33. The expression $\log_5 19$ is equivalent to

A. $\dfrac{\log 5}{\log 19}$

B. $\dfrac{\log_5 19}{\log 5}$

C. $\dfrac{\log_2 5}{\log_2 19}$

D. $\dfrac{\log_2 19}{\log_2 5}$

34. Written in logarithmic form, the equation $p = 4q^m$ is equal to

A. $m = \log_{4q} p$

B. $m = \log_q\left(\dfrac{p}{4}\right)$

C. $m = \log_q(4p)$

D. $m = \log_q(p - 4)$

Not for Reproduction

35. If $\log_3 y = c - \log_3 x$, where $y > 0$ and $x > 0$, then y is equal to

A. $c - x$

B. $\dfrac{c}{x}$

C. $\dfrac{c^3}{x}$

D. $\dfrac{3^c}{x}$

36. If $\log_3 x = 15$, then $\log_3\left(\dfrac{1}{3}x\right)$ is equal to

A. 14

B. 12

C. 5

D. -15

Use the following information to answer the next question.

The relationship between the length and mass of a particular species of snakes is

$$\log m = \log a + 3\log l$$

where a is a given constant

m is the mass of the snake in grams

l is the length of the snake in metres

37. This relationship can also be written as

A. $\log\left(\dfrac{m}{al^3}\right) = 0$

B. $\log\left(\dfrac{m}{3al}\right) = 0$

C. $\log\left(\dfrac{am}{l^3}\right) = 0$

D. $\log\left(\dfrac{am}{3l}\right) = 0$

38. The expression $2\log 3 - \dfrac{1}{2}\log 16 + \log 12$ is written as a single logarithmic expression as

A. $\log 5$

B. $\log 15$

C. $\log 27$

D. $\log 30$

39. The expression $4\log_b 2b - \log_b(1.6b)$, where $b > 0$, $b \neq 1$, is equivalent to

A. $\log_b 14.4 + 3$

B. $\log_b 3.75 + 3$

C. $\log_b 10 + \log_b 3$

D. $\log_b 10 + 3$

Numerical Response

40. What is the value of the expression $\log_4(64)^{50}$? _____

(Record your answer as a **whole** number.)

41. What is the value of the expression $\log_4 \dfrac{1}{12} + \log_4 \dfrac{3}{16}$?

A. -4

B. -3

C. 3

D. 4

42. Which of the following statements regarding the graph of $y = \left(\dfrac{1}{4}\right)^x$ is **true**?

  A. The equation of the vertical asymptote of the graph is $x = 0$.

  B. The graph has an x-intercept located at the point $(1, 0)$.

  C. The graph passes through the point $(-2, 16)$.

  D. The range of the graph is $y < 0$.

43. As the value of x increases, the function $f(x) = \log_b x$ will change from decreasing to increasing when the value of base b changes from

  A. $b = 2$ to $b = 3$

  B. $b = \dfrac{1}{2}$ to $b = \dfrac{1}{3}$

  C. $b = 2$ to $b = \dfrac{1}{3}$

  D. $b = \dfrac{1}{2}$ to $b = 3$

44. Which of the following statements regarding the graph of $y = \log_8 x$ is **true**?

  A. The range of the graph is $y > 0$.

  B. The y-intercept of the graph is $(0, 1)$.

  C. The equation of the vertical asymptote of the graph is $x = 0$.

  D. The graph passes through the point $\left(\dfrac{1}{8}, -2\right)$.

45. Campbell wants to use a graphing calculator to verify his sketch of the graph of $y = 5\log_2\left(\dfrac{x}{10} + 60\right)$, but his calculator accepts only common logarithms. Which of the following equations is equivalent to Campbell's function?

  A. $y = 5\left(\dfrac{\log 2}{\log\left(\dfrac{x}{10} + 60\right)}\right)$

  B. $y = 5\left(\dfrac{\log\left(\dfrac{x}{10} + 60\right)}{\log 2}\right)$

  C. $y = 5\left(\dfrac{\log\left(\dfrac{x}{10} + 60\right)}{2}\right)$

  D. $y = 5\left(\dfrac{2}{\log\left(\dfrac{x}{10} + 60\right)}\right)$

46. The graph of $y = a^{x-2}$ has a y-intercept of

  A. $\dfrac{1}{a^2}$

  B. $-\dfrac{1}{a^2}$

  C. $-a^2$

  D. 2

Copyright Protected

47. The graph of $y = \log_4 x$, where $x > 0$, lies entirely

- **A.** above the x-axis
- **B.** below the x-axis
- **C.** to the left of the y-axis
- **D.** to the right of the y-axis

48. An investment of \$1 000 is earning 4% interest per annum compounded annually. If the value, V, of the investment after t years is given by $V = 1\ 000(1.04)^t$, then t, written as a function of V, is

- **A.** $t = \dfrac{\log(V)}{3} - \log(1.04)$
- **B.** $t = \dfrac{\log(V)}{3\log(1.04)}$
- **C.** $t = \log(V) - 3 - \log(1.04)$
- **D.** $t = \dfrac{\log(V) - 3}{\log(1.04)}$

49. In the equation $\log_{(x+2)} 5 = 10$, the value of x, correct to the nearest hundredth, is

- **A.** −0.42
- **B.** −0.83
- **C.** −1.41
- **D.** 1.50

Use the following information to answer the next question.

> By applying logarithm laws, the equation $4\log_3(x+6) - 2\log_3(7x+9) = 5$ can be written as a polynomial so that it can be solved for x.

50. What is the degree of the polynomial?

- **A.** 2
- **B.** 3
- **C.** 4
- **D.** 5

51. If $\log_5(125x) = 25$, then the value of x is

- **A.** 5^{28}
- **B.** 5^{22}
- **C.** $5^{\frac{25}{3}}$
- **D.** 5

Use the following information to answer the next question.

> **Half-life of Phosphorus-32**
>
> $A(t) = A_0\left(\dfrac{1}{2}\right)^{\frac{t}{h}}$, where
>
> $A(t) =$ the mass present at time t
> $A_0 = A(0)$
> $t =$ time
> $h =$ half-life of phosphorus-32

52. The half-life of phosphorus-32 is 14.3 days. The length of time that it will take 96.2 g of phosphorus-32 to decay to 12.5 g, to the nearest day, is

- **A.** 8 days
- **B.** 26 days
- **C.** 42 days
- **D.** 52 days

Copyright Protected

*Use the following information to answer
the next question.*

The pH scale describes the acidity or basicity of a particular solution. The pH of a solution is the negative logarithm of the concentration of hydrogen ions, $[H^+]$. In terms of an equation, this can be written as $pH = -\log[H^+]$.

53. If the pH of pure water is 7, then what is the pH of a solution that is 20 times more acidic than pure water?

A. 1.5

B. 5.7

C. 7.5

D. 8.3

54. If the polynomial $P(x) = 2x^4 + x^3 - 4x^2 + 1$ is divided by $x + \dfrac{1}{2}$, then the remainder is

A. $-\dfrac{1}{2}$

B. 0

C. $\dfrac{1}{4}$

D. 3

Numerical Response

55. If $x + 4$ is a factor of the polynomial $P(x) = x^4 + 3x^3 - Kx^2 + 7x - 4$, then the value of K is _____.
(Record your answer as a **whole** number.)

*Use the following information to answer
the next question.*

Fred divides $P(x) = x^3 + 2x^2 + x + 6$ by $(x + 2)$ as follows:

$$
\begin{array}{r}
x^2 + 1 \\
x+2\overline{\smash{)}x^3 + 2x^2 + 1x + 6} \\
\underline{x^3 + 2x^2} \\
0 + 1x + 6 \\
\underline{1x + 2} \\
4
\end{array}
$$

56. Fred's calculation demonstrates that

A. $(x + 2)$ is a factor of P

B. $(x^2 + 1)$ is a factor of P

C. $P(-2) = 0$

D. $P(-2) = 4$

*Use the following information to answer
the next question.*

The partial graph of a cubic polynomial function, $y = P(x)$, is shown below.

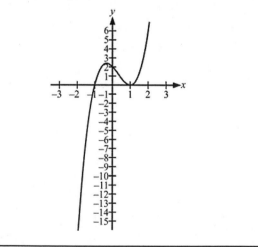

57. When $P(x)$ is divided by $(x + 2)$, the remainder is

A. negative   B. zero

C. positive   D. undefined

Not for Reproduction

Use the following information to answer the next question.

Trey is given the function

$f(x) = x^2 - \sqrt{3}x^3 + x^{-4} + 5x^{\frac{5}{4}}$. He believes that $f(x)$ is not a polynomial function for the following reasons:

1. The function contains a non-integral coefficient, $\sqrt{3}$.

2. The function contains a negative power of x, -4.

3. The function contains a fractional power of x, $\dfrac{5}{4}$.

4. The function does not contain a constant term.

58. Which of Trey's reasons about why $f(x)$ is not a polynomial function are **true**?

  A. I and II

  B. II and III

  C. I, II, and III

  D. I, III, and IV

Use the following information to answer the next question.

The graph of a polynomial function is shown.

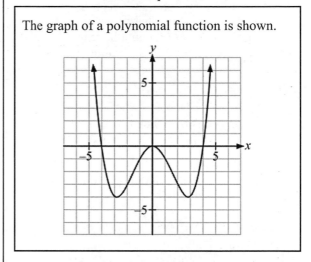

59. Which of the following statements about the given graph is **true**?

  A. The roots at $x = -4$ and $x = 4$ have a multiplicity of 1, and the root at $x = 0$ has a multiplicity of 4.

  B. The roots at $x = -4$ and $x = 4$ have a multiplicity of 2, and the root at $x = 0$ has a multiplicity of 1.

  C. The roots at $x = -4$ and $x = 4$ have a multiplicity of 3, and the root at $x = 0$ has a multiplicity of 2.

  D. The roots at $x = -4$ and $x = 4$ have a multiplicity of 4, and the root at $x = 0$ has a multiplicity of 4.

60. If $3x$ is a factor of the polynomial $P(x)$, then one x-intercept of the graph of P must be

  A. 3

  B. $\dfrac{1}{3}$

  C. 0

  D. -3

Copyright Protected

61. If a polynomial function P is of degree five, then the greatest number of x-intercepts that the graph of $y = P(x)$ could have is _____. (Record your answer as a **whole** number.)

62. If the graph of $y = \sqrt{x}$ is vertically stretched about the x-axis by a factor of a, $a > 0$, $a \neq 1$, then the graph of $y = \sqrt{x}$ and the graph of the transformed function will have the same

A. domain, range, x-intercept, and y-intercept

B. x-intercept and y-intercept, but a different domain and range

C. domain and x-intercept, but a different range and y-intercept

D. range and y-intercept, but a different domain and x-intercept

63. Which of the following statements about the graphs of $y = 5\sqrt{x}$ and $y = -5\sqrt{x}$ is **true**?

A. They have the same domain and range.

B. They have different domains and ranges.

C. They have the same domain but different ranges.

D. They have different domains but the same range.

64. If the function $y = \sqrt{5x - 2}$ is written in the form $y = a\sqrt{x - c}$, what are the values of a and c?

A. $a = \sqrt{5}$, $c = \dfrac{2}{5}$

B. $a = \sqrt{5}$, $c = 2$

C. $a = 5$, $c = \dfrac{2}{5}$

D. $a = 5$, $c = 2$

65. The solution to $3\sqrt{x + 3} = 2x + 1$, rounded to the nearest **hundredth**, is _____.

66. When the function $f(x) = x + 2$ is transformed to $y = \dfrac{1}{f(x)}$, the equation of the vertical asymptote is

A. $x = 0$

B. $x = 2$

C. $x = \dfrac{1}{2}$

D. $x = -2$

67. What is the equation of the horizontal asymptote for the graph of $f(x) = \dfrac{5x - 2}{3x - 2}$?

A. $y = \dfrac{5}{3}$

B. $y = 1$

C. $y = \dfrac{2}{3}$

D. $y = 0$

Not for Reproduction

Use the following information to answer the next question.

Two functions, $f(x) = \dfrac{1}{x} + 1$ and

$g(x) = \dfrac{(x+1)^2(x-2)}{x(x+1)(x-2)}$, are given.

The graph of $y = f(x)$ is shown.

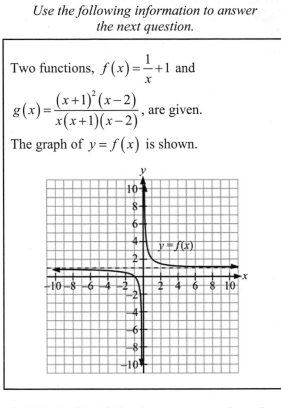

68. Which of the following statements about the graph of $y = g(x)$ is **true**?

A. The graph of $y = g(x)$ has more vertical asymptotes than the graph of $y = f(x)$.

B. The graph of $y = g(x)$ is identical to the graph of $y = f(x)$.

C. The graph of $y = g(x)$ contains the point $(-1, 0)$.

D. The graph of $y = g(x)$ has a hole at $x = 2$.

Numerical Response

69. The smallest solution value to the equation

$2x - 5 = \dfrac{x+1}{x-2}$ is _____.

(Record your answer to the nearest **tenth**.)

Use the following information to answer the next question.

The graph of $y = f(x)$ is given.

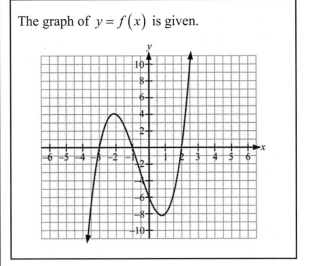

Written Response

70. If the x-intercepts on the graph of $y = f(x)$ are integral, what are the x-intercepts of the graph of $y = f(x-7)$?

Copyright Protected

Written Response

71. Sketch the graph of $y = -3(2)^{x+2} - 1$.

Written Response

73. Given the function $P(x) = x^3 - 2x^2 - 5x + 6$, where $P(-2) = 0$, what is the complete factorization of $P(x)$?

Written Response

72. Solve $\log_6(x) + \log_6(x+5) = 2$.

Not for Reproduction

ANSWERS AND SOLUTIONS—PRACTICE QUESTIONS

1. D	16. B	31. B	46. A	61. 5
2. C	17. B	32. D	47. D	62. A
3. C	18. A	33. D	48. D	63. C
4. C	19. A	34. B	49. B	64. A
5. C	20. 17	35. D	50. C	65. 3.25
6. 2.5	21. 132	36. A	51. B	66. D
7. C	22. C	37. A	52. C	67. A
8. D	23. B	38. C	53. B	68. D
9. B	24. C	39. D	54. B	69. 1.2
10. B	25. B	40. 150	55. 2	70. WR
11. D	26. A	41. B	56. D	71. WR
12. D	27. D	42. C	57. A	72. WR
13. C	28. C	43. D	58. B	73. WR
14. D	29. B	44. C	59. A	
15. B	30. D	45. B	60. C	

1. D

Step 1

Substitute $2x-6$ for $h(x)$ and x^2-9 for $g(x)$ in the equation $f(x)=h(x)g(x)$.

$$f(x)=h(x)g(x)$$
$$f(x)=(2x-6)(x^2-9)$$

Step 2
Expand using FOIL.

$$f(x)=(2x-6)(x^2-9)$$
$$f(x)=2x^3-18x-6x^2+54$$
$$f(x)=2x^3-6x^2-18x+54$$

2. C

Step 1

Substitute x^2-25 for $g(x)$ and $x+5$ for $h(x)$ in the equation $f(x)=\dfrac{g(x)}{h(x)}$.

$$f(x)=\frac{g(x)}{h(x)}$$
$$f(x)=\frac{x^2-25}{x+5}$$

Step 2
State the non-permissible value or values.
$$x+5\neq0$$
$$x\neq-5$$

The non-permissible value of x is -5.

Step 3
Factor the numerator, and reduce.

$$f(x)=\frac{x^2-25}{x+5}$$
$$f(x)=\frac{(x-5)(x+5)}{x+5}$$
$$f(x)=x-5$$

3. C

Step 1

Substitute x^2-2x+1 for $g(x)$ and x^2+3x-4 for $h(x)$ into the equation $f(x)=g(x)-h(x)$.

$$f(x)=g(x)-h(x)$$
$$f(x)=(x^2-2x+1)-(x^2+3x-4)$$

Step 2

Subtract, and simplify by collecting like terms.

$f(x) = (x^2 - 2x + 1) - (x^2 + 3x - 4)$

$f(x) = x^2 - 2x + 1 - x^2 - 3x + 4$

$f(x) = x^2 - x^2 - 2x - 3x + 1 + 4$

$f(x) = -5x + 5$

4. C

Step 1

Replace x in $g(x)$ with the function $f(x) = x - 1$.

$g(x) = (x - 2)^2$

$g(f(x)) = ((x - 1) - 2)^2$

Step 2

Simplify.

$g(f(x)) = ((x - 1) - 2)^2$

$g(f(x)) = (x - 1 - 2)^2$

$g(f(x)) = (x - 3)^2$

$g(f(x)) = x^2 - 6x + 9$

5. C

Step 1

Calculate the value of $f(-6)$.

Substitute -6 into the function $f(x)$ wherever the variable x appears, and then simplify the expression.

$f(x) = \frac{1}{2}x^2 - 10$

$f(-6) = \frac{1}{2}(-6)^2 - 10$

$f(-6) = \frac{1}{2}(36) - 10$

$f(-6) = 18 - 10$

$f(-6) = 8$

Step 2

Calculate the value of $f(f(-6))$.

Since $f(-6) = 8$, $f(f(-6)) = f(8)$.

Substitute 8 into the function $f(x)$ wherever the variable x appears, and then simplify the expression.

$f(x) = \frac{1}{2}x^2 - 10$

$f(8) = \frac{1}{2}(8)^2 - 10$

$f(8) = \frac{1}{2}(64) - 10$

$f(8) = 32 - 10$

$f(8) = 22$

Therefore, $f(f(-6)) = 22$.

6. 2.5

Step 1

Determine the expression for $g(f(x))$.

Substitute $3x - 7$ into the function $g(x)$ wherever the variable x appears, and simplify the expression.

$g(x) = 5 - 2x$

$g(f(x)) = 5 - 2(3x - 7)$

$g(f(x)) = 5 - 6x + 14$

$g(f(x)) = 19 - 6x$

Step 2

Solve for x.

Given that $g(f(x)) = 4$, equate the expression for $g(f(x))$ to 4.

$g(f(x)) = 19 - 6x$

$4 = 19 - 6x$

$-15 = -6x$

$2.5 = x$

7. C

Step 1

Determine how to obtain the graph of $y = (x - 3)^3 + 4$ from the graph of $y = x^3$.

The equation $y = (x - 3)^3 + 4$ is of the form $y = f(x - h) + k$, where $k = 4$ and $h = 3$.

Therefore, the graph of $y = x^3$ is translated 3 units to the right and 4 units up.

Not for Reproduction

Step 2

Determine the location of the point (x, y) on the graph of $y = x^3$ after the translations.

When the graph moves 3 units to the right, the x-coordinate increases by 3. When the graph moves 4 units up, the y-coordinate increases by 4.

Therefore, the location of the translated point (x, y) on the graph of $y = (x-3)^3 + 4$ will be $(x + 3, y + 4)$.

8. D

When $x + 6$ is substituted for x in the equation $y = f(x)$, the graph of $y = f(x)$ will be translated 6 units to the left.

The point $(5, 4)$ is on the graph of $y = f(x+6)$, so it has been shifted 6 units to the left. Therefore, the corresponding point on the graph of $y = f(x)$ is 6 units to the right of $(5, 4)$.

In other words, the x-value of the corresponding point is $5 + 6 = 11$, and the y-value is 4. The coordinates of the corresponding point on the graph of $y = f(x)$ are $(11, 4)$.

9. B

Step 1

Determine how to obtain the graph of $y = f(x-3)+2$ from the graph of $y = f(x)$.

The equation $y = f(x-3)+2$ is of the form $y = f(x-c)+d$, where $c = 3$ and $d = 2$.

Therefore, the graph of $y = f(x-3)+2$ is formed from $y = f(x)$ by a horizontal translation 3 units right and a vertical translation 2 units up.

Step 2

Determine the range of the transformed function.

The horizontal translation will not affect the range of the function, but the vertical translation will cause each point on the graph of $y = f(x)$ to shift up by 2 units.

Therefore, the range of g is as follows:
$g(x) \geq -11 + 2$
$g(x) \geq -9$

10. B

Step 1

Rewrite the equation $y + 1 = f(x) - 4$ in the form $y - k = f(x)$.

$y + 1 = f(x) - 4$
$y + 5 = f(x)$

Step 2

Determine how to obtain the graph of $y + 1 = f(x) - 4$ from the graph of $y = f(x)$.

When the equation $y + 1 = f(x) - 4$ is rewritten in the form $y - k = f(x)$, $k = -5$.

Therefore, the graph of $y + 1 = f(x) - 4$ can be drawn by translating the graph of $y = f(x)$ down by 5 units.

11. D

Step 1

Substitute $\frac{1}{2}y$ for y in the equation $y = f(x)$.

$y = f(x)$
$\frac{1}{2}y = f(x)$

Step 2

Determine how to obtain the graph of $\frac{1}{2}y = f(x)$ from the graph of $y = f(x)$.

The equation $\frac{1}{2}y = f(x)$ can be written in the form $y = 2f(x)$, where $a = 2$.

Therefore, the graph of $\frac{1}{2}y = f(x)$ is formed from $y = f(x)$ by stretching it vertically about the x-axis by a factor of 2.

12. D

Step 1

Determine how to obtain the graph of $y = f\left(\frac{1}{3}x\right)$ from the graph of $y = f(x)$.

The equation $y = f\left(\dfrac{1}{3}x\right)$ is in the form

$y = f(bx)$, where $b = \dfrac{1}{3}$. Therefore, the graph of

$y = f\left(\dfrac{1}{3}x\right)$ is formed from $y = f(x)$ by

stretching it horizontally about the y-axis by a factor of 3.

Step 2
Determine the location of the point $(-3, 9)$ after the transformation.

When the graph of $y = f(x)$ is stretched horizontally by a factor of 3, every point (x, y) is transformed to point $(3x, y)$.

Therefore, point $(-3, 9)$ is transformed to point

$(3(-3), 9) = (-9, 9)$ on the graph of $y = f\left(\dfrac{1}{3}x\right)$.

13. C

Step 1
Identify appropriate points on the graph of $y = f(x)$.

Possible points on the graph of $y = f(x)$ are $(0, 0)$, $(2, 4)$, and $(4, 0)$.

Step 2
For each of the ordered pairs $(0, 0)$, $(2, 4)$, and $(4, 0)$, determine the corresponding point on the graph of $y = f\left(\dfrac{1}{2}x\right)$.

The graph of $y = f(x)$ must be stretched horizontally about the y-axis by a factor of 2 (the reciprocal of $\dfrac{1}{2}$ is 2) in order to obtain the

graph of $y = f\left(\dfrac{1}{2}x\right)$. Thus, any point (x, y) on the

graph of $y = f(x)$ will be transformed to the corresponding point (x, y) $(2 \times x, y) = (2x, y)$ on the

graph of $y = f\left(\dfrac{1}{2}x\right)$.

Point $(0, 0)$ corresponds to the point $(2 \times 0, 0) = (0, 0)$.

Point $(2, 4)$ corresponds to the point $(2 \times 2, 4) = (4, 4)$.

Point $(4, 0)$ corresponds to the point $(2 \times 4, 0) = (8, 0)$.

Step 3

Sketch the graph of $y = f\left(\dfrac{1}{2}x\right)$ by making

use of the points $(0, 0)$, $(4, 4)$, and $(8, 0)$.

The graph of $y = f\left(\dfrac{1}{2}x\right)$ can be sketched

as follows:

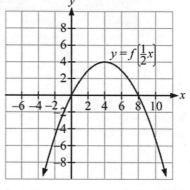

Step 4
Compare the domain and range of the graphs.

The graph of $y = f(x)$ is a parabola opening downward, and by observation, it can be seen that its domain is $x \in \mathbb{R}$, and its range is $y \le 4$.

The graph of $y = f\left(\dfrac{1}{2}x\right)$ is also a parabola

opening downward and by observation, it can be seen that its domain is $x \in \mathbb{R}$, and its range is $y \le 4$.

The graphs of $y = f(x)$ and $y = f\left(\dfrac{1}{2}x\right)$ have

the same domain and range.

14. D

Step 1
Identify the ordered pairs that define the x-intercepts of the graph $y = f(x)$.

Since the graph of $y = f(x)$ crosses the x-axis where $x = -1$ and $x = 5$, the x-intercepts of the graph of $y = f(x)$ are located at the ordered pairs $(-1, 0)$ and $(5, 0)$.

Copyright Protected

Not for Reproduction

Step 2

Determine the x-intercepts of the transformed graph.

Since the graph of $y = f(x)$ is vertically stretched about the x-axis by a factor of $\dfrac{1}{5}$, a point (x, y) on the graph of $y = f(x)$ will be transformed to the corresponding point $\left(x, \dfrac{1}{5} \times y\right) = \left(x, \dfrac{1}{5}y\right)$ on the graph of the transformed function. Thus, the ordered pair $(-1, 0)$ corresponds to the point $\left(-1, 0 \times \dfrac{1}{5}\right) = (-1, 0)$, and the point $(5, 0)$ corresponds to the point $\left(5, 0 \times \dfrac{1}{5}\right) = (5, 0)$ on the graph of the transformed function. It then follows that the x-intercepts of the graph of the transformed function are also located at the ordered pair $(-1, 0)$ and $(5, 0)$.

15. B

Step 1

Apply the horizontal stretch.

The graph of $y = 8x^2 + 3$ is horizontally stretched by a factor of 4, so replace x with $\dfrac{1}{4}x$.

$$y = 8x^2 + 3$$
$$y = 8\left(\dfrac{1}{4}x\right)^2 + 3$$
$$y = 8\left(\dfrac{x}{4}\right)^2 + 3$$

Step 2

Apply the vertical stretch.

The graph of $y = 8x^2 + 3$ is vertically stretched by a factor 2, so replace y in $y = 8\left(\dfrac{x}{4}\right)^2 + 3$ with $\dfrac{1}{2}y$.

$$y = 8\left(\dfrac{x}{4}\right)^2 + 3$$
$$\dfrac{1}{2}y = 8\left(\dfrac{x}{4}\right)^2 + 3$$

Step 3

Isolate y, and simplify.

$$\dfrac{1}{2}y = 8\left(\dfrac{x}{4}\right)^2 + 3$$
$$y = 2\left[8\left(\dfrac{x}{4}\right)^2 + 3\right]$$
$$y = 2\left[8\left(\dfrac{x^2}{16}\right) + 3\right]$$
$$y = 2\left(\dfrac{1}{2}x^2 + 3\right)$$
$$y = x^2 + 6$$

Therefore, the equation of the transformed graph is $y = x^2 + 6$.

16. B

Step 1

Apply the vertical stretch about the x-axis by a factor of 3 to the equation $y = \dfrac{1}{x}$.

Replace y with $\dfrac{1}{3}y$ in the equation $y = \dfrac{1}{x}$, and then solve for y.

$$\dfrac{1}{3}y = \dfrac{1}{x}$$
$$y = \dfrac{3}{x}$$

Step 2

Apply the reflection in the x-axis.

Replace y with $-y$ in the equation $y = \dfrac{3}{x}$, and then solve for y.

$$-y = \dfrac{3}{x}$$
$$y = -\dfrac{3}{x}$$

Step 3

Apply the translation 4 units right and 2 units down.

Replace x with $x-4$ and y with $y+2$ in the equation $y=-\dfrac{3}{x}$. Then, solve for y.

$$y=-\frac{3}{x}$$
$$(y+2)=-\frac{3}{(x-4)}$$
$$y=-\frac{3}{x-4}-2$$

Step 4

Simplify the equation $y=-\dfrac{3}{x-4}-2$.

$$y=-\frac{3}{x-4}-2$$
$$y=\frac{-3}{x-4}-\frac{2(x-4)}{x-4}$$
$$y=\frac{-3-2x+8}{x-4}$$
$$y=\frac{-2x+5}{x-4}$$

17. B

Determine the transformations applied to the graph of $y=f(x)$ to arrive at the graph of $y=f\left(\dfrac{1}{4}x-1\right)$, and then apply those transformations to the point $(2,-8)$.

Step 1

Rewrite the function $y=f\left(\dfrac{1}{4}x-1\right)$ in the form $y=f\big(b(x-h)\big)$.

$$y=f\left(\frac{1}{4}x-1\right)$$
$$y=f\left(\frac{1}{4}(x-4)\right)$$

Step 2

Determine the transformations applied to the graph of $y=f(x)$ to arrive at the graph of $y=f\left(\dfrac{1}{4}(x-4)\right)$.

To obtain the transformed function $y=f\left(\dfrac{1}{4}(x-4)\right)$, you need to substitute $\dfrac{1}{4}x$ for x and then substitute $x-4$ for x in the equation $y=f(x)$.

When $\dfrac{1}{4}x$ is substituted for x, the graph of $y=f(x)$ is horizontally stretched about the y-axis by a factor of 4.

When $x-4$ is substituted for x, the graph of $y=f(x)$ is translated 4 units to the right.

Step 3
Apply the stretch.

Since it is a horizontal stretch, multiply the x-coordinate by the stretch factor of 4.
$(2\times4,-8)=(8,-8)$

Step 4
Apply the translation.

The graph of the transformed function moves 4 units to the right, so add 4 to the x-coordinate.
$(8+4,-8)=(12,-8)$

Therefore, the point $(2,-8)$ on the graph of $y=f(x)$ will be transformed to $(12,-8)$ on the graph of $y=f\left(\dfrac{1}{4}x-1\right)$.

18. A

Step 1
Apply the horizontal stretch.

Since the graph of $y=f(x)$ is stretched horizontally about the y-axis by a factor of $\dfrac{1}{4}$, substitute $4x$ for x in the equation $y=f(x)$.

The resulting equation is $y=f(4x)$.

Step 2
Apply the vertical stretch.

Since the graph of $y=f(4x)$ is stretched vertically about the x-axis by a factor of 3, substitute $\dfrac{1}{3}y$ for y in the equation $y=f(4x)$.

The resulting equation is $\dfrac{1}{3}y=f(4x)$,

or $y=3f(4x)$.

Step 3
Apply the vertical reflection.

Substitute $-y$ for y in the equation $y=3f(4x)$ to reflect the graph $y=3f(4x)$ in the x-axis.

Copyright Protected

Not for Reproduction

The resulting equation is $-y = 3f(4x)$, which is equivalent to $y = -3f(4x)$.

Step 4
Apply the translations.

To translate the graph of $y = -3f(4x)$ 5 units left and 2 units down, substitute $x + 5$ for x and $y + 2$ for y in the equation $y = -3f(4x)$.

The equation of the transformed function is $y + 2 = -3f(4(x+5))$, or $y = -3f(4(x+5)) - 2$.

The equation $y = -3f(4(x+5)) - 2$ can then be written as $y = -3f(4x + 20) - 2$.

19. A

Step 1
Determine the necessary substitutions to obtain the equation $y = 9(x-7)^2$ from the equation $y = x^2$.

Multiplying both sides of the equation $y = 9(x-7)^2$ by $\frac{1}{9}$ gives the equivalent equation $\frac{1}{9}y = (x-7)^2$.

To obtain $\frac{1}{9}y = (x-7)^2$ from the equation $y = x^2$, substitute $\frac{1}{9}y$ for y and $x + 7$, or $x - (-7)$, for x.

Step 2
Describe the transformations needed to arrive at the graph of $y = 9(x-7)^2$ from the graph of $y = x^2$.

When y is replaced with $\frac{1}{9}y$ in the equation $y = x^2$, the result is a vertical stretch about the x-axis by a factor of 9.

When x is replaced with $x + 7$, or $x - (-7)$, the result is a horizontal translation 7 units left.

Therefore, the transformations needed to arrive at the graph of $y = 9(x-7)^2$ from the graph of $y = x^2$ are a vertical stretch about the x-axis by a factor of 9 and then a horizontal translation of 7 units left.

20. 17

Step 1
Apply the horizontal stretch.

When $y = f(x)$ is stretched horizontally, the x-coordinate is multiplied by the stretch factor, and the y-coordinate stays the same.

A horizontal stretch by a factor of 4 will transform the point $(-4, 2)$ to $(-4 \times 4, 2)$, or $(-16, 2)$.

Step 2
Apply the vertical translation.

When $y = f(x)$ is translated vertically, the x-coordinate stays the same, and the distance of the translation is added to or subtracted from the y-coordinate.

The vertical translation 3 units down will transform the point $(-16, 2)$ to $(-16, 2 - 3)$, or $(-16, -1)$.

Step 3
Calculate the value of $|p + q|$.

The point (p, q) on the transformed graph is $(-16, -1)$. This means that $p = -16$ and $q = -1$.
$$|p + q|$$
$$= |-16 + (-1)|$$
$$= |-17|$$
$$= 17$$

Therefore, the value of $|p + q|$ is 17.

21. 132

Step 1
Sketch the graph of equation 1.

Equation 1 is $y = f(-x)$. In order to obtain the equation $y = f(-x)$ from the equation $y = f(x)$, it is necessary to substitute $-x$ for x in the equation $y = f(x)$.

All of the x-coordinates are multiplied by –1, and the graph of $y = f(x)$ is reflected across the y-axis.

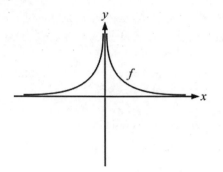

Step 2
Sketch the graph of equation 2.

Equation 2 is $y = -f(x)$. In order to obtain the equation $y = -f(x)$ from the equation $y = f(x)$, it is necessary to substitute $-y$ for y in the equation $y = f(x)$.

All of the y-coordinates are multiplied by –1, and the graph of $y = f(x)$ is reflected across the x-axis.

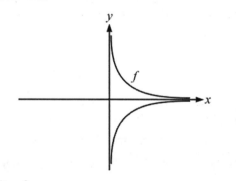

Step 3
Sketch the graph of equation 3.

Equation 3 is $y = -f(-x)$. In order to obtain the equation $y = -f(-x)$ from the equation $y = f(x)$, it is necessary to substitute $-x$ for x and $-y$ for y in the equation $y = f(x)$.

The x- and y-coordinates are multiplied by –1, and the graph of $y = f(x)$ is reflected across the x- axis and then across the y-axis.

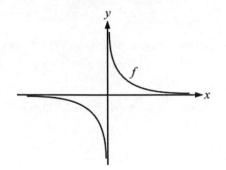

Step 4
Fill in the blanks of the original question.

The equations that produced the portions of the design found in quadrants II, III, and IV, are 1, 3, and 2, respectively.

Therefore, recorded as a three-digit number, this is 132.

22. C

In order to obtain the equation $y = f(-x)$ from the equation $y = f(x)$, it is necessary to substitute $-x$ for x in the equation $y = f(x)$.

When $-x$ is substituted for x in the equation $y = f(x)$, the graph of $y = f(x)$ will be reflected in the y-axis. Therefore, the ordered pair (x, y) on the graph of $y = f(x)$ will be transformed to the ordered pair $(-x, y)$ on the graph of $y = f(-x)$.

Since the ordered pair $(3, -5)$ is on the graph of $y = f(x)$, the ordered pair $(-3, -5)$ will be on the graph of $y = f(-x)$.

23. B

To produce a graph that is a reflection across the line $y = x$, the x- and y-coordinates on the graph of the original function must be interchanged. Therefore, the point $(-2, 7)$ corresponds to the transformed point $(7, -2)$ on the reflected graph.

Copyright Protected

Not for Reproduction

24. C

Step 1
Determine the transformations applied to the graph of $y = f(x)$ in order to transform it to the graph of $y = f(-x)$.

In order to obtain the equation $y = f(-x)$ from the equation $y = f(x)$, it is necessary to substitute $-x$ for x in the equation $y = f(x)$. When $-x$ is substituted for x in the equation $y = f(x)$, the graph of $y = f(x)$ will be reflected in the y-axis.

Therefore, the ordered pair (x, y) on the graph of $y = f(x)$ will be transformed to the ordered pair $(-x, y)$ on the graph of $y = f(-x)$.

Step 2
Identify particular ordered pairs on the graph of $y = f(x)$.

The ordered pairs $(-6, 3)$, $(-3, 0)$, and $(0, 3)$ are on the graph of $y = f(x)$.

Step 3
Apply the reflection in the y-axis to the points on the graph of $y = f(x)$.

Since an ordered pair (x, y) on the graph of $y = f(x)$ will be transformed to the ordered pair $(-x, y)$ on the graph of $y = f(-x)$, it follows that the ordered pairs $(6, 3)$, $(3, 0)$, and $(0, 3)$ will be on the graph of $y = f(-x)$.

The following graph contains these ordered pairs:

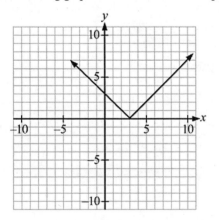

25. B

Step 1
Write the set of ordered pairs that define function f.

Since $0 \leq x \leq 3$, where x is an integer, begin by substituting each of the values 0, 1, 2, and 3 for x in the equation $f(x) = x^2 - 4$ as follows:

$$f(x) = x^2 - 4$$
$$f(0) = (0)^2 - 4 = -4$$
$$f(1) = (1)^2 - 4 = -3$$
$$f(2) = (2)^2 - 4 = 0$$
$$f(3) = (3)^2 - 4 = 5$$

Step 2
Write the set of ordered pairs that could define function f.
$$\{(0, -4), (1, -3), (2, 0), (3, 5)\}$$

Step 3
Write the set of ordered pairs that define $f^{-1}(x)$.

In order to write the ordered pairs that define $f^{-1}(x)$, it is necessary to interchange the x- and y-values in the ordered pairs that define function f. Therefore, the set of ordered pairs that could define the inverse function, $f^{-1}(x)$, is

$$\{(-4, 0), (-3, 1), (0, 2), (5, 3)\}.$$

26. A

The inverse of function A is obtained by interchanging the x- and y-values in the ordered pairs.
$$(-2, 0) \rightarrow (0, -2)$$
$$(0, 3) \rightarrow (3, 0)$$
$$(2, 0) \rightarrow (0, 2)$$
$$(4, 6) \rightarrow (6, 4)$$
$$(6, 8) \rightarrow (8, 6)$$

Therefore, the inverse of function A is defined by $\{(0, -2), (3, 0), (0, 2), (6, 4), (8, 6)\}$.

27. D

Step 1

Determine the inverse of the function.
Interchange the values of x and y, and solve for y.

$$x = 2 - \sqrt{y}$$
$$x - 2 = -\sqrt{y}$$
$$-x + 2 = \sqrt{y}$$
$$(-x + 2)^2 = y$$
$$x^2 - 4x + 4 = y$$

The equation of the inverse function is
$y = x^2 - 4x + 4$.

Step 2

Determine the domain and range of the inverse function.

When the inverse of a function is defined, the x- and y-variables of the domain and range of the original function are also interchanged to become the range and domain of the inverse.

The domain and range for $y = 2 - \sqrt{x}$ are $x \geq 0$ and $y \leq 2$, respectively. Therefore, the domain and range on the inverse function are $x \leq 2$ and $y \geq 0$, respectively.

The inverse of $y = 2 - \sqrt{x}$, where $x \geq 0$ and $y \leq 2$, is $y = x^2 - 4x + 4$, where $x \leq 2$ and $y \geq 0$.

28. C

Step 1

Replace $f(x)$ with y.

$$f(x) = \frac{6}{x - 7}$$
$$y = \frac{6}{x - 7}$$

Step 2

Interchange x and y.

$$y = \frac{6}{x - 7}$$
$$x = \frac{6}{y - 7}$$

Step 3

Solve for y.

$$x = \frac{6}{y - 7}$$
$$x(y - 7) = 6$$
$$y - 7 = \frac{6}{x}$$
$$y = \frac{6}{x} + 7$$
$$y = \frac{6}{x} + \frac{7x}{x}$$
$$y = \frac{6 + 7x}{x}$$

Therefore, the inverse function is $f^{-1}(x) = \dfrac{7x + 6}{x}$.

29. B

Step 1

Replace $f(x)$ with y.

$$f(x) = \frac{1}{2}(x + 6)^2 - 5$$
$$y = \frac{1}{2}(x + 6)^2 - 5$$

Step 2

Interchange x and y.

$$y = \frac{1}{2}(x + 6)^2 - 5$$
$$x = \frac{1}{2}(y + 6)^2 - 5$$

Step 3

Solve for y.

$$x = \frac{1}{2}(y + 6)^2 - 5$$
$$x + 5 = \frac{1}{2}(y + 6)^2$$
$$2x + 10 = (y + 6)^2$$
$$\pm\sqrt{2x + 10} = y + 6$$
$$\pm\sqrt{2x + 10} - 6 = y$$
$$y = \pm\sqrt{2x + 10} - 6$$

Note that y cannot be replaced by $f^{-1}(x)$ since the inverse is not a function.

Copyright Protected

Not for Reproduction

30. D

Step 1
Sketch the inverse graph, $y = F(x)$.

To identify points on the graph of $y = F(x)$, interchange the x- and y-values of the coordinates of the points on the graph of $y = f(x)$.

Points on the graph of $y = f(x)$ are $(-6, 2)$, $(-1, 7)$, and $(4, 2)$. Therefore, points on the graph of $y = F$ are $(2, -6)$, $(7, -1)$, and $(2, 4)$.

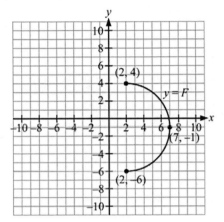

Step 2
Sketch a graph for each of the given restrictions.

When the domain of $f(x)$ is restricted to $x \geq -1$, only points in the interval $-1 \leq x \leq 4$ are included. On the inverse graph, this corresponds to a range restricted to $-1 \leq y \leq 4$. With this restriction, F is a function.

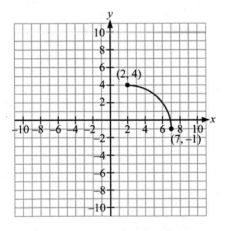

When the domain of $f(x)$ is restricted to $x \leq -1$, only points in the interval $-6 \leq x \leq -1$ are included. On the inverse graph, this corresponds to a range restricted to $-6 \leq y \leq -1$. With this restriction, F is a function.

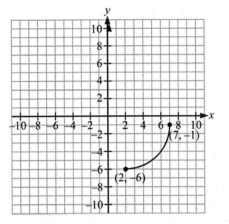

When the domain of $f(x)$ is restricted to $x \geq, 2$ only points in the interval $2 \leq x \leq 4$ are included. On the inverse graph, this corresponds to a range restricted to $2 \leq y \leq 4$. With this restriction, F is a function.

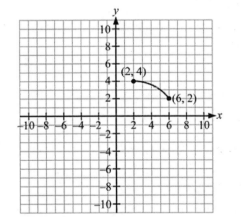

When the domain of $f(x)$ is restricted to $x \leq 2$, only points in the interval $-6 \leq x \leq 2$ are included. On the inverse graph, this corresponds to a range restricted to $-6 \leq y \leq 2$. This graph does not represent a function.

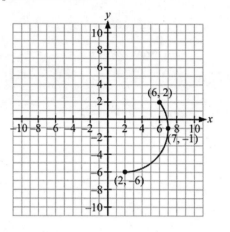

31. B

Step 1

Substitute $y = 0$ into the equation $y = \log_b x$.

$y = \log_b x$
$0 = \log_b x$

Step 2

Solve for x.

The equation $0 = \log_b x$ can be written in exponential form as $x = b^0$.

$x = b^0$
$x = 1$

Therefore, the x-intercept is 1.

32. D

The exponential equation $y = b^x$ can be written in logarithmic form as $x = \log_b y$.

Therefore, $81^{\frac{3}{4}} = 27$ can be written in logarithmic form as $\log_{81}(27) = \frac{3}{4}$.

33. D

Apply the change of base rule, $\log_b(a) = \dfrac{\log_c(a)}{\log_c(b)}$, to $\log_5 19$.

$\log_5 19 = \dfrac{\log_2 19}{\log_2 5}$, where $x > 0, x \neq 1$

The expression that correctly applies the change of base rule is $\dfrac{\log_2 19}{\log_2 5}$.

34. B

Step 1

Rewrite the equation $p = 4q^m$ as $\dfrac{p}{4} = q^m$.

Step 2

Write $\dfrac{p}{4} = q^m$ in logarithmic form. Recall that $x = a^y$ is equivalent to $y = \log_a x$.

Thus, $\dfrac{p}{4} = q^m$ is equivalent to $m = \log_q\left(\dfrac{p}{4}\right)$.

35. D

Step 1

Rewrite the equation so the logarithms are all on one side.

$$\log_3 y = c - \log_3 x$$
$$\log_3 y + \log_3 x = c$$

Step 2

Apply the product law of logarithms.

$$\log_3 y + \log_3 x = c$$
$$\log_3(yx) = c$$

Step 3

Rewrite the equation in exponential form, and solve for y.

$$\log_3(yx) = c$$
$$3^c = yx$$
$$\frac{3^c}{x} = y$$

Not for Reproduction

36. A

Step 1
Apply the product law of logarithms in reverse.
$$\log_3\left(\frac{1}{3}x\right) = \log_3\frac{1}{3} + \log_3 x$$

Step 2
Evaluate each term, and simplify.
$$\log_3\frac{1}{3} + \log_3 x$$
$$= \log_3(3^{-1}) + \log_3 x$$
$$= -1 + 15$$
$$= 14$$

37. A

Step 1
Apply the power law of logarithms.
$$\log m = \log a + 3\log l$$
$$\log m = \log a + \log(l^3)$$

Step 2
Apply the product law of logarithms.
$$\log m = \log a + \log(l^3)$$
$$\log m = \log(al^3)$$

Step 3
Subtract $\log(al^3)$ from both sides of the equation, and apply the quotient law of logarithms.
$$\log m = \log(al^3)$$
$$\log m - \log(al^3) = 0$$
$$\log\left(\frac{m}{al^3}\right) = 0$$

38. C

Step 1
Apply the power law of logarithms to the first two terms of the expression.
$$2\log 3 - \frac{1}{2}\log 16 + \log 12$$
$$= \log 3^2 - \log 16^{\frac{1}{2}} + \log 12$$

Step 2
Simplify the first two terms of the expression.
$$\log 3^2 - \log 16^{\frac{1}{2}} + \log 12$$
$$= \log 9 - \log 4 + \log 12$$

Step 3
Apply the product law and the quotient law of logarithms, and then simplify the resulting expression.
$$\log 9 - \log 4 + \log 12$$
$$= \log\left(\frac{9 \times 12}{4}\right)$$
$$= \log 27$$

39. D

Step 1
Apply the power law of logarithms.
$$4\log_b 2b - \log_b(1.6b)$$
$$= \log_b(2b)^4 - \log_b(1.6b)$$

Step 2
Apply the quotient law of logarithms.
$$\log_b(2b)^4 - \log_b(1.6b)$$
$$= \log_b\left(\frac{(2b)^4}{1.6b}\right)$$

Step 3
Simplify.
$$\log_b\left(\frac{(2b)^4}{1.6b}\right)$$
$$= \log_b\left(\frac{16b^4}{1.6b}\right)$$
$$= \log_b(10b^3)$$

Step 4
Apply the product law of logarithms, and simplify.
$$\log_b(10b^3)$$
$$= \log_b 10 + \log_b b^3$$
$$= \log_b 10 + 3$$

40. 150

Step 1
Apply the power law of logarithms.
$$\log_4 (64)^{50}$$
$$= 50 \log_4 64$$

Step 2
Evaluate.

Since $4^3 = 64$, $\log_4 64 = 3$.
$$50 \log_4 64$$
$$= 50(3)$$
$$= 150$$

The value of the expression $\log_4 (64)^{50}$ is 150.

41. B

Step 1
Simplify the given expression by writing it as a single logarithm.
$$\log_4 \frac{1}{12} + \log_4 \frac{3}{16}$$
$$= \log_4 \left(\left(\frac{1}{12} \right) \left(\frac{3}{16} \right) \right)$$
$$= \log_4 \left(\frac{3}{192} \right)$$
$$= \log_4 \left(\frac{1}{64} \right)$$

Step 2
Evaluate $\log_4 \left(\frac{1}{64} \right)$.
$$\log_4 \left(\frac{1}{64} \right) = -3$$

42. C

Analyze each statement to determine which one is true.

Step 1
Determine the equation of the vertical asymptote.

The graph of $y = \left(\frac{1}{4} \right)^x$ does not have a vertical asymptote. Therefore, statement **A** is false.

Step 2
Determine the x-intercept.

Since $0 \neq \left(\frac{1}{4} \right)^1$, the point $(1,0)$ is not an x-intercept.

Therefore, statement **B** is false.

Step 3
Determine if the graph passes through the point $(-2, 16)$.

In the equation $y = \left(\frac{1}{4} \right)^x$, substitute -2 for x and 16 for y.
$$y = \left(\frac{1}{4} \right)^x$$
$$16 = \left(\frac{1}{4} \right)^{-2}$$
$$16 = \left(4^{-1} \right)^{-2}$$
$$16 = 4^2$$
$$16 = 16$$

Since the left-hand side is equal to the right-hand side, the graph of $y = \left(\frac{1}{4} \right)^x$ passes through the ordered pair $(-2, 16)$. Therefore, statement **C** is true.

Step 4
Determine the range of the graph of $y = \left(\frac{1}{4} \right)^x$.

The range of the function $y = b^x$ is $y > 0$.

Since $y = \left(\frac{1}{4} \right)^x$ is of the form $y = b^x$, the range of the graph is $y > 0$, not $y < 0$. Therefore, statement **D** is false.

43. D

The function $f(x) = \log_b x$ is increasing when $b > 1$ and decreasing when $0 < b < 1$. Therefore, the change from a decreasing to an increasing function would occur when the value of b changes from $\frac{1}{2}$ to 3.

44. C

Step 1
Analyze the first statement.

The graph of $y = \log_b x$, where $b > 0$, has a range of $y \in R$. Since $y = \log_8 x$ is of the form $y = \log_b x$, the range of the graph of $y = \log_8 x$ is $y \in R$, not $y > 0$.

Statement **A** is false.

Copyright Protected

Not for Reproduction

Step 2
Analyze statement **B**.

The graph of $y = \log_b x$, where $b > 0$, has a vertical asymptote at $x = 0$ (y-axis). Therefore, $y = \log_8 x$ does not have a y-intercept.

Statement **B** is false.

Step 3
Analyze statement **C**.

The graph of $y = \log_b x$, where $b > 0$, has a vertical asymptote at $x = 0$ (y-axis). Therefore, the vertical asymptote of $y = \log_8 x$ is $x = 0$.

Statement **C** is true.

Step 4
Analyze statement **D**.

In the equation $y = \log_8 x$, substitute $\frac{1}{8}$ for x and -2 for y in the equation, and convert it to exponential form.

$$-2 = \log_8\left(\frac{1}{8}\right)$$

$$8^{-2} = \frac{1}{8}$$

Since $8^{-2} \neq \frac{1}{8}$, the graph of $y - \log_8 x$ docs not pass through $\left(\frac{1}{8}, -2\right)$.

Statement **D** is false.

45. B

Apply the change of base formula, $\log_b a = \dfrac{\log_c a}{\log_c b}$, using base 10 so that a calculator can be used.

The function $y = 5\log_2\left(\dfrac{x}{10} + 60\right)$ can be written using common logarithms as

$$y = 5\left(\frac{\log\left(\dfrac{x}{10} + 60\right)}{\log 2}\right).$$

46. A

Determine the y-intercept of the graph by substituting $x = 0$ into the equation $y = a^{x-2}$.

$y = a^{x-2}$
$y = a^{0-2}$
$y = a^{-2}$
$y = \dfrac{1}{a^2}$

Therefore, the y-intercept is $\dfrac{1}{a^2}$.

47. D

The function $y = \log_4 x$ is of the form $y = \log_b x$, where the value of b is 4, which is greater than 1. Therefore, the graph of $y = \log_4 x$ is increasing and has range of $y \in R$. It is given that $x > 0$. Therefore, the graph lies entirely to the right of the y-axis.

48. D

Step 1
Take the logarithm of both sides of the equation $V = 1\,000(1.04)^t$.

$V = 1\,000(1.04)^t$
$\log V = \log\left(1\,000(1.04)^t\right)$

Step 2
Apply the product law of logarithms.

$\log V = \log\left(1\,000(1.04)^t\right)$
$\log V = \log 1\,000 + \log(1.04)^t$

Step 3
Apply the power law of logarithms.

$\log V = \log 1\,000 + \log(1.04)^t$
$\log V = \log 1\,000 + t(\log 1.04)$

Step 4
Solve for t.

$\log V = \log 1\,000 + t(\log 1.04)$
$\log V = 3 + t(\log 1.04)$
$\log V - 3 = t(\log 1.04)$
$\dfrac{\log V - 3}{\log 1.04} = t$

49. B

Step 1

Convert the equation $\log_{(x+2)} 5 = 10$ to exponential form.

$$\log_{(x+2)} 5 = 10$$
$$(x+2)^{10} = 5$$

Step 2

Solve for x.

$$(x+2)^{10} = 5$$
$$x+2 = \sqrt[10]{5}$$
$$x = \sqrt[10]{5} - 2$$
$$x \approx -0.83$$

50. C

Step 1

Apply the power law of logarithms.

$$4\log_3(x+6) - 2\log_3(7x+9) = 5$$
$$\log_3(x+6)^4 - \log_3(7x+9)^2 = 5$$

Step 2

Apply the quotient law of logarithms.

$$\log_3(x+6)^4 - \log_3(7x+9)^2 = 5$$
$$\log_3\left(\frac{(x+6)^4}{(7x+9)^2}\right) = 5$$

Step 3

Rewrite the equation in exponential form.

$$\log_3\left(\frac{(x+6)^4}{(7x+9)^2}\right) = 5$$
$$3^5 = \frac{(x+6)^4}{(7x+9)^2}$$

Step 4

Multiply both sides of the equation by $(7x+9)^2$.

$$3^5 = \frac{(x+6)^4}{(7x+9)^2}$$
$$3^5(7x+9)^2 = (x+6)^4$$

Step 5

Determine the degree of the polynomial.

When expanded, the left side of the equation $3^5(7x+9)^2 = (x+6)^4$ will have a degree of 2, and the right side will have a degree of 4. As a result, the term in the equation with the highest degree will have a degree of 4.

Therefore, after simplifying so that either the left-hand side or the right-hand side is equal to 0, the equation will have the form of a polynomial of degree 4.

51. B

Step 1

Express $\log_5(125x) = 25$ in exponential form.

$$\log_5(125x) = 25$$
$$5^{25} = 125x$$

Step 2

Solve for x in the expression $5^{25} = 125x$.

$$5^{25} = 125x$$
$$5^{25} = 5^3 x$$
$$\frac{5^{25}}{5^3} = x$$
$$5^{(25-3)} = x$$
$$5^{22} = x$$

52. C

The half-life formula for a radioactive substance is

$$A(t) = A_0\left(\frac{1}{2}\right)^{\frac{t}{h}}, \text{ where } A(t) = \text{mass at time } t,$$

$A_0 = A(0)$, $t = $ time, and $h = $ half-life of substance.

Step 1

Let $h = 14.3$ days, $A_0 = 96.2$ g, and $A(t) = 12.5$ g

in the equation $A(t) = A_0\left(\frac{1}{2}\right)^{\frac{t}{h}}$.

$$A(t) = A_0\left(\frac{1}{2}\right)^{\frac{t}{h}}$$
$$12.5 = 96.2\left(\frac{1}{2}\right)^{\frac{t}{14.3}}$$

Copyright Protected

Not for Reproduction

Step 2
Divide each side by 96.2.

$$12.5 = 96.2\left(\frac{1}{2}\right)^{\frac{t}{14.3}}$$

$$\frac{12.5}{96.2} = \left(\frac{1}{2}\right)^{\frac{t}{14.3}}$$

Step 3
Take the log of both sides of the equation.

$$\frac{12.5}{96.2} = \left(\frac{1}{2}\right)^{\frac{t}{14.3}}$$

$$\log\left(\frac{12.5}{96.2}\right) = \log\left(\frac{1}{2}\right)^{\frac{t}{14.3}}$$

Step 4
Apply the power law of logarithms to the right side of the equation.

$$\log\left(\frac{12.5}{96.2}\right) = \log\left(\frac{1}{2}\right)^{\frac{t}{14.3}}$$

$$\log\left(\frac{12.5}{96.2}\right) = \frac{t}{14.3}\log\left(\frac{1}{2}\right)$$

Step 5
Solve for t.

$$\log\left(\frac{12.5}{96.2}\right) = \frac{t}{14.3}\log\left(\frac{1}{2}\right)$$

$$14.3\log\left(\frac{12.5}{96.2}\right) = t\log\left(\frac{1}{2}\right)$$

$$\frac{14.3\log\left(\frac{12.5}{96.2}\right)}{\log\left(\frac{1}{2}\right)} = t$$

$$t \approx 42 \text{ days}$$

Therefore, it will take about 42 days for 96.2 g of phosphorus-32 to decay to 12.5 g.

53. B

Step 1
Determine the [H+] for pure water by applying the formula pH $= -\log$[H+].

Substitute 7 for pH, and then solve for [H+].

$$\text{pH} = -\log$$
$$7 = -\log[H^+]$$
$$-7 = \log[H^+]$$
$$10^{-7} = [H^+]_{water}$$

Step 2
Determine the [H+] for the more acidic solution.

Let x be the pH of the acidic solution. Substitute x for pH in the formula pH $= -\log$[H+], and then solve for [H+].

$$\text{pH} = -\log[H^+]$$
$$x = -\log[H^+]$$
$$-x = \log[H^+]$$
$$10^{-x} = [H^+]_{acicdic\ solution}$$

Step 3
Write an equation to relate the [H+] of water and the more acidic solution.

The [H+] for water is 10^{-7}, and the [H+] for the acidic solution is 10^{-x}. The value of [H+] for the acidic solution is 20 times as great as [H+] for water. Therefore, $20\left(10^{-7}\right) = 10^{-x}$.

Step 4
Solve for x.

Rewrite the equation so that both powers are on the same side, and then apply the quotient law of exponents.

$$20\left(10^{-7}\right) = 10^{-x}$$
$$20 = \frac{10^{-x}}{10^{-7}}$$
$$20 = 10^{-x-(-7)}$$
$$20 = 10^{-x+7}$$

Take the common logarithm of each side of the equation, apply the power law of logarithms, and then solve for x.

$$20 = 10^{-x+7}$$
$$\log 20 = \log\left(10^{-x+7}\right)$$
$$\log 20 = (-x+7)\log 10$$
$$\frac{\log 20}{\log 10} = -x + 7$$
$$x = 7 - \frac{\log 20}{\log 10}$$
$$x \approx 5.7$$

Therefore, a solution that is 20 times as acidic as water has a pH of approximately 5.7.

Copyright Protected

54. B

According to the remainder theorem, when $P(x)$ is divided by a binomial of the form $x - a$, the remainder is $P(a)$. In this case, $P(x)$ is divided by $x + \dfrac{1}{2}$, or $x - \left(-\dfrac{1}{2}\right)$, so $a = -\dfrac{1}{2}$.

Substitute $x = -\dfrac{1}{2}$ into $P(x)$ to find the remainder.

$$P(x) = 2x^4 + x^3 + 4x^2 + 1$$

$$P\left(-\frac{1}{2}\right) = 2\left(-\frac{1}{2}\right)^4 + \left(-\frac{1}{2}\right)^3 + 4\left(-\frac{1}{2}\right)^2 + 1$$

$$P\left(-\frac{1}{2}\right) = 2\left(\frac{1}{16}\right) + \left(-\frac{1}{8}\right) - 4\left(\frac{1}{4}\right) + 1$$

$$P\left(-\frac{1}{2}\right) = \frac{2}{16} - \frac{1}{8} - \frac{4}{4} + 1$$

$$P\left(-\frac{1}{2}\right) = \frac{1}{8} - \frac{1}{8} - 1 + 1$$

$$P\left(-\frac{1}{2}\right) = 0$$

Therefore, the remainder is 0.

55. 2

Step 1
Apply the factor theorem.

If $P(a) = 0$ for the polynomial $P(x)$, then $(x - a)$ is a factor of $P(x)$.

The binomial $x + 4 = x - (-4)$ is a factor of $P(x)$, so $P(-4) = 0$.

Step 2
Let $x = -4$ in $P(x)$, and set it equal to 0.

$$P(x) = x^4 + 3x^3 - Kx^2 + 7x - 4$$

$$P(-4) = (-4)^4 + 3(-4)^3 - K(-4)^2 + 7(-4) - 4$$

$$0 = (256) + 3(-64) - K(16) + 7(-4) - 4$$

$$0 = 256 - 192 - 16K - 28 - 4$$

$$0 = 32 - 16K$$

Step 3
Solve for K.

$$0 = 32 - 16K$$

$$16K = 32$$

$$K = \frac{32}{16}$$

$$K = 2$$

Therefore, the value of K in the polynomial $P(x) = x^4 + 3x^3 - Kx^2 + 7x - 4$ is 2.

56. D

According to the remainder theorem, when $P(x)$ is divided by a binomial of the form $x - a$, the remainder is $P(a)$.

Since $P(x)$ is divided by $x + 2 = x - (-2)$, $a = -2$.

When $P(x)$ is divided by $x + 2$, the remainder will be equal to $P(-2)$.

Since the remainder obtained by Fred is 4, his calculation demonstrates that $P(-2) = 4$.

57. A

According to the remainder theorem, when $P(x)$ is divided by a binomial of the form $x - a$, the remainder is $P(a)$.

If $P(x)$ is divided by $x + 2 = x - (-2)$, then $a = -2$, and the reminder will be $P(-2)$.

By looking at the graph of $y = P(x)$, it can be seen that the point $(-2, P(-2))$ lies in the third quadrant, so $P(-2)$ must be a negative number.

Thus, the remainder when $P(x)$ is divided by $x + 2$ is negative.

58. B

A polynomial function is a function that can be written in the form $f(x) = a_n x^n + a_{n-1} x^{n-1} + a_{n-2} x^{n-2} + \ldots + a_2 x^2 + a_1 x + a_0$, where the variables $a_0, a_1, a_2, \ldots a_n$ are real numbers, and all exponents of the x-variables are whole numbers.

The non-integral coefficient, $\sqrt{3}$, in the given function, $f(x) = x^2 - \sqrt{3}x^3 + x^{-4} + 5x^{\frac{5}{4}}$ is a real number. The constant term in the function is $a_0 = 0$.

However, $f(x)$ is not a polynomial function because it contains a negative exponent and a fractional exponent.

59. A

Step 1
Determine the behaviour of the graph at the x-intercepts.

At $x = -4$ and $x = 4$, the graph crosses straight though the x-axis.

At $x = 0$, the graph is tangent to the x-axis.

Not for Reproduction

Step 2
Determine the multiplicity of the roots.

When the graph crosses straight through the x-axis, the multiplicity of the root is 1. Therefore, the multiplicity of the roots at $x = -4$ and $x = 4$ is 1.

When the graph is tangent to the x-axis, the multiplicity of the root is an even number. Since the graph is tangent to the x-axis at the origin, the multiplicity of the root $x = 0$ is an even number.

It is necessary that the roots at $x = -4$ and $x = 4$ have a multiplicity of 1. It is also possible that the root at $x = 0$ has a multiplicity of 4.

60. C

When a polynomial is written in the factored form, $f(x) = a(x - r_1)(x - r_2)(x - r_3)...(x - r_n)$, where r_1, r_2, r_3,..., r_n are real numbers, the x-intercepts of the graph of the function are r_1, r_2, r_3,..., r_n.

If $3x = 3(x - 0)$ is a factor of $P(x)$, then 0 must be an x-intercept of the graph.

61. 5

The degree of a polynomial, P, is equal to the sum of the multiplicities of the zeros.

It is given that P is a polynomial of degree 5, so the sum of the multiplicities of its zeros is 5. Therefore, P can have at most 5 zeros.

Since each real zero corresponds to an x-intercept on the graph of $y = P(x)$, it follows that there can be at most 5 x-intercepts on the graph.

62. A

Step 1
Determine the domain, range, and intercepts of $y = \sqrt{x}$.

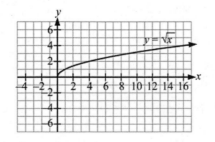

The graph of $y = \sqrt{x}$ has a domain of $x \geq 0$, a range of $y \geq 0$, and the x- and y-intercepts are both at $(0, 0)$.

Step 2
Determine the domain of the transformed function.

When the graph of $y = \sqrt{x}$ is vertically stretched by a factor of a, the y-coordinate of every point is multiplied by a. The x-coordinates do not change, so the domain $x \geq 0$ does not change.

Step 3
Determine the range of the transformed function.

The range of $y = \sqrt{x}$ is $y \geq 0$. When the y-coordinates are multiplied by a, where $a > 0$, all of the y-coordinates will still be greater than 0, so the range $y \geq 0$ does not change.

Step 4
Determine the intercepts of the transformed function.

The x- and y- intercepts of $y = \sqrt{x}$ are both at $(0, 0)$. When the y-coordinate is multiplied by a, the result is $(0, 0)$, so the x- and y- coordinates do not change.

Therefore, the graph of the transformed function will have the same domain, range, x-intercept, and y-intercept as the graph of $y = \sqrt{x}$.

63. C

The graph of $y = -5\sqrt{x}$ is simply the graph of $y = 5\sqrt{x}$ reflected in the x-axis. Thus, the graphs of $y = 5\sqrt{x}$ and $y = -5\sqrt{x}$ are as shown.

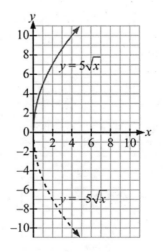

According to the given graphs, the domain of both graphs is $x \geq 0$. However, the range of the graph of $y = 5\sqrt{x}$ is $y \geq 0$, while the range of $y = -5\sqrt{x}$ is $y \leq 0$.

The graphs of $y = 5\sqrt{x}$ and $y = -5\sqrt{x}$ have the same domain but different ranges.

64. A

Step 1
Factor 5 out of $5x - 2$.
$$y = \sqrt{5x - 2}$$
$$y = \sqrt{5\left(x - \frac{2}{5}\right)}$$

Step 2
Simplify 5 out of the radicand.
$$y = \sqrt{5\left(x - \frac{2}{5}\right)}$$
$$y = \sqrt{5}\sqrt{x - \frac{2}{5}}$$

The function $y = \sqrt{5x - 2}$ written in the form $y = a\sqrt{x - c}$ is $y = \sqrt{5}\sqrt{x - \frac{2}{5}}$. The values of a and c are $\sqrt{5}$ and $\frac{2}{5}$, respectively.

65. 3.25

The equation can be solved using a TI-83 or similar calculator. When solving radical equations graphically, the solution is the x-value at the point of intersection between the graphs of the two functions.

Step 1
Graph the corresponding equations.

Press $\boxed{Y=}$, and enter $Y_1 = 3\sqrt{\ } (X + 3)$ and $Y_2 = 2X + 1$. Press $\boxed{ZOOM}$, and select 6:ZStandard.

The graphs of the two functions will appear as follows.

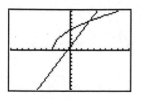

Step 2
Determine where the graphs intersect.

Observe that there is only one intersection point. To find the point of intersection, press $\boxed{2nd}$ $\boxed{TRACE}$, and select 5:intersect.

Use the arrow button to move to the point of intersection, and press $\boxed{ENTER}$ three times to find the intersection point.

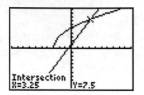

The x-value of the intersection point is 3.25.

66. D

The transformed function is $y = \dfrac{1}{f(x)} = \dfrac{1}{x + 2}$.

The graph of the function has a vertical asymptote where $x + 2 = 0$, or $x = -2$.

67. A

Step 1
Determine the degree of the numerator and the degree of the denominator.

The degree of the numerator, $5x - 2$, is 1.

The degree of the denominator, $3x - 2$, is 1.

Step 2
Determine the equation for the horizontal asymptote.

Since the degree of the numerator is equal to the degree of the denominator, the horizontal asymptote occurs at $y = \dfrac{a}{b}$, where a and b are the leading coefficients of the numerator and denominator, respectively.

$$y = \frac{a}{b}$$
$$y = \frac{5}{3}$$

The equation of the horizontal asymptote is $y = \dfrac{5}{3}$.

Copyright Protected

Not for Reproduction

68. D

Step 1

Identify the non-permissible values for

$$g(x) = \frac{(x+1)^2(x-2)}{x(x+1)(x-2)},$$ and reduce the function to

lowest terms.

The function is not defined for $x = 0$, $x = -1$, and $x = 2$, since the denominator cannot be 0.

Simplify the function by cancelling the common factors, $(x + 1)$ and $(x - 2)$, in the numerator and denominator.

$$g(x) = \frac{(x+1)^2(x-2)}{x(x+1)(x-2)}$$

$$g(x) = \frac{x+1}{x},$$ where $x \neq 0$, $x \neq -1$, and $x \neq 2$

This can also be written as $g(x) = \frac{1}{x} + 1$, where

$x \neq 0$, $x \neq -1$, and $x \neq 2$.

Step 2

Determine if the graph of $g(x)$ will have a vertical asymptote or a hole for each non-permissible value of x.

The factor x remains in the denominator after $g(x)$ is reduced, so $x = 0$ is a vertical asymptote.

The factor $(x - 2)$ cancels out of the numerator and denominator after $g(x)$ is reduced, so there is a hole at $x = 2$. A factor of $(x + 1)$ remains in the numerator, but one factor of $(x + 1)$ is cancelled out of the numerator and denominator. Therefore there is also a hole at $x = 1$.

Step 3

Describe the graph of each function.

The graph of $y = g(x)$ will have the same shape as the graph of $y = \frac{1}{x} + 1$, but it will contain two holes.

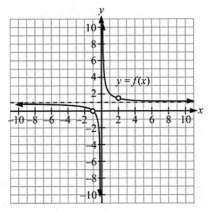

The graph of $y = g(x)$ has the same number of vertical asymptotes as the graph of

$y = f(x) = \frac{1}{x} + 1$. However, the graphs are not

identical, since $y = g(x)$ contains two holes.

The graph of $y = g(x)$ does not pass through the point $(-1, 0)$, since one of the holes occurs at $x = -1$. The other hole is at $x = 2$.

Therefore, the only true statement is that the graph of $y = g(x)$ has a hole at $x = 2$.

69. 1.2

Use a TI-83 or similar calculator to graph the

equation $2x - 5 = \frac{x+1}{x-2}$. One way to do this is to

separate the equation into two functions,

$f(x) = 2x - 5$ and $g(x) = \frac{x+1}{x-2}$, and then graph

both functions. To find the solution to the problem, determine the points of intersection of the two functions.

Step 1

Determine the non-permissible values.

Since $x - 2$ is part of the denominator, determine the value of x when it equals 0.

$$x - 2 = 0$$
$$x = 2$$

Therefore, the only non-permissible value is 2.

Copyright Protected

Step 2

Use the calculator to graph $f(x) = 2x - 5$ and

$g(x) = \dfrac{x+1}{x-2}$.

Press $\boxed{Y=}$, and enter $2X - 5$ in Y_1 and $(X+1)/(X-2)$ in Y_2. Press $\boxed{WINDOW}$, and enter a window setting that will show the points of intersection of the two curves. An appropriate window setting in this case would be $x:[-5, 5, 1]$ and $y:[-3, 3, 1]$. Press $\boxed{GRAPH}$ to generate the graphs.

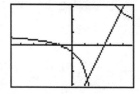

Step 3

Determine the smallest point of intersection of the graphs. The x-coordinates of the point of intersection give the solution value.

Press $\boxed{2nd}$ $\boxed{TRACE}$ to access the CALC menu, and select 5:intersect. Move the cursor to a point on the curve of $f(x) = 2x - 5$ that is at or near one of the points of intersection, and press $\boxed{ENTER}$. Then, move the cursor to a point on the curve of $g(x) = \dfrac{x+1}{x-2}$ that is at or near the same point of intersection, and press $\boxed{ENTER}$ twice. The coordinates of the smallest point of intersection will be given.

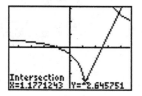

Rounded to the nearest tenth, the smallest point of intersection is $(1.2, -2.6)$. Therefore, the smallest solution value is 1.2.

---

70. **WR**

Step 1
Determine the x-intercepts of the graph of $y = f(x)$.

The x-intercepts of the graph are $(-3, 0)$, $(-1, 0)$, and $(2, 0)$.

Step 2
Determine how the graph of $y = f(x-7)$ can be obtained from the graph of $y = f(x)$.

In order to generate the equation $y = f(x-7)$ from the equation $y = f(x)$, it is necessary to substitute $x - 7$ for x in the equation $y = f(x)$. Therefore, the graph of $y = f(x)$ must be translated 7 units to the right in order to arrive at the graph of $y = f(x-7)$.

Step 3
Determine the x-intercepts of the graph of $y = f(x-7)$.

Since the graph of $y = f(x-7)$ is 7 units to the right of the graph of $y = f(x)$, the x-intercepts of $y = f(x-7)$ are located at the ordered pairs $(-3 + 7, 0) = (4, 0)$, $(-1 + 7, 0) = (6, 0)$, and $(2 + 7, 0) = (9, 0)$.

71. **WR**

Sketch the graph of $y = -3(2)^{x+2} - 1$ by applying transformations to the graph of $y = 2^x$.

Step 1
Identify the transformations applied to $y = 2^x$ to get $y = -3(2)^{x+2} - 1$.

By comparing $y = -3(2)^{x+2} - 1$ to $y = aB^{b(x-c)} + d$, you can determine that $a = -3$, $b = 1$, $c = -2$, and $d = -1$.

Therefore, the graph is vertically stretched by a factor of 3, reflected in the x-axis, and translated 2 units left and 1 unit down.

Not for Reproduction

Step 2

Sketch the graph of $y = 2^x$.

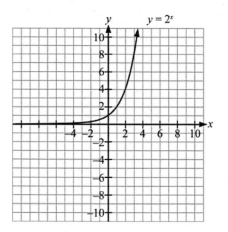

Step 3

Vertically stretch the graph of $y = 2^x$ by a factor of 3. The equation of the resulting graph is $y = 3(2)^x$.

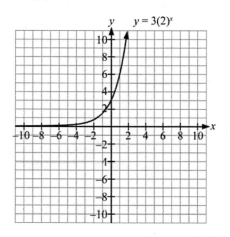

Step 4

Reflect the graph of $y = 3(2)^x$ in the x-axis. The equation of the resulting graph is $y = -3(2)^x$.

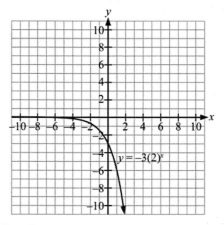

Step 5

Translate the graph of $y = -3(2)^x$ horizontally 2 units to the left. The equation of the resulting graph is $y = -3(2)^{x+2}$.

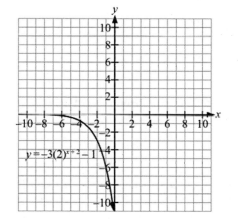

Step 6

Translate the graph of $y = -3(2)^{x+2}$ vertically 1 unit down. The equation of the resulting graph is $y = -3(2)^{x+2} - 1$.

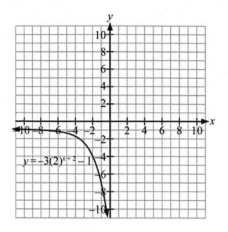

72. WR

Step 1

Use the laws of logarithms to combine the logarithmic expressions.

Since these expressions are being added, apply the product law of logarithms to write them as a single logarithm.

$$\log_6(x) + \log_6(x+5) = 2$$
$$\log_6\left[(x)(x+5)\right] = 2$$

Expand the expression in the square brackets.

$$\log_6\left[(x)(x+5)\right] = 2$$
$$\log_6\left(x^2 + 5x\right) = 2$$

Step 2

Write the logarithmic equation in exponential form.

The equation in exponential form is $6^2 = x^2 + 5x$, or $x^2 + 5x = 36$.

Step 3

Solve the exponential equation.

Subtract 36 from both sides of the equation to gather all terms to one side.
$$x^2 + 5x - 36 = 0$$

Factor the polynomial.
$$(x+9)(x-4) = 0$$

Solve for x.
$$x = 4 \text{ or } x = -9$$

Step 4

Check for extraneous roots.

Substitute each solution into the original equation to see if the LHS = RHS.

Verify if $x = 4$ is a solution. Substitute 4 for x into the left side of the original equation, and simplify.

LHS	RHS
$\log_6(x) + \log_6(x+5)$ $= \log_6(4) + \log_6(4+5)$ $= \log_6(4 \times 9)$ $= \log_6(36)$ $= 2$	2

Since the LHS = RHS, the solution $x = 4$ is verified.

Verify if $x = -9$ is a solution. Substitute -9 into the left side of the original equation, and simplify.

LHS	RHS
$\log_6(x) + \log_6(x+5)$ $= \log_6(-9) + \log_6(-9+5)$	2

The expression $\log_6(-9)$ cannot be evaluated because the logarithm of a negative number is not a real number, which means that $x = -9$ is an extraneous root and not part of the solution.

Thus, the only solution to the equation $\log_6(x) + \log_6(x+5) = 2$ is $x = 4$.

Copyright Protected

Not for Reproduction

73. **WR**

Step 1

Use the factor theorem.

If $P(a) = 0$, then $x - a$ is a factor of $P(x)$.

Since $P(-2) = 0$, $(x + 2)$ is a factor of $P(x)$.

Step 2

Use synthetic division to determine the other factor.

$$
\begin{array}{r|rrrr}
-2 & 1 & -2 & -5 & -6 \\
   & \downarrow & -2 & 8 & -6 \\
\hline
   & 1 & -4 & 3 & 0
\end{array}
$$

This means $P(x) = \left(x^2 - 4x + 3\right)(x + 2)$.

Step 3

Factor the quadratic expression to complete the factorization of $P(x)$.

$$x^2 - 4x + 3 = (x - 3)(x - 1)$$

This means $P(x) = (x + 2)(x - 3)(x - 1)$.

UNIT TEST—RELATIONS AND FUNCTIONS

1. Given the functions $f(x) = x^2 + 1$ and $g(x) = \sqrt{x+4}$, which of the following statements is **true**?

   A. The function $f(x)$ has the same domain as the function $f(g(x))$, but a different range.

   B. The function $g(x)$ has the same domain as the function $f(g(x))$, but a different range.

   C. The function $f(x)$ has the same domain and the same range as the function $f(g(x))$.

   D. The function $g(x)$ has the same domain and the same range as the function $f(g(x))$.

2. If (a, b) is a point on the graph of $y = f(x)$, which of the following points is on the graph of $y = f(x+2)$?

   A. $(a+2, b)$

   B. $(a-2, b)$

   C. $(a, b+2)$

   D. $(a, b-2)$

Use the following information to answer the next question.

The graph of $y = f(x)$ has a domain of $4 \le x \le 9$ and a range of $1 \le y \le 8$.

3. What is the domain and range of $y - 4 = f(x)$, respectively?

   A. $0 \le x \le 5, 1 \le y \le 8$

   B. $4 \le x \le 9, -3 \le y \le 4$

   C. $4 \le x \le 9, 5 \le y \le 12$

   D. $8 \le x \le 13, 1 \le y \le 8$

Use the following information to answer the next question.

The point (2, 4) is on the graph of $y = x^2$. When the graph of $y = x^2$ is transformed to $y - 3 = x^2$, the coordinates of the point (2, 4) are transformed to the point (a, b).

Numerical Response

4. The value of $a + b$ is _____.
   (Record your answer as a **whole** number.)

5. What is the value of the smallest x-intercept of the graph of the transformed function after the graph of $f(x) = x^2 - 3x - 18$ is stretched horizontally about the y-axis by a factor of $\frac{1}{3}$?

   A. 0

   B. −1

   C. −3

   D. −9

Use the following information to answer the next question.

The graph of $y = f(x)$ passes through the point (6, 2).

6. The stretch factor that will transform the point (6, 2) to (6, 4) is a

   A. vertical stretch about the x-axis by a factor of 2

   B. vertical stretch about the x-axis by a factor of $\frac{1}{2}$

   C. horizontal stretch about the y-axis by a factor of 2

   D. horizontal stretch about the y-axis by a factor of $\frac{1}{2}$

Copyright Protected

Not for Reproduction

7. Which of the following pairs of transformations will produce a different image if the order in which they are performed is reversed?

   A. A horizontal translation and then a vertical translation

   B. A horizontal stretch about the y-axis and then a horizontal translation

   C. A horizontal stretch about the y-axis and then a reflection in the x-axis

   D. A vertical stretch about the x-axis and then a horizontal stretch about the y-axis

Use the following information to answer the next question.

The graph of $y = x^2$ and a transformation of it are shown.

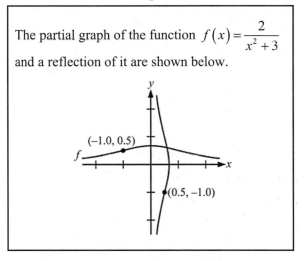

The two graphs are congruent, and the vertex of the transformed graph is at $(-3, -1)$.

8. The equation of the transformed graph is

   A. $y = -(x+3)^2 - 1$

   B. $y = -(x+3)^2 + 1$

   C. $y = (-x+3)^2 - 1$

   D. $y = (-x+3)^2 + 1$

9. The graph of $y = f(x)$ is transformed to the graph of $y = 3f(2x-8)-1$. Which point on the graph of $y = 3f(2x-8)-1$ corresponds to the point $(-2, 6)$ on the graph of $y = f(x)$?

   A. $(-4, 17)$

   B. $(-4, 18)$

   C. $(3, 17)$

   D. $(3, 18)$

10. If $y = f(x)$, where $f(x) = 2 - \sqrt{x-7}$, then what is the x-intercept of $y = -f(x)$?

    A. 3

    B. -3

    C. 11

    D. -11

Use the following information to answer the next question.

The partial graph of the function $f(x) = \dfrac{2}{x^2 + 3}$ and a reflection of it are shown below.

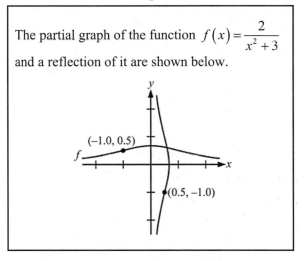

11. An expression for this reflection of graph f is

    A. $x = y$

    B. $x = f(y)$

    C. $y = f(-x)$

    D. $y = -f(x)$

Copyright Protected

12. Which of the following statements about the inverse of $f(x) = x^2 + 4$ and its domain is **true**?

A. It is not a function, and its domain is $x \geq 0$.

B. It is not a function, and its domain is $x \geq 4$.

C. It is a function, and its domain is $x \geq 0$.

D. It is a function, and its domain is $x \geq 4$.

Use the following information to answer the next question.

A function is defined as follows:

y is determined by adding 4 to x and then multiplying by 6.

13. After interchanging x and y, which of the following operations are required to determine the inverse of the given function?

A. Divide x by 6, and then add 4 to y.

B. Divide x by 6, and then subtract 4 from y.

C. Subtract 4 from y, and then divide x by 6.

D. Subtract 4 from y, and then multiply x by 6.

14. If $\log_x \dfrac{64}{27} = -\dfrac{3}{2}$, then the value of x is

A. $\dfrac{16}{9}$

B. $\dfrac{9}{16}$

C. $-\dfrac{9}{16}$

D. $-\dfrac{25}{16}$

Numerical Response

15. The value of $\dfrac{\log_6 1\,000}{\log_6 10}$ is _____.

(Record your answer as a **whole** number.)

16. If $\log_7 x = m + \log_7 n$, where $x > 0$ and $n > 0$, then x is equal to

A. $7^m n$

B. $7^n m$

C. $7mn$

D. $m^7 n$

17. A student wants to use a graphing calculator to graph $y = \log_5 x$. If the calculator accepts only common logarithms, then an equivalent equation that could be used to obtain the graph is

A. $y = \dfrac{\log x}{\log 5}$

B. $y = \log x - \log 5$

C. $y = 5 \log x$

D. $y = \dfrac{\log x}{5}$

18. Where $A > 0$ and $A \neq 1$, the expression $3\log_A(2A) - \log_A(1.6A)$ is equivalent to

A. $\log_A 5 + 2$

B. $\log_A 6.4 - 2$

C. $\log_A 12.8 + 2$

D. $\log 5 + 2 \log A$

Not for Reproduction

The partial graph of the exponential function $f(x) = 4^x$ is shown below.

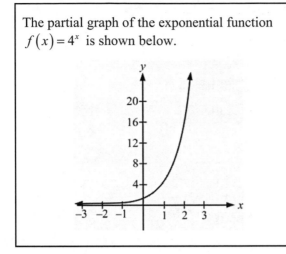

19. The domain of the inverse function is

A. $x > 0$, $x \in R$

B. $x < 0$, $x \in R$

C. $x \geq 0$, $x \in R$

D. $x \in R$

20. The graphs of the logarithmic functions
$y = \log_b x$, $b > 1$ and $y = \log_a x$, $0 < a < 1$
will intersect at the ordered pair

A. $(0, 0)$

B. $(0, 1)$

C. $(1, 0)$

D. $(1, 1)$

21. Which of the following statements about the graph of the inverse of the function $y = 5^x$ is **false**?

A. The x-intercept of the graph is 1.

B. The domain of the graph is $x \in R$.

C. The graph passes through the point $(25, 2)$.

D. The graph has a vertical asymptote of $x = 0$.

An earthquake in country A was measured to be 86 times more intense than an earthquake in country B.

Numerical Response

22. If the earthquake in country B was a magnitude 4.1 earthquake, then the magnitude of the earthquake in country A, to the nearest tenth, is _____.
(Record your answer to **one** decimal place.)

The partial graphs of $f(x) = 1 + 3\log_2 x$ and $g(x) = 4 - \log_2 x$ are shown below. The graphs intersect at point A.

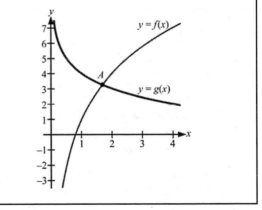

23. Based on the information above, the x-coordinate of point A can be determined by solving

A. $3\log_2 x + 1 = 0$

B. $4 - \log_2 x = 0$

C. $\log_2 x = \dfrac{5}{2}$

D. $\log_2 x = \dfrac{3}{4}$

24. The atmospheric pressure P, in kilopascals (kPa), at a distance d, in kilometres above Earth, is given by the formula $P = 100\left(10^{-0.0542d}\right)$. A particular plane is designed to fly safely when the atmospheric pressure is greater than 15 kPa. The plane can fly safely to a maximum height of

A. 15.5 km
B. 15.2 km
C. 10.9 km
D. 2.8 km

25. The zeros of a cubic polynomial function P are 1, $\sqrt{5}$, and $-\sqrt{5}$. If $P(x) = x^3 + bx^2 + cx + d$, then $P(2)$ is equal to

A. −3
B. −1
C. 1
D. 3

Use the following information to answer the next question.

For the polynomial $P(x) = 3x^3 - 2x^2 - x - 15$, $P(2) = -1$.

26. Based on the given information, which of the following statements is **true**?

A. When $P(x)$ is divided by $x + 2$, the remainder is −1.

B. When $P(x)$ is divided by $x - 2$, the remainder is −1.

C. When $P(x)$ is divided by $x + 2$, the remainder is 1.

D. When $P(x)$ is divided by $x - 2$, the remainder is 1.

27. If $G(x) = 8x^4 + 3x^2 - x + k$, then the value of k that will make −1 a zero of G is

A. −12
B. −10
C. 10
D. 12

28. Which of the following graphs could represent the function $y = \sqrt{x} + d$, where $d > 0$?

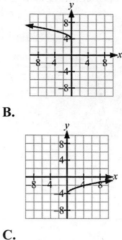

A.

B.

C.

D.

29. Rounded to the nearest tenth, what is the solution to $\sqrt[3]{x^2 + 5} = -2x$?

A. $x = -1.3$
B. $x = -0.9$
C. $x = 0.9$
D. $x = 1.3$

30. How many horizontal asymptotes does the graph of the function $f(x) = \dfrac{3x^2 - 5}{x + 5}$ have?

A. 0
B. 1
C. 2
D. 3

Copyright Protected

Not for Reproduction

Use the following information to answer the next question.

Marcel sketched the graphs of the function

$f(x) = \dfrac{x+5}{x(x+5)}$ and the function

$g(x) = \dfrac{(x+3)(x-2)}{x(x+3)(x-2)}$ on separate grids.

31. Assuming Marcel correctly graphed each function, which of the following statements about his sketches is **true**?

A. The graphs of $y = f(x)$ and $y = g(x)$ are

congruent to the graph of $y = \dfrac{1}{x}$.

B. The graph of $y = f(x)$ has one hole, and the graph of $y = g(x)$ has two holes.

C. The graphs of $y = f(x)$ and $y = g(x)$ are each discontinuous at the same number of points.

D. The graph of $y = f(x)$ has two vertical asymptotes, and the graph of $y = g(x)$ has three vertical asymptotes.

Use the following information to answer the next question.

The graph of the rational function

$f(x) = \dfrac{x+2}{2x-10}$ has a vertical asymptote at

$x = a$ and a horizontal asymptote at $y = \dfrac{b}{c}$,

where $\dfrac{b}{c}$ is reduced to lowest terms and

$a, b, c \in \mathrm{R}$.

Numerical Response

32. The value of $a + b + c$ is _____.
(Record your answer as a **whole** number.)

Written Response

33. Given $y = x^2 - x - 3$, write the equation representing the graph of this function reflected in the *y*-axis.

Use the following information to answer the next question.

A mathematics class was asked to solve the following equation.

$$3^{x+2} = 6^x$$

The attempts of two students to solve the equation are shown below. Each student made one error that led to an incorrect solution.

Student A	Student B

Student A

$3^{x+2} = 6^x$
$3^{x+2} = 3^{2x}$
$x + 2 = 2x$
$\quad 2 = 2x - x$
$\quad x = 2$

Student B

$3^{x+2} = 6^x$
$\log 3^{x+2} = \log 6^x$
$x + 2\log 3 = x\log 6$
$2\log 3 = -x + x\log 6$
$2\log 3 = x(-1 + \log 6)$
$$\frac{2\log 3}{(-1 + \log 6)} = x$$

x is approximately -4.3

Written Response

34. Identify the error that was made by each student and state why each error leads to an incorrect answer.

Written Response

35. If $f(x) = 6 - 4x$ and $g(x) = \dfrac{1}{2}x - 3$, what is the value of $g\left(f\left(-\dfrac{1}{2}\right)\right)$?

Copyright Protected

Not for Reproduction

Written Response

36. Tristan is building a shed. He constructs a wooden frame in the shape of a rectangular prism. The width of the frame is 1 m less than the height. The length of the frame is 1 m more than half the height of the frame.

a) Create a function that models the volume of the shed as a function of the height.

b) If the volume of the shed is 15 m³, determine the dimensions of the frame.

Written Response

37. What transformations were applied to $y = \sqrt{x}$ to get $y = 4\sqrt{x-2} + 1$?

Copyright Protected

ANSWERS AND SOLUTIONS—UNIT TEST

1. B	9. C	17. A	25. B	33. WR
2. B	10. C	18. A	26. B	34. WR
3. C	11. B	19. A	27. A	35. WR
4. 9	12. B	20. C	28. D	36. WR
5. B	13. B	21. B	29. B	37. WR
6. A	14. B	22. 6.0	30. A	
7. B	15. 3	23. D	31. B	
8. A	16. A	24. B	32. 8	

1. B

Step 1

Determine the domain and range of $f(x) = x^2 + 1$.

This is a quadratic function with the domain $x \in \mathrm{R}$. The range is $y \geq 1$.

Step 2

Determine the domain and range of $g(x) = \sqrt{x+4}$.

The function is not defined for $x + 4 < 0$, or $x < -4$. Therefore, the domain is $x \geq -4$. The range is $y \geq 0$.

Step 3

Determine the domain and range of $f(g(x))$.

$$f(g(x))$$
$$= f\left(\sqrt{x+4}\right)$$
$$= \left(\sqrt{x+4}\right)^2 + 1$$
$$= (x+4) + 1$$
$$= x + 5$$

For $f(g(x))$, the domain is $x \geq -4$, because the domain is restricted by the domain of $g(x)$.

Because of this restriction on the domain, the range of $f(g(x))$ is restricted to $y \geq 1$.

Step 4

Compare the domains of the three functions.

The function $f(x)$ has the domain $x \in \mathrm{R}$.

The functions $g(x)$ and $f(g(x))$ both have the domains $x \geq -4$.

Step 5

Compare the ranges of the three functions.

The functions $f(x)$ and $f(g(x))$ both have the ranges $y \geq 1$. The function $g(x)$ has the range $y \geq 0$.

Therefore, the statement "the function $g(x)$ has the same domain as the function $f(g(x))$, but a different range" is true.

2. B

Step 1

Determine how to obtain the graph of $y = f(x+2)$ from the graph of $y = f(x)$.

The equation $y = f(x+2)$ is in the form $y = f(x-h)$, where $h = -2$. Therefore, the graph of $y = f(x+2)$ is formed from $y = f(x)$ by translating it 2 units to the left.

Step 2

Determine the location of the translation of each point (a, b).

When the graph is translated 2 units to the left, each of the x-coordinates decreases by 2, and the y-coordinates do not change.

Therefore, each point (a, b) on the graph of $y = f(x)$ will be transformed to the point $(a - 2, b)$ on the graph of $y = f(x+2)$.

3. C

Step 1

Determine how to obtain the graph of $y - 4 = f(x)$ from the graph of $y = f(x)$.

The equation $y - 4 = f(x)$ is in the form $y - k = f(x)$, where $k = 4$. Therefore, the graph of $y - 4 = f(x)$ is formed from $y = f(x)$ by translating it 4 units up.

Step 2

Determine the domain of $y - 4 = f(x)$.

The graph is not translated to the left or right, so the domain of the graph will not change. The domain of $y - 4 = f(x)$ is still $4 \leq x \leq 9$.

Step 3

Determine the range of $y - 4 = f(x)$.

The graph is translated 4 units up, so each of the limits of the range needs to be 4 units greater.

Therefore, the range is $(1 + 4) \leq y \leq (8 + 4)$, or $5 \leq y \leq 12$.

4. 9

Step 1

Determine how to obtain the graph of $y - 3 = x^2$ from the graph of $y = x^2$.

The equation $y - 3 = x^2$ is in the form $y - k = f(x)$, where $k = 3$ and $f(x) = x^2$. Therefore, the graph of $y - 3 = x^2$ is formed from $y = x^2$ by translating it 3 units up.

Step 2

Determine the location of the translation of $(2, 4)$.

When the graph is translated 3 units up, each of the y-coordinates increases by 3, and the x-coordinates do not change. Since $(2, 4)$ is on the graph of $y = x^2$, the graph of $y - 3 = x^2$ will contain the point $(2, 4 + 3) = (2, 7)$.

Step 3

Determine the value of $a + b$.

Point (a, b) is equal to point $(2, 7)$, so $a = 2$ and $b = 7$. To find the sum of the points, add them together.

$a + b$
$= 2 + 7$
$= 9$

Therefore, the value of $a + b = 9$.

5. B

Step 1

Determine the x-intercepts of the graph of $f(x) = x^2 - 3x - 18$.

Substitute 0 for y in the equation $y = x^2 - 3x - 18$.

$0 = x^2 - 3x - 18$

Solve for x by first factoring $x^2 - 3x - 18$.

$0 = (x - 6)(x + 3)$

$x - 6 = 0$ or $x + 3 = 0$
$x = 6$ $x = -3$

The x-intercepts of the graph of $f(x) = x^2 - 2x - 15$ are located at the ordered pairs $(6, 0)$ and $(-3, 0)$.

Step 2

If the graph of $y = f(x)$ is stretched horizontally about the y-axis by a factor of $\frac{1}{3}$, the ordered pair (x, y) on the graph of $y = f(x)$ corresponds to the ordered pair $\left(\frac{1}{3}x, y\right)$ on the graph of the transformed function.

Thus, the x-intercepts of the graph of the transformed function are located at the ordered pairs $\left(\frac{1}{3}(6), 0\right) = (2, 0)$ and $\left(\frac{1}{3}(-3), 0\right) = (-1, 0)$.

Step 3

Determine the smallest x-intercept of the transformed graph.

The smallest x-intercept is -1.

6. A

Step 1
Determine the type of stretch.

The x-coordinate of the ordered pairs (6, 2) and (6, 4) is 6. Therefore, the ordered pair (6, 4) can be obtained from the ordered pair (6, 2) by a vertical stretch about the x-axis.

Step 2
Determine the stretch factor.

The y-coordinate of (6, 4) is equal to the y-coordinate of (6, 2) multiplied by 2.

Therefore, the graph of $y = f(x)$ must be vertically stretched about the x-axis by a factor of 2 in order for the ordered pair (6, 2) to be transformed to the ordered pair (6, 4).

7. B

In general, stretches and reflections must be completed prior to any translations. Thus, a horizontal stretch about the y-axis and then a horizontal translation should produce different images if performed in reverse.

This can also be shown algebraically.

Step 1
Show how the equation of $y = f(x)$ changes if the stretch is applied before the translation.

If the graph of $y = f(x)$ is horizontally stretched by a factor of b about the y-axis, the resulting equation is $y = f\left(\dfrac{1}{b}x\right)$.

If the graph of $y = f\left(\dfrac{1}{b}x\right)$ is translated horizontally c units, the resulting equation is $y = f\left(\dfrac{1}{b}(x-c)\right)$.

Step 2
Show how the equation of $y = f(x)$ changes if the translation is applied before the stretch.

When the graph of $y = f(x)$ is translated horizontally c units, the resulting equation is $y = f(x-c)$.

If the graph of $y = f(x-c)$ is horizontally stretched about the y-axis by a factor of b, the resulting equation is $y = f\left(\dfrac{1}{b}x - c\right)$.

Step 3
Compare the two equations.

The equation $y = f\left(\dfrac{1}{b}(x-c)\right)$ and $y = f\left(\dfrac{1}{b}x - c\right)$ are not equal. Therefore, if the order in which the transformations are performed is reversed, the resulting graphs will be different.

8. A

Step 1
Decide which transformations were applied to $y = x^2$ to obtain the transformed graph.

The transformed graph is obtained by applying a reflection and a translation. In general, reflections must be applied before translations.

The graph of $y = x^2$ was reflected across the x-axis and then translated 3 units left and 1 unit down.

Step 2
Apply the reflection.

Substitute $-y$ for y in the equation $y = x^2$, since the graph of $y = x^2$ is reflected in the x-axis.
$$y = x^2$$
$$(-y) = x^2$$
$$y = -x^2$$

Step 3
Apply the vertical translation.

The graph of $y = -x^2$ is translated 1 unit down, so substitute $y + 1$ for y.
$$y = -x^2$$
$$y + 1 = -x^2$$

Step 4
Apply the horizontal translation.

The graph of $y + 1 = -x$ is translated 3 units to the left, so substitute $x + 3$ for x.
$$y + 1 = -(x)^2$$
$$y + 1 = -(x+3)^2$$

Copyright Protected

Not for Reproduction

Step 5
Isolate y.

$$y + 1 = -(x+3)^2$$
$$y = -(x+3)^2 - 1$$

Therefore, the equation of the transformed graph is $y = -(x+3)^2 - 1$.

9. C

Step 1
Rewrite the equation $y = 3f(2x-8) - 1$.

The equation $y = 3f(2x-8) - 1$ can be rewritten as $y = 3f(2(x-4)) - 1$.

Step 2
Describe how to obtain the graph of $y = 3f(2(x-4)) - 1$ from $y = f(x)$.

The graph of $y = 3f(2(x-4)) - 1$ is obtained from the graph of $y = f(x)$ by a vertical stretch factor of 3, a horizontal stretch factor of $\dfrac{1}{2}$, and a translation 4 units right and 1 unit down.

Step 3
Apply the horizontal and vertical stretches to the point $(-2, 6)$.

Multiply -2 by $\dfrac{1}{2}$ and 6 by 3.

$$(-2, 6) \rightarrow \left(\left(-2 \times \dfrac{1}{2}\right), (6 \times 3)\right) = (-1, 18)$$

Step 4
Apply the horizontal and vertical translations to the point $(-1, 18)$.

Add 4 to -1, and subtract 1 from 18.

$$(-1, 18) \rightarrow ((-1+4), (18-1)) = (3, 17)$$

The point $(3, 17)$ on the graph of $y = 3f(2x-8) - 1$ corresponds to the point $(-2, 6)$ on the graph of $y = f(x)$.

10. C

Step 1
Determine the x-intercept of the graph of $y = f(x)$.

Substitute 0 for y in the equation $y = 2 - \sqrt{x-7}$, and solve for x.

$$y = 2 - \sqrt{x-7}$$
$$0 = 2 - \sqrt{x-7}$$
$$2 = \sqrt{x-7}$$
$$4 = x - 7$$
$$x = 11$$

The x-intercept occurs at the ordered pair $(11, 0)$.

Step 2
Determine the x-intercepts of the transformed equation.

The graph of $y = -f(x)$ is the reflection of the graph of $y = f(x)$ about the x-axis. As a result, a point (x, y) on the graph of $y = f(x)$ becomes point $(x, -y)$ on the graph of $y = -f(x)$.

Thus, the x-intercept $(11, 0)$ on the graph of $y = f(x)$ becomes point $(11, -0) = (11, 0)$ on the graph of $y = -f(x)$.

The x-intercepts of the graph of $y = f(x)$ are invariant points when the graph of $y = f(x)$ is reflected in the x-axis.

The x-intercept of $y = -f(x)$ is also $(11, 0)$, or $x = 11$.

11. B

The graph shows point $(-1, 0.5)$ on $f(x)$ transformed to point $(0.5, -1)$ on its reflection. Therefore, the reflection is in the line $y = x$ (*i.e.*, the inverse relation). This is described by the equation $x = f(y)$.

Copyright Protected

12. B

Step 1

Describe the graph of $f(x) = x^2 + 4$.

The graph of the function $f(x) = x^2 + 4$ is a parabola opening upward with a vertex at $(0, 4)$. As such, the domain of the function is $x \in \mathbb{R}$, and its range is $x \geq 4$.

Step 2

Determine if the inverse of $f(x) = x^2 + 4$ is a function.

The inverse of the given function is a parabola with the same vertex, but opening to the right. This means it is not a function because when $x > 4$, there are two y-values for every x-value.

Step 3

Determine the domain of the inverse of $f(x) = x^2 + 4$.

The domain of the inverse of a function is the same as the range of the original function. The range of $f(x) = x^2 + 4$ is $y \geq 4$, so the domain of its inverse is $x \geq 4$.

Therefore, the inverse of $f(x) = x^2 + 4$ is not a function, and its domain is $x \geq 4$.

13. B

Step 1

Write the function as an equation.

To find y, add 4 to x, and then multiply by 6. This is expressed as $y = 6(x + 4)$.

Step 2

Find the equation of the inverse of the function.

Interchange x and y.
$$y = 6(x + 4)$$
$$x = 6(y + 4)$$

Solve for y.
$$x = 6(y + 4)$$
$$\frac{x}{6} = y + 4$$
$$\frac{x}{6} - 4 = y$$

Step 3

Describe the operations in words.

To determine the inverse, divide x by 6, then subtract 4 from y.

In this case, dividing by 6 must be done first, since multiplying by 6 was the last operation performed on the original function. Then, the reverse of adding 4, which is subtracting 4, must be performed.

14. B

Step 1

Write the equation $\log_x \dfrac{64}{27} = -\dfrac{3}{2}$ in exponential form. Remember that $\log_a x = y$ is equivalent to $x = a^y$.

$$\frac{64}{27} = x^{-\frac{3}{2}}$$

Step 2

Isolate x.

Since $-\dfrac{3}{2} \times -\dfrac{2}{3} = 1$, the equation $\dfrac{64}{27} = x^{-\frac{3}{2}}$ can be isolated for x as follows:

$$\frac{64}{27} = x^{-\frac{3}{2}}$$
$$\left(\frac{64}{27}\right)^{-\frac{2}{3}} = \left(x^{-\frac{3}{2}}\right)^{-\frac{2}{3}}$$
$$\left(\frac{64}{27}\right)^{-\frac{2}{3}} = x$$

Step 3

Apply the negative exponent rule to the left side of the equation.

$$\left(\frac{64}{27}\right)^{-\frac{2}{3}} = x$$
$$\left(\frac{27}{64}\right)^{\frac{2}{3}} = x$$

Step 4

Apply the rule for rational exponents to the left side of the equation.

$$\left(\frac{27}{64}\right)^{\frac{2}{3}} = x$$
$$\left(\sqrt[3]{\frac{27}{64}}\right)^2 = x$$

Not for Reproduction

Step 5

Evaluate $\left(\sqrt[3]{\dfrac{27}{64}} \right)^2$.

$$\left(\sqrt[3]{\dfrac{27}{64}} \right)^2$$
$$= \left(\dfrac{3}{4} \right)^2$$
$$= \dfrac{9}{16}$$

Therefore, $x = \dfrac{9}{16}$.

15. 3

Notice that $\dfrac{\log_6 1\,000}{\log_6 10}$ is a logarithmic expression in which both logarithms have the same base: base 6.

Step 1
Use the change of base formula to rewrite the expression as a single logarithm with base 10.

$$\dfrac{\log_c a}{\log_c b} = \log_b a$$
$$\dfrac{\log_6 1\,000}{\log_6 10} = \log_{10} 1\,000$$

Step 2
Evaluate.

$$\log_{10} 1\,000 = 3$$

16. A

Step 1
Group all the expressions involving logarithms on the same side of the equation, and isolate the variable m on the opposite side of the equation.
$$\log_7 x - \log_7 n = m$$

Step 2
Apply the quotient law of logarithms.
$$\log_7 x - \log_7 n = m$$
$$\log_7 \left(\dfrac{x}{n} \right) = m$$

Step 3
Write $\log_7 \left(\dfrac{x}{n} \right) = m$ in exponential form.

$$\log_7 \left(\dfrac{x}{n} \right) = m$$
$$7^m = \dfrac{x}{n}$$

Step 4
Solve for x.

$$7^m = \dfrac{x}{n}$$
$$7^m n = x$$

Therefore, the variable x is equal to $7^m n$.

17. A

Apply the change of base formula, $\log_b a = \dfrac{\log_c a}{\log_c b}$, to the equation $y = \log_5 x$.

$$y = \log_5 x$$
$$y = \dfrac{\log x}{\log 5}$$

18. A

Step 1
Apply the power law of logarithms in reverse to the first term of the expression.
$$3\log_A (2A) - \log_A (1.6A)$$
$$= \log_A (2A)^3 - \log_A (1.6A)$$

Step 2
Simplify the power $(2A)^3$ by applying the power of a power law for exponents.
$$\log_A (2A)^3 - \log_A (1.6A)$$
$$= \log_A (8A^3) - \log_A (1.6A)$$

Step 3
Apply the quotient law of logarithms, and then simplify the resulting expression using the quotient rule for exponents.
$$\log_A (8A^3) - \log_A (1.6A)$$
$$= \log_A \left(\dfrac{8A^3}{1.6A} \right)$$
$$= \log_A (5A^2)$$

Step 4
Apply the product law of logarithms.
$$\log_A (5A^2) = \log_A 5 + \log_A A^2$$

Copyright Protected

Step 5

Apply the power law of logarithms to the second term of the expression.

$\log_A 5 + \log_A A^2$
$= \log_A 5 + 2 \log_A A$

Step 6

Since $\log_A A = 1$, substitute 1 for $\log_A A$.

$\log_A 5 + 2 \log_A A$
$= \log_A 5 + 2(1)$
$= \log_A 5 + 2$

19. A

The range of $f(x) = 4^x$ becomes the domain of f^{-1}. Since the range of $f(x) = 4^x$ is $y > 0$, $y \in \mathrm{R}$, the domain of the inverse function f^{-1} is $x > 0$, $x \in \mathrm{R}$.

20. C

The equation $y = \log_b x$ is equivalent to $b^y = x$.

The equation $y = \log_a x$ is equivalent to $a^y = x$.

Each of these graphs will have an x-intercept of 1, since $b^0 = 1$ and $a^0 = 1$.

Therefore, the two graphs will intersect at the ordered pair (1, 0).

21. B

Graph the function $y = 5^x$ and its inverse, $y = \log_5 x$.

The reflection of $y = 5^x$ is formed by a reflection across the line $y = x$, as shown.

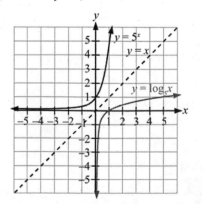

The graph of $y = \log_5 x$ has the x-intercept of 1.

Since $5^2 = 25$, the point (2, 25) is on the graph of $y = 5^x$, so the point (25, 2) is on the graph of $y = \log_5 x$.

The graph of $y = \log_5 x$ has a vertical asymptote at the y-axis, which has the equation $x = 0$. Therefore, the domain is $x > 0$, not $x \in \mathrm{R}$.

22. 6.0

The intensity of an earthquake is measured using the Richter scale with the formula $I = I_r (10)^m$, where I is the intensity of the earthquake, I_r is the reference intensity of a very small and barely measurable earthquake, and m is the magnitude on the Richter scale.

Step 1

Let I_A represent the intensity of the earthquake in country A.

Substitute I_A for I in the exponential equation $I = I_r (10)^m$.

$I_A = I_r (10)^m$

Step 2

Let I_B represent the intensity of the earthquake in country B.

Substitute I_B for I and 4.1 for m in the exponential equation $I = I_r (10)^m$.

$I_B = I_r (10)^{4.1}$

Step 3

It is given that the earthquake in country A is 86 times more intense than the earthquake in country B. Write a ratio that compares the intensity of the earthquakes.

$\dfrac{I_A}{I_B} = 86$

Step 4

Substitute $I_r (10)^m$ for I_A and $I_r (10)^{4.1}$ for I_B in the equation $\dfrac{I_A}{I_B} = 86$.

$\dfrac{I_r (10)^m}{I_r (10)^{4.1}} = 86$

Not for Reproduction

Step 5
Cancel the I_r variables.
$$\frac{(10)^m}{(10)^{4.1}} = 86$$

Step 6
Apply the quotient law of exponents.
$$(10)^{m-4.1} = 86$$

Step 7
Rewrite the exponential equation in logarithmic form.
$$\log_{10} 86 = m - 4.1$$

Step 8
Evaluate $\log_{10} 86$, and solve for m.
$$1.934 \approx m - 4.1$$
$$6.034 \approx m$$

The earthquake in country A was approximately a magnitude 6.0 earthquake.

23. D

The point of intersection is at point A. At point A, $f(x) = g(x)$.

Step 1
Substitute $f(x) = 1 + 3\log_2 x$ and
$g(x) = 4 - \log_2 x$ into $f(x) = g(x)$.
$$f(x) = g(x)$$
$$1 + 3\log_2 x = 4 - \log_2 x$$

Step 2
Simplify the equation $1 + 3\log_2 x = 4 - \log_2 x$.
$$1 + 3\log_2 x = 4 - \log_2 x$$
$$3\log_2 x + \log_2 x = 4 - 1$$
$$4\log_2 x = 3$$
$$\log_2 x = \frac{3}{4}$$

24. B

Pressure P in (kPa) is given by the formula
$$P = 100\left(10^{-0.0542d}\right).$$

Step 1
Since the pressure has to be greater than 15 kPa, substitute $100\left(10^{-0.0542d}\right)$ for P into the inequality $P > 15$ kPa.
$$P > 15$$
$$100\left(10^{-0.0542d}\right) > 15$$
$$10^{-0.0542d} > \frac{15}{100}$$
$$10^{-0.0542d} > 0.15$$

Step 2
Take the logarithm of both sides.
$$10^{-0.0542d} > 0.15$$
$$\log 10^{-0.0542d} > \log 0.15$$

Step 3
Solve for d.
$$\log 10^{-0.0542d} > \log 0.15$$
$$(-0.0542d)\log 10 > \log 0.15$$
$$-0.0542d > \log 0.15$$
$$d < \frac{\log 0.15}{-0.0542}$$
$$d < 15.201\ldots$$

Therefore, the plane can safely fly to a maximum height of approximately 15.2 km.

25. B

Step 1
Write the equation of the function.

The graph of the function has zeros at 1, $\sqrt{5}$, and $-\sqrt{5}$. These correspond to roots of the equation of the function. Since three distinct roots of the cubic function are known, each root must have multiplicity of 1.

Since the leading coefficient of the function $P(x) = x^3 + bx^2 + cx + d$ is 1, the factored form can be written as $P(x) = (x-1)\left(x - \sqrt{5}\right)\left(x + \sqrt{5}\right)$.

Step 2
Evaluate $P(2)$.
$$P(2) = (2-1)\left(2 - \sqrt{5}\right)\left(2 + \sqrt{5}\right)$$
$$P(2) = (1)\left(2^2 - \left(\sqrt{5}\right)^2\right)$$
$$P(2) = 4 - 5$$
$$P(2) = -1$$

Therefore, the value of $P(2)$ is equal to -1.

26. B

Apply the remainder theorem.

When a polynomial function $P(x)$ is divided by $(x - a)$, the remainder is $P(a)$.

Given that $P(2) = -1$, when the polynomial $P(x)$ is divided by $x - 2$, the remainder is -1.

27. A

If -1 is a zero of G, the point $(-1, 0)$ lies on the graph of G. Substitute $G(x) = 0$ and $x = -1$ into the equation, and solve for k.

$$G(x) = 8x^4 + 3x^2 - x + k$$
$$0 = 8(-1)^4 + 3(-1)^2 - (-1) + k$$
$$0 = 8 + 3 + 1 + k$$
$$0 = 12 + k$$
$$-12 = k$$

28. D

When the graph of $y = \sqrt{x}$ is transformed to the graph of $y = \sqrt{x} + d$, the change in the value of d causes a vertical translation. Since $d > 0$, the graph of $y = \sqrt{x}$ will shift upward. The domain, $x \geq 0$, remains unchanged, and the range becomes $y \geq d$. The graph of $y = \sqrt{x} + d$, where $d > 0$, will be in quadrant I.

Therefore, the following graph could represent the graph of the function $y = \sqrt{x} + d$, where $d > 0$.

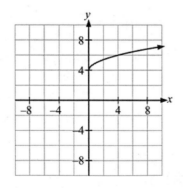

29. B

Step 1
Graph the corresponding equations.

Using a TI-83 or similar calculator, press $\boxed{Y=}$, and enter the equations $Y_1 = \sqrt[3]{}\left(X\,\char`\^\,2 + 5\right)$ and $Y_2 = -2X$.

To enter the equation $Y_1 = \sqrt[3]{}\left(X\,\char`\^\,2 + 5\right)$, press $\boxed{MATH}$, select $4{:}\sqrt[3]{}($, and then enter the rest of the equation.

Press $\boxed{ZOOM}$, and select 6:ZStandard.

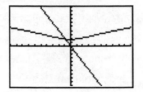

Step 2
Determine where the graphs intersect.

Press $\boxed{2nd}$ $\boxed{TRACE}$ to access the CALC menu, select 5:intersect, and move the cursor close to the point of intersection.

Press $\boxed{ENTER}$ three times to find the point of intersection.

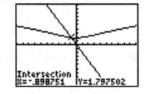

The intersection of the two graphs occurs at $(-0.898751, 1.797502)$. Therefore, rounded to the nearest tenth, the solution to $\sqrt[3]{x^2 + 5} = -2x$ is $x = -0.9$.

30. A

Step 1
Determine the degree of the numerator and the denominator.

The degree of the numerator, $3x^2 - 5$, is 2.

The degree of the denominator, $x + 5$, is 1.

Step 2
Determine the number of horizontal asymptotes.

Since the degree of the numerator is greater than the degree of the denominator, there are no horizontal asymptotes.

31. B

Step 1
Identify the non-permissible values for $f(x) = \dfrac{x+5}{x(x+5)}$, and reduce the function to lowest terms.

Copyright Protected

Not for Reproduction

The function is not defined for $x = 0$ and $x = -5$, since the denominator cannot be zero.

Simplify the function, cancelling the common factor, $(x + 5)$, in the numerator and denominator.

$$f(x) = \frac{x+5}{x(x+5)}$$

$$f(x) = \frac{1}{x}, \text{ where } x \neq 0 \text{ and } x \neq -5$$

Step 2

Identify the non-permissible values for

$$g(x) = \frac{(x+3)(x-2)}{x(x+3)(x-2)}, \text{ and reduce the function to}$$

lowest terms.

The function is not defined for $x = 0$, $x = -3$, and $x = 2$.

Simplify the function, cancelling the common factors, $(x + 3)$ and $(x - 2)$, in the numerator and denominator.

$$g(x) = \frac{(x+3)(x-2)}{x(x+3)(x-2)}$$

$$f(x) = \frac{1}{x}, \text{ where } x \neq 0, x \neq -3, \text{ and } x \neq 2$$

Step 3

Determine if the graph of $f(x)$ will have a vertical asymptote or a hole for each non-permissible value of x.

The factor x remains in the denominator after $f(x)$ is reduced, so $x = 0$ is a vertical asymptote.

The factor $(x + 5)$ cancels out of the numerator and denominator after $f(x)$ is reduced, so there is a hole at $x = -5$.

Step 4

Determine if the graph of $g(x)$ will have a vertical asymptote or a hole for each non-permissible value of x.

The factor x remains in the denominator after $g(x)$ is reduced, so $x = 0$ is a vertical asymptote.

The factors $(x + 3)$ and $(x - 2)$ cancel out of the numerator and denominator after $g(x)$ is reduced, so there are holes at $x = -3$, and $x = 2$.

Step 5

Describe the graph of each function.

The graph of $y = f(x)$ will be identical to the graph of $y = \frac{1}{x}$, but there will be a hole at $x = -5$.

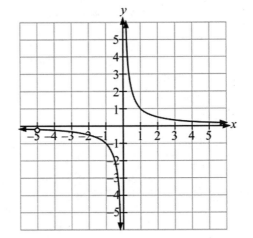

The graph of $y = g(x)$ will be identical to the graph of $y = \frac{1}{x}$, but there will be holes at $x = -3$ and $x = 2$.

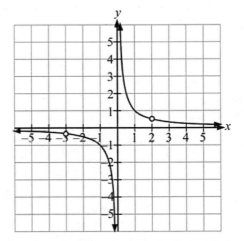

Therefore, the only statement that is true is that the graph of $y = f(x)$ has one hole and the graph of $y = g(x)$ has two holes.

32. 8

Step 1
Determine the vertical asymptote.

Since the function $f(x) = \dfrac{x+2}{2x-10}$ is in the form

$f(x) = \dfrac{ax+c}{mx+b}$, it has a vertical asymptote when
$mx + b = 0$.

Substitute 2 for m and -10 for b in the equation
$mx + b = 0$, and solve for x.

$$2x - 10 = 0$$
$$2x = 10$$
$$x = 5$$

Step 2
Determine the horizontal asymptote.

The degree of the numerator $x + 2$ is 1, and the degree of the denominator $2x - 10$ is 1. Since the degree of the numerator is equal to the degree of the denominator, the horizontal asymptote occurs

at $y = \dfrac{a}{b}$, where a and b are the leading

coefficients of the numerator and denominator, respectively.

$$y = \dfrac{a}{b}$$
$$y = \dfrac{1}{2}$$

The horizontal asymptote is at $y = \dfrac{1}{2}$.

Step 3
Determine the value of $a + b + c$.

The graph of the rational function $f(x) = \dfrac{x+2}{2x-10}$

has a vertical asymptote at $x = a$ and a horizontal

asymptote at $y = \dfrac{b}{c}$. Therefore, $a = 5$, $b = 1$, and

$c = 2$.

The value of $a + b + c$ is equal to $5 + 1 + 2 = 8$.

33. WR

Step 1
Substitute $-x$ for x in the equation $y = x^2 - x - 3$.
When $-x$ is substituted for x, the graph of
$y = x^2 - x - 3$ is reflected in the y-axis.

$$y = (-x)^2 - (-x) - 3$$

Step 2
Simplify the equation $y = (-x)^2 - (-x) - 3$.

$$y = x^2 + x - 3$$

34. WR

Student A
Student A stated that $6^x = 3^{2x}$, which would
indicate that $6 = 3^2$. This is not correct.

Student B
In the third line of the solution, the student did
not realize that $\log 3$ was multiplied by $(x + 2)$,
so in line 4 the student incorrectly subtracted x.

35. WR

Step 1
Determine the value of $f\left(-\dfrac{1}{2}\right)$.

Substitute $-\dfrac{1}{2}$ for x in $f(x)$.

$$f(x) = 6 - 4x$$
$$f\left(-\dfrac{1}{2}\right) = 6 - 4\left(-\dfrac{1}{2}\right)$$

Evaluate.

$$6 - 4\left(-\dfrac{1}{2}\right)$$
$$= 6 + 2$$
$$= 8$$

Step 2
Determine the value of $g\left(f\left(-\dfrac{1}{2}\right)\right)$, or $g(8)$.

Substitute 8 for x in $g(x)$.

$$g(x) = \dfrac{1}{2}x - 3$$
$$g(8) = \dfrac{1}{2}(8) - 3$$

Copyright Protected

Not for Reproduction

Evaluate.

$$\frac{1}{2}(8)-3$$
$$=4-3$$
$$=1$$

Therefore, $g\left(f\left(-\frac{1}{2}\right)\right)=1$.

36. **WR**

a) Step 1
Determine the independent and dependent variables.

The independent variable, x, is the height, and the dependent variable, $V(x)$, is the volume of the shed.

Step 2
Draw a diagram.

Let x equal the height of the frame.

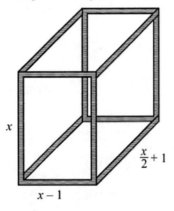

Step 3
Determine a function that models the volume of the shed's frame.

Volume = length × width × height

$$V(x)=\left(\frac{x}{2}+1\right)(x-1)(x)$$

The volume can be represented as the function $V(x)=\left(\frac{x}{2}+1\right)(x-1)(x)$, where x represents the height of the frame.

b) Step 1
Write an equation for the volume of the shed.

The volume function is

$V(x)=\left(\frac{x}{2}+1\right)(x-1)(x)$. Since the volume of the shed is 15 m³, substitute 15 for $V(x)$ in the volume function.

$$V(x)=\left(\frac{x}{2}+1\right)(x-1)(x)$$
$$15=\left(\frac{x}{2}+1\right)(x-1)(x)$$

Step 2
Graph the related function on a TI-83 or similar calculator.

To identify the related function, subtract 15 from both sides of the volume equation.

$$15=\left(\frac{x}{2}+1\right)(x-1)(x)$$
$$0=\left(\frac{x}{2}+1\right)(x-1)(x)-15$$

Press $\boxed{Y=}$, and input the equation as $Y_1 = (X/2 + 1)(X-1)(X) - 15$.

You can use the window settings of $x : [-5, 5, 1]$ and $y : [-20, 10, 1]$ and press $\boxed{\text{GRAPH}}$ to obtain this window.

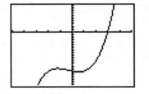

The height, x, corresponds to the x-intercept.

Step 3
Determine the zeros of the graph.

Press $\boxed{\text{2nd}}$ $\boxed{\text{TRACE}}$, and select 2:zero.

When asked for a left bound, move the cursor to the left of the x-intercept, and press $\boxed{\text{ENTER}}$. When asked for the right bound, move the cursor to the right of the first zero, and press $\boxed{\text{ENTER}}$.

Press ENTER after the "Guess?" prompt.

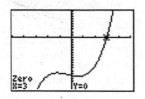

The x-intercept occurs at $x = 3$.

Step 4
Determine the dimensions of the frame.

Since the zero of the graph represents the height, the height of the frame is 3 m.

The length of the frame is $\dfrac{3}{2} + 1 = 2.5 \text{ m}$.

The width is $3 - 1 = 2$ m.

37. **WR**

The function $y = a\sqrt{x - c} + d$ is a transformation of the basic square root function $y = \sqrt{x}$, where the parameters a, c, and d represent specific transformations.

Step 1
Determine the transformation caused by parameter a.

A change in a causes a vertical stretch by a factor of a and reflects the graph in the x-axis if it is negative.

Since $a = 4$, the graph of the function is stretched vertically about the x-axis by a factor of 4.

Step 2
Determine the transformation caused by parameter c.

A change in c causes a horizontal translation c units to the right when c is positive and c units to the left when c is negative.

Since $c = 2$, the graph of the function is translated 2 units to the right.

Step 3
Determine the transformation caused by parameter d.

A change in d causes a vertical translation d units up when d is positive and d units down when d is negative.

Since $d = 1$, the graph of the function is translated 1 unit up.

The transformations applied to $y = \sqrt{x}$ to get $y = 4\sqrt{x - 2} + 1$ were a vertical stretch by a factor of 4 and a translation 2 units to the right and 1 unit up.

Copyright Protected

Permutations, Combinations and Binomial Theorem

PERMUTATIONS, COMBINATIONS AND BINOMIAL THEOREM

Table of Correlations				
Specific Expectation	**Practice Questions**	**Unit Test Questions**	**Practice Test 1**	**Practice Test 2**
It is expected that students will:				
Develop algebraic and numeric reasoning that involves combinatorics.				
PC.1 Apply the fundamental counting principle to solve problems.	1, 2, 3, 4, 5, 6, 26	1, 2, 3	32	31
PC.2 Determine the number of permutations of n elements taken r at a time to solve problems.	7, 8, 9, 10, 11, 12	4, 5, 12, 14	33	32, 33
PC.3 Determine the number of combinations of n different elements taken r at a time to solve problems.	13, 14, 15, 16, 17, 25	6, 7, 8	34, 35	34, 35
PC.4 Expand powers of a binomial in a variety of ways, including using the binomial theorem (restricted to exponents that are natural numbers).	18, 19, 20, 21, 22, 23, 24	9, 10, 11, 13	36, 37	36, 37

Copyright Protected

Not for Reproduction

PERMUTATIONS, COMBINATIONS AND BINOMIAL THEOREM

PC.1 Apply the fundamental counting principle to solve problems.

FUNDAMENTAL COUNTING PRINCIPLE

The fundamental counting principle states that if a task is made up of several stages in which there are m ways to accomplish stage 1, n ways to accomplish stage 2, p ways to accomplish stage 3, and so on, then the total ways to accomplish the entire task (stage 1, stage 2, stage 3, and so on) is $m \times n \times p \times \ldots$.

For example, if a lock has a three-digit code and each digit has 10 different possibilities, then there are a total of $10 \times 10 \times 10 = 1\,000$ different possible lock codes.

Practice Questions: 1–6, 26

PC.2 Determine the number of permutations of n elements taken r at a time to solve problems.

PERMUTATIONS

The arrangement of a set of objects in a particular order is called a permutation. For example, three different letters, a, b, and c, can be arranged in six different three-letter sequences:

$(a, b, c)\ (a, c, b)\ (b, a, c)\ (b, c, a)\ (c, a, b)\ (c, b, a)$

The number of permutations of n distinct objects taken n at a time is $n!$. The number of permutations of n distinct objects taken r at a time, which is denoted as $_nP_r$, is given by the formula

$$_nP_r = \frac{n!}{(n-r)!}, \text{ where } n \geq r.$$

Example

Determine the number of permutations of 7 marbles taken 3 at a time.

Solution

Step 1

Apply the formula $_nP_r = \dfrac{n!}{(n-r)!}$.

Substitute 7 for n and 3 for r.

$$_nP_r = \frac{n!}{(n-r)!}$$

$$_7P_3 = \frac{7!}{(7-3)!}$$

$$_7P_3 = \frac{7!}{4!}$$

Step 2

Evaluate $\dfrac{7!}{4!}$.

$$_7P_3 = \frac{7!}{4!}$$

$$_7P_3 = \frac{7 \times 6 \times 5 \times 4!}{4!}$$

$$_7P_3 = 7 \times 6 \times 5$$

$$_7P_3 = 210$$

When some of the objects to be arranged are identical, the number of distinct permutations of n objects can be calculated using the formula

$\dfrac{n!}{a!\,b!\,c!\ldots}$, where a objects are one kind, b objects are a second kind, c objects are a third kind, and so on.

Example

How many different 7-letter arrangements
can be made from all the letters in the word
TORONTO?

Solution

In the word TORONTO , there are 2 Ts and 3 Os.
Therefore, the number of 7-letter arrangements
is $\dfrac{7!}{2!3!} = \dfrac{5\,040}{12} = 420$.

Practice Questions: 7–12

PC.3   *Determine the number of combinations
of n different elements taken r at a time
to solve problems.*

COMBINATIONS

A combination is a selection of objects from a
larger set in which the order does not matter.

For example, there are three different outcomes
when selecting two different letters from *a*, *b*,
and *c*:
{*a, b*} {*a, c*} {*b, c*}

In other words, there are three combinations of
three letters selected two at a time. In general, the
number of combinations of *n* objects taken *r* at a
time is $_nC_r = \dfrac{n!}{(n-r)!\,r!}$, where $n \geq r$.

The notation $_nC_r$ can also be written as $\dbinom{n}{r}$.

Example

What is the number of diagonals in an 8-sided
regular polygon with 8 vertices?

Solution

The number of lines formed by joining any two
vertices on an 8-sided polygon is $_8C_2$. However, a
diagonal in a regular polygon is formed by joining
two vertices that are not adjacent.

Therefore, since the regular polygon has 8 sides,
the number of diagonals is

$_8C_2 - 8 = \dfrac{8!}{2!(8-2)!} - 8 = 20$.

Practice Questions: 13–17, 25

PC. 4.   *Expand powers of a binomial in a variety
of ways, including using the binomial
theorem (restricted to exponents that are
natural numbers).*

BINOMIAL THEOREM

The binomial theorem states that the expansion of
$(x+y)^n$, where *n* is a non-negative integer, is
expressed as

$(x+y)^n = {}_nC_0 x^n + {}_nC_1 x^{n-1}y + {}_nC_2 x^{n-2}y^2 + \ldots + {}_nC_n y^n.$

The expansion of $(x+y)^n$ has $(n+1)$ terms, and
the coefficients of the terms can be found from the
rows of Pascal's triangle. The given diagram
shows the first six rows of Pascal's triangle.

$$
\begin{array}{ccccccccccc}
&&&&&1&&&&&\\
&&&&1&&1&&&&\\
&&&1&&2&&1&&&\\
&&1&&3&&3&&1&&\\
&1&&4&&6&&4&&1&\\
1&&5&&10&&10&&5&&1\\
\end{array}
$$

Every entry in Pascal's triangle is also a
combination.

$$
\begin{array}{ccccccccccc}
&&&&&_0C_0&&&&&\\
&&&&_1C_0&&_1C_1&&&&\\
&&&_2C_0&&_2C_1&&_2C_2&&&\\
&&_3C_0&&_3C_1&&_3C_2&&_3C_3&&\\
&_4C_0&&_4C_1&&_4C_2&&_4C_3&&_4C_4&\\
_5C_0&&_5C_1&&_5C_2&&_5C_3&&_5C_4&&_5C_5\\
\end{array}
$$

The general term of the expansion of $(x+y)^n$,
where *n* is a non-negative integer, is given by
$t_{k+1} = {}_nC_k x^{n-k} y^k$. This formula can be used to
solve problems related to specific terms of any
binomial expansion.

Copyright Protected

Not for Reproduction

Example

What is the term in the expansion of $(a+b)^5$ that contains a^3?

Solution

The general term of the expansion of $(a+b)^5$ is $t_{k+1} = {}_5C_k a^{5-k}b^k$. Since the term that contains a^3 is required, then a^{5-k} must be equal to a^3, which means the value of k is 2.

Let $k=2$ in the general term, and simplify.
$$t_{k+1} = {}_5C_k a^{5-k}b^k$$
$$t_{2+1} = {}_5C_2 a^{5-2}b^2$$
$$t_3 = 10a^3b^2$$

The term that contains a^3 in the expansion of $(a+b)^5$ is $10a^3b^2$.

Practice Questions: 18–24

PRACTICE QUESTIONS—PERMUTATIONS, COMBINATIONS AND BINOMIAL THEOREM

1. A university student is doing research on birth order and gender in families with 2, 3, and 4 children. Each family is designated by a code, which is assigned based on the number of children, their birth order, and their sex. For example, the code MFM is given to families with 3 children where the first- and last-born children are male and the middle child is female. If the student needs a code for families with 2 children, 3 children, and 4 children, then what is the maximum number of possible codes?

   A. 12 codes

   B. 16 codes

   C. 24 codes

   D. 28 codes

2. All telephone numbers are preceded by a 3-digit area code. In the original Bell Telephone System of assigning area codes, the first digit could be any number from 2 to 9, the second digit was either 0 or 1, and the third digit could be any number except 0. In this system, the number of different area codes possible was

   A. 126

   B. 144

   C. 160

   D. 576

Use the following information to answer the next question.

> A password for a certain computer program needs to be an arrangement of 4 characters consisting of letters and digits from 0 to 9.

3. If the letter y is considered to be a consonant, what is the number of 4-character passwords that either begin with a consonant or have no consonants at all?

   A. 50 625

   B. 456 976

   C. 979 776

   D. 1 030 401

4. Assume that in a given set of 3-digit area codes, the middle digit of each code is either "0" or "1." Which of the following conditions on the digits would result in exactly 180 area codes?

   A. The first digit cannot be zero, and the third digit must be different from the first.

   B. There are no restrictions on the possible values.

   C. All three digits must be different.

   D. The first digit cannot be zero.

Numerical Response

5. An airline company requires flight attendants to wear a pair of pants, a shirt, a tie, and a blazer. The flight attendants have a choice of 3 different pairs of pants, 5 different shirts, 4 different ties, and 2 different blazers. The maximum number of different outfits that a flight attendant could create using the items provided is _____ outfits. (Record your answer as a **whole** number.)

Copyright Protected

Not for Reproduction

Numerical Response

6. The number of 3-digit numbers **less than 400** that can be formed if the last digit is either 4 or 5 is _____.
(Record your answer as a **whole** number.)

7. The value of n in the equation $_nP_2 = 110$ is

A. -10 B. -1

C. 5   D. 11

8. If all of the letters in the word **DIPLOMA** are used, then the number of different 7-letter arrangements that can be made beginning with 3 vowels is

A. 24

B. 144

C. 720

D. 5 040

Use the following information to answer the next question.

Jen is having a party at her house and expects that 7 friends will come. She wants to give each friend a gift. She has 8 gifts to give away, but decides she really likes 1 particular gift and keeps it for herself.

9. How many different ways can Jen randomly give each friend a gift?

A. 5 040

B. 40 320

C. $7! \times 6! \times 5! \times 4! \times 3! \times 2! \times 1!$

D. $8! \times 7! \times 6! \times 5! \times 4! \times 3! \times 2! \times 1!$

Use the following information to answer the next question.

A ship has 6 different-coloured flags on board. To send signals, the ship's crew arranges some or all of the flags vertically on a flagpole.

10. How many different signals can be made if at least 4 flags must be used at a time?

A. 15   B. 360

C. 516   D. 1 800

Use the following information to answer the next question.

A car dealership manager wants to line up 9 cars in a row along one side of the dealership. All the cars are identical except for colour: 2 are red, 3 are blue, and 4 are black.

11. The number of different possible arrangements of the 9 cars is

A. 210

B. 1 260

C. 15 120

D. 362 880

Numerical Response

12. The **difference** between the number of arrangements using all of the letters in **FACTOR** and the number of arrangements using all of the letters in **DIVIDE** is _____.
(Record your answer as a **whole** number.)

13. The value of $_aC_5$, where $a \in N$ and $a > 5$, is equal to the value of

A. $_5C_a$

B. $_{a-5}C_5$

C. $_aC_{a-5}$

D. $_aC_{5-a}$

Copyright Protected

Use the following information to answer the next question.

A family is getting family photos taken. The family consists of a mother, a father, 4 sons, 3 daughters, and the family dog.

14. The photographer can use combinations to solve the problem of taking a photo in which

  A. all of the family is arranged in a line

  B. 5 of the 7 children are posing with the dog

  C. the mother, father, and daughters are placed in a line

  D. all of the children are lined up with the boys and girls alternating

Use the following information to answer the next question.

A restaurant offers ice-cream sundaes with 9 different topping choices.

15. Which of the following expressions represents the number of 3-topping sundaes a customer can order?

  A. $\dfrac{9!}{6!3!}$

  B. $\dfrac{9!}{6!}$

  C. $\dfrac{9!3!}{6!}$

  D. $\dfrac{9!}{3!}$

Use the following information to answer the next question.

At a garage sale, Marcie finds a box containing 7 old records. She decides to purchase 3 of the records. She pays for the records and puts them in her bag.

16. How many different groups of 3 records can Marcie possibly have in her bag?

  A. 21   **B.** 35

  C. 210   **D.** 420

Use the following information to answer the next question.

During the regular season of a recreational soccer league, each team plays every other team only once. The total number of games in the regular season is 45.

17. How many teams are in this league?

  A. 6

  B. 8

  C. 10

  D. 12

18. When expanded, which of the following expressions would have the coefficients 1, 4, 6, 4, and 1?

  A. $(a+b)^2$

  B. $(a+b)^3$

  C. $(a+b)^4$

  D. $(a+b)^5$

19. The expansion of $(2x-y)^{2p-5}$ has 18 terms. What is the value of p?

  A. 5

  B. 6

  C. 11

  D. 12

20. Which of the following expressions is the expanded form of $(5a-3b)^3$?

  A. $5a^3 - 9a^2b + 45ab^2 - 3b^3$

  B. $125a^3 - 45a^2b + 45ab^2 - 27b^3$

  C. $125a^3 - 225a^2b + 135ab^2 - 27b^3$

  D. $375a^3 - 225a^2b + 135ab^2 - 81b^3$

Not for Reproduction

21. If $(x-1)^5 = a_5x^5 + a_4x^4 + a_3x^3 + a_2x^2 + a_1x + a_0$, then the value of $a_5 + a_4 + a_3 + a_2 + a_1 + a_0$ is

   A. −32

   B. 0

   C. 1

   D. 32

22. What is the constant term of the expansion of $\left(a^4 - \dfrac{2}{a^3}\right)^{14}$?

   A. −768 768

   B. −3 003

   C. 3 003

   D. 768 768

23. The term of the expansion of $(x-y)^4$ that contains x^2 is

   A. $6x^2y$

   B. $6x^2y^2$

   C. $-6x^2y^2$

   D. $-6x^2y^3$

Numerical Response

24. A term of the binomial expansion $(ax+y)^8$, where $a > 0$, is $112x^2y^6$. The value of a, correct to the nearest whole number, is _____.
(Record your answer as a **whole** number.)

Written Response

25. The general staff in a hospital consists of 3 doctors and 12 nurses. How many different teams of 2 doctors and 5 nurses can be formed if a particular doctor must be included on each team and 2 particular nurses are on vacation and cannot be part of the teams?

Copyright Protected

Use the following information to answer the next question.

A certain province has particular rules for its licence plates. Each licence plate has 5 characters. The first three characters must be letters such that the first and third letters are consonants and the second letter is a vowel. The next two characters must be odd digits that cannot be the same.

Written Response

26. If there are 21 consonants and 5 vowels in the alphabet, how many different licence plates are possible, given these restrictions?

Not for Reproduction

ANSWERS AND SOLUTIONS—PRACTICE QUESTIONS

1. D	7. D	13. C	19. C	25. WR
2. B	8. B	14. B	20. C	26. WR
3. D	9. A	15. A	21. B	
4. D	10. D	16. B	22. D	
5. 120	11. B	17. C	23. B	
6. 60	12. 540	18. C	24. 2	

1. D

Step 1
Determine the number of codes for the families consisting of 2 children.

Each child can be either a male or a female. Therefore, the number of possible codes for families with 2 children is $2 \times 2 = 4$.

Step 2
Determine the number of codes for the families consisting of 3 children.

The number of possible codes for families with 3 children is $2 \times 2 \times 2 = 8$.

Step 3
Determine the number of codes for the families consisting of 4 children.

The number of possible orders for families with 4 children is $2 \times 2 \times 2 \times 2 = 16$.

Step 4
Determine the maximum number of codes for families of 2, 3, and 4 children.

Add the number of possible codes for each family. $4 + 8 + 16 = 28$

Therefore, the maximum number of codes for families of 2, 3, and 4 children is 28.

2. B

Step 1
Determine the number of possibilities for the first digit.

The first digit can be 2, 3, 4, 5, 6, 7, 8, or 9. Thus, there are 8 possibilities for the first digit.

Step 2
Determine the number of possibilities for the second digit.

The second digit can be either a 0 or a 1; therefore, there are 2 possibilities for the second digit.

Step 3
Determine the number of possibilities for the third digit.

The third digit can be 1, 2, 3, 4, 5, 6, 7, 8, or 9; therefore, there are 9 possibilities for the third digit.

Step 4
Determine the number of different area codes possible.

Applying the fundamental counting principle, the number of different area codes possible is $8 \times 2 \times 9 = 144$.

3. D

Step 1
Determine the number of 4-character passwords that begin with a consonant.

The alphabet contains 21 consonants, so the first character has 21 possibilities. The next three characters can be any letter or digit, which allows for $26 + 10 = 36$ possibilities for the next three characters.

Apply the fundamental counting principle to find the number of 4-character passwords that begin with a consonant.
$21 \times 36 \times 36 \times 36 = 979\,776$

Step 2
Determine the number of 4-character passwords that have no consonants.

There are 5 vowels in the alphabet. All four characters can be any vowel or number, which allows for $5 + 10 = 15$ possibilities for each character.

Apply the fundamental counting principle to find the number of 4-character passwords that have no consonants.
$15 \times 15 \times 15 \times 15 = 50\ 625$

Step 3
Determine the total number of possible passwords.

The total number of 4-character passwords that either begin with a consonant or have no consonants at all can be found by adding the two possibilities together.
$979\ 776 + 50\ 625 = 1\ 030\ 401$

4. **D**

If the middle digit of each code is either 0 or 1, then there are only 2 possible middle digits.

Step 1
Examine alternative A.

Since the first digit cannot be 0 and the third digit must be different from the first, there are 9 possibilities for the first digit and 9 possibilities for the third digit. Hence, the number of possible codes is $9 \times 2 \times 9 = 162$.

Step 2
Examine alternative B.

Since there are no restrictions on the possible values, there are 10 possibilities for both the first and third digits. Hence, the number of possible codes is $10 \times 2 \times 10 = 200$.

Step 3
Examine alternative C.

Since all three digits must be different, there are 9 possibilities for the first digit and 8 possibilities for the third digit. Hence, the number of possible codes is $9 \times 2 \times 8 = 144$.

Step 4
Examine alternative D.

Since the first digit cannot be 0, there are 9 possibilities for the first digit and 10 possibilities for the third digit. Hence, the number of possible codes is $9 \times 2 \times 10 = 180$.

Thus, the first digit cannot be 0.

5. 120

Step 1
Determine the number of choices for each type of apparel.

The flight attendants can choose from 3 different pairs of pants, 5 different shirts, 4 different ties, and 2 different blazers.

Step 2
Apply the fundamental counting principle to find the maximum number of different outfits.

Multiply the number of choices for each apparel item.
$3 \times 5 \times 4 \times 2 = 120$

Therefore, the maximum number of different outfits that a flight attendant can create is 120.

6. 60

Step 1
Determine the number of possibilities for the first digit.

The first digit can be 1, 2, or 3. Thus, there are 3 possibilities for the first digit.

Step 2
Determine the number of possibilities for the second digit.

The second digit can be 0, 1, 2, 3, 4, 5, 6, 7, 8, or 9. Thus, there are 10 possibilities for the second digit.

Step 3
Determine the number of possibilities for the third digit.

The third digit can be 4 or 5. Thus, there are 2 possibilities for the third digit.

Step 4
Determine the total number of 3-digit numbers less than 400.

Applying the fundamental counting principle, the total number of 3-digit numbers less than 400 is $3 \times 10 \times 2 = 60$.

Copyright Protected

Not for Reproduction

7. D

Step 1

Apply the formula $_nP_r = \dfrac{n!}{(n-r)!}$.

In the equation $_nP_2 = 110$, rewrite $_nP_2$ as $\dfrac{n!}{(n-2)!}$.

$$_nP_2 = 110$$
$$\frac{n!}{(n-2)!} = 110$$

Step 2

Rewrite $n!$ as $n(n-1)(n-2)!$.

$$\frac{n!}{(n-2)!} = 110$$
$$\frac{n(n-1)(n-2)!}{(n-2)!} = 110$$

Step 3

Divide out the common factors, and solve for n.

$$\frac{n(n-1)(n-2)!}{(n-2)!} = 110$$
$$n(n-1) = 110$$
$$n^2 - n = 110$$
$$n^2 - n - 110 = 0$$

Factor $n^2 - n - 110 = 0$, and apply the zero product property to each factor.

$$(n+10)(n-11) = 0$$
$$n + 10 = 0 \qquad n - 11 = 0$$
$$n = -10 \qquad n = 11$$

Since $n \geq 2$, the value of n is 11.

8. B

Step 1

Determine the number of arrangements for the first three letters.

The first three letters must be vowels. There are 3 vowels in the word DIPLOMA. Therefore, the number of arrangements for the first three letters is 3!.

Step 2

Determine the number of arrangements for the remaining letters.

The remaining four letters have 4! possible arrangements.

Step 3

Calculate the total number of 7-letter arrangements possible.
$$3! \times 4! = 144$$

9. A

Since Jen is keeping 1 specific item, there are only 7 items to give to 7 people. The number of permutations of n different items is $n!$ Therefore, the total ways that Jen can give 7 gifts to 7 friends is 7! = 5 040.

10. D

To make signals with at least 4 flags means that the signals could consist of 4, 5, or 6 flags.

Step 1

Express each possible flag set as a permutation.

To make a signal with 4 flags, arrange 4 flags from the given 6. The number of permutations of 6 flags taken 4 at a time is $_6P_4$.

To make a signal with 5 flags, arrange 5 flags from the given 6. This can be expressed as $_6P_5$.

To make a signal with 6 flags, arrange 6 flags from the given 6. This can be expressed as $_6P_6$.

Step 2

Determine the total number of different signals that can be made.

Since signals can be made with 4, 5, or 6 flags, the permutations must be added together.

$$_6P_4 + {}_6P_5 + {}_6P_6$$
$$= \frac{6!}{(6-4)!} + \frac{6!}{(6-5)!} + \frac{6!}{(6-6)!}$$
$$= \frac{6!}{2!} + \frac{6!}{1!} + \frac{6!}{0!}$$
$$= 360 + 720 + 720$$
$$= 1\,800$$

Therefore, the total number of different signals that can be made is 1 800.

11. B

Since there are 2 red cars, 3 blue cars, and 4 black cars, the total number of different arrangements is $\dfrac{9!}{4!\,3!\,2!} = 1\,260$.

12. 540

Step 1

Determine the number of arrangements from the word FACTOR.

All of the letters in the word FACTOR are distinct. Therefore, the number of possible arrangements using all 6 letters is $6! = 720$.

Step 2

Determine the number of arrangements from the word DIVIDE.

In the word DIVIDE, there are 2 Ds and 2 Is. Therefore, the number of possible arrangements, given these identical elements, is $\dfrac{6!}{2!\,2!} = 180$.

Step 3

Determine the difference.
$720 - 180 = 540$

13. C

Step 1

In the formula $_nC_r = \dfrac{n!}{(n-r)!\,r!}$, let $n = a$

and $r = 5$.

$$_nC_r = \frac{n!}{(n-r)!\,r!}$$

$$_aC_5 = \frac{a!}{(a-5)!\,5!}$$

Step 2

Rewrite $5!$ as $(a - a + 5)!$.

$$_aC_5 = \frac{a!}{(a-5)!\,5!}$$

$$_aC_5 = \frac{a!}{(a-5)!\,(a-a+5)!}$$

Step 3

Rewrite $(a - a + 5)!$ as $(a - (a - 5))!$.

$$_aC_5 = \frac{a!}{(a-5)!\,(a-a+5)!}$$

$$_aC_5 = \frac{a!}{(a-5)!\,(a-(a-5))!}$$

Step 4

Apply the formula $_nC_r = \dfrac{n!}{(n-r)!\,r!}$.

$$_aC_5 = \frac{a!}{(a-5)!\,(a-(a-5))!}$$

$$_aC_5 = \frac{a!}{(a-(a-5))!\,(a-5)!}$$

$$_aC_5 = {_aC_{a-5}}$$

14. B

In a combination problem, the order in which the selections are made does not matter.

Choosing 5 children from 7 for a picture with the dog is a situation in which the order is not important. Therefore, it can be solved with combinations.

The other alternatives all involve arranging family members in a row, where a change in the order makes a different arrangement. These are examples of permutation problems.

15. A

In the formula $_nC_r = \dfrac{n!}{(n-r)!\,r!}$, let $n = 9$ and

$r = 3$.

$$_9C_3 = \frac{9!}{(9-3)!\,3!}$$

$$_9C_3 = \frac{9!}{6!\,3!}$$

The expression $\dfrac{9!}{6!\,3!}$ represents the number of 3-topping sundaes a customer can order.

16. B

The order in which the records are purchased does not matter. Therefore, Marcie can possibly have $_7C_3 = 35$ different groups of 3 records in her bag.

Not for Reproduction

17. C

Step 1

Determine the number of games for n teams if each team plays every other team only once. The order in which the teams are chosen does not matter; therefore, the total number of games will be $_nC_2$.

Step 2

Solve for n.

The total number of games in a regular season is 45. In the formula $_nC_r = \dfrac{n!}{(n-r)!\,r!}$, let $_nC_r = 45$ and $r = 2$, and then solve for n.

$$_nC_r = \frac{n!}{(n-r)!\,r!}$$
$$45 = \frac{n!}{(n-2)!\,2!}$$
$$45 = \frac{n(n-1)(n-2)!}{(n-2)!\,2}$$
$$45 = \frac{n(n-1)}{2}$$
$$90 = (n)(n-1)$$
$$0 = n^2 - n - 90$$
$$0 = (n-10)(n+9)$$

Therefore, $n = 10$ or $n = -9$. However, since n cannot be a negative number, the answer is 10 teams.

18. C

The coefficients for the terms of the expansion of $(x+y)^n$ come from the $(n+1)^{\text{th}}$ row of Pascal's triangle.

$$1$$
$$1 \quad 1$$
$$1 \quad 2 \quad 1$$
$$1 \quad 3 \quad 3 \quad 1$$
$$1 \quad 4 \quad 6 \quad 4 \quad 1$$
$$1 \quad 5 \quad 10 \quad 10 \quad 5 \quad 1$$

The coefficients 1, 4, 6, 4, and 1 make up the fifth row of the triangle. Therefore, the binomial is raised to the power of $5 - 1 = 4$.

19. C

Step 1

Determine the value of p.

The expansion of the binomial $(x+y)^n$ has $(n+1)$ terms. This expansion has 18 terms. Therefore, the value of n is as follows:
$$n + 1 = 18$$
$$n = 18 - 1$$
$$n = 17$$

Step 2

Determine the value of p.

The exponent of $(2x - y)^{2p-5}$ is $2p - 5$.

Equate the exponent $2p - 5$ to 17, and solve for p.
$$2p - 5 = 17$$
$$2p = 22$$
$$\frac{2p}{2} = \frac{22}{2}$$
$$p = 11$$

20. C

Step 1

Apply the binomial theorem. Let $n = 3$, $x = 5a$, and $y = -3b$.

$$(5a - 3b)^3$$
$$= {_3C_0}(5a)^3 + {_3C_1}(5a)^2(-3b)$$
$$\quad + {_3C_2}(5a)^1(-3b)^2 + {_3C_3}(-3b)^3$$

Step 2

Simplify.

$$(5a - 3b)^3$$
$$= {_3C_0}(5a)^3 + {_3C_1}(5a)^2(-3b)$$
$$\quad + {_3C_2}(5a)^1(-3b)^2 + {_3C_3}(-3b)^3$$
$$= (1)(125a^3) + (3)(25a^2)(-3b)$$
$$\quad + (3)(5a)(9b^2) + (1)(-27b^3)$$
$$= 125a^3 - 225a^2b + 135ab^2 - 27b^3$$

21. B

Step 1

Apply the binomial theorem. Let $n = 5$ and $y = -1$.

$$(x-1)^5$$
$$= {}_5C_0x^5 + {}_5C_1x^4(-1) + {}_5C_2x^3(-1)^2$$
$$\quad + {}_5C_3x^2(-1)^3 + {}_5C_4x^1(-1)^4 + {}_5C_5(-1)^5$$

Step 2

Simplify.

$$(x-1)^5$$
$$= {}_5C_0x^5 + {}_5C_1x^4(-1) + {}_5C_2x^3(-1)^2$$
$$\quad + {}_5C_3x^2(-1)^3 + {}_5C_4x^1(-1)^4 + {}_5C_5(-1)^5$$
$$= 1x^5 + 5x^4(-1) + 10x^3(-1)^2$$
$$\quad + 10x^2(-1)^3 + 5x^1(-1)^4 + 1(-1)^5$$
$$= x^5 - 5x^4 + 10x^3 - 10x^2 + 5x + 1$$

Step 3

Calculate the total value of the coefficients.

$$a_5 + a_4 + a_3 + a_2 + a_1 + a_0$$
$$= 1 - 5 + 10 - 10 + 5 - 1$$
$$= 0$$

22. D

Step 1

Determine the general term for the expansion

of $\left(a^4 - \dfrac{2}{a^3}\right)^{14}$.

In the formula $t_{k+1} = {}_nC_k x^{n-k}y^k$, let $n = 14$, $x = a^4$,

and $y = \dfrac{2}{a^3}$.

$$t_{k+1} = {}_nC_k x^{n-k}y^k$$
$$t_{k+1} = {}_{14}C_k \left(a^4\right)^{14-k}\left(\frac{2}{a^3}\right)^k$$

Step 2

Simplify the general term.

$$t_{k+1} = {}_{14}C_k \left(a^4\right)^{14-k}\left(\frac{2}{a^3}\right)^k$$
$$t_{k+1} = {}_{14}C_k \left(a^{56-4k}\right)\left(\frac{2^k}{a^{3k}}\right)$$
$$t_{k+1} = {}_{14}C_k \, 2^k \left(\frac{a^{56-4k}}{a^{3k}}\right)$$
$$t_{k+1} = {}_{14}C_k \, 2^k \left(a^{56-4k-3k}\right)$$
$$t_{k+1} = {}_{14}C_k \, 2^k \left(a^{56-7k}\right)$$

Step 3

Determine the value of k.

The constant term of an expansion has a degree of 0. This means the expression a^{56-7k} must have a degree of 0.

Equate the exponent of a^{56-7k} to 0, and solve for k.
$$56 - 7k = 0$$
$$56 = 7k$$
$$k = 8$$

Step 4

Determine the constant term of the expansion.

Let $k = 8$ in the general term, and simplify.

$$t_{k+1} = {}_{14}C_k \left(a^4\right)^{14-k}\left(\frac{2}{a^3}\right)^k$$
$$t_{8+1} = {}_{14}C_8 \left(a^4\right)^{14-8}\left(\frac{2}{a^3}\right)^8$$
$$t_9 = (3\ 003)\left(a^{24}\right)\left(\frac{256}{a^{24}}\right)$$
$$t_9 = (3\ 003)(256)$$
$$t_9 = 768\ 768$$

23. B

Step 1

Determine the general term of the expansion.

In the formula $t_{k+1} = {}_nC_k x^{n-k}y^k$, let $n = 4$ and $y = -y$.

$$t_{k+1} = {}_nC_k x^{n-k}y^k$$
$$t_{k+1} = {}_4C_k x^{4-k}(-y)^k$$

Step 2

Determine the term in the expansion that contains x^2.

The expression x^{4-k} must be equal to x^2, which means the value of k is 2.

In the general term, let $k = 2$, and simplify.

$$t_{k+1} = {}_4C_k x^{4-k}(-y)^k$$
$$t_{2+1} = {}_4C_2 x^{4-2}(-y)^2$$
$$t_3 = 6x^2y^2$$

Copyright Protected

Not for Reproduction

24. 2

Step 1

Determine the general term of the expansion.

In the formula $t_{k+1} = {}_nC_k x^{n-k} y^k$, let $n = 8$, $x = ax$, and $y = y$.

$t_{k+1} = {}_nC_k x^{n-k} y^k$

$t_{k+1} = {}_8C_k (ax)^{8-k} y^k$

Step 2

Determine the value of k that gives the term $112x^2 y^6$.

The expression y^k must be equal to y^6, which means the value of k is 6.

Step 3

In the general term $t_{k+1} = {}_8C_k (ax)^{8-k} y^k$, let $k = 6$, and simplify.

$t_{k+1} = {}_8C_k (ax)^{8-k} y^k$

$t_{6+1} = {}_8C_6 (ax)^{8-6} y^6$

$t_7 = {}_8C_6 (ax)^2 y^6$

$t_7 = {}_8C_6 a^2 x^2 y^6$

Step 4

Determine the value of a.

The value of ${}_8C_6 a^2$ is equal to the coefficient, 112.

$_8C_6 a^2 = 112$

$28a^2 = 112$

$a^2 = 4$

$a = \pm 2$

Since $a > 0$, the value of a is 2.

25. WR

The order in which the doctors and nurses are selected does not matter; therefore, the given question is a combination problem.

Step 1

Determine the number of possible selections for the doctors.

Since one particular doctor must be included, the other doctor on the team must be selected from the two remaining doctors. This can be represented by ${}_2C_1$.

Step 2

Determine the number of possible selections for the nurses.

Since two nurses cannot be part of the team, the 5 required nurses must be selected from the 10 available nurses. This can be represented by ${}_{10}C_5$.

Step 3

Determine the number of possible doctor-nurse teams that can be formed.

The number of possible doctor-nurse teams can be determined by applying the fundamental counting principle.

${}_1C_1 \times {}_2C_1 \times {}_{10}C_5 = 504$

Thus, there are 504 different doctor-nurse teams that can be formed.

Copyright Protected

26. WR

Step 1
List the stages of the task.

The task is to make a 5-character licence plate that fits the given restrictions. This task has five stages:

1) Select the first character. There are 21 consonants in the alphabet, so there are 21 choices for the first character.

2) Select the second character. This letter must be a vowel. There are 5 vowels, so there are 5 choices for the second character.

3) Select the third character. Since the third character must be a consonant, there are 21 choices for the third character.

4) Select the fourth character. An odd digit must be selected. Since there are 5 odd digits (1, 3, 5, 7, and 9), there are 5 choices for the fourth character.

5) Select the fifth character. From the remaining 4 odd digits, there are 4 choices for the fifth character.

Step 2
Determine the number of possible licence plates for this particular province.

Apply the fundamental counting principle. Multiply the number of choices for each character on the licence plate.
$21 \times 5 \times 21 \times 5 \times 4 = 44\ 110$

There are 44 100 possible licence plates for this particular province.

UNIT TEST—PERMUTATIONS, COMBINATIONS AND BINOMIAL THEOREM

1. If a standard 6-sided die is rolled 5 times, what is the number of possible results in which either all even numbers or all odd numbers are rolled?

   A. 243

   B. 486

   C. 23 328

   D. 44 656

2. Codes with 4 digits are to be made from the digits 1, 2, 3, 4, 5, 6, and 7. If repetitions are **not** permitted and each code must contain 2 odd digits followed by 2 even digits, then the number of codes that can be formed is

   A. 72 codes

   B. 144 codes

   C. 210 codes

   D. 840 codes

3. A set of 3 different Mathematics books, 4 different Physics books, and 2 different English books are arranged on a shelf. If the books on each subject are to be kept together, then the number of different arrangements possible for the books is

   A. 288

   B. 864

   C. 1 260

   D. 1 728

4. If the Davis family consists of 4 daughters, 3 sons, a mother, and a father, what is the number of possible arrangements of the family members when they are standing in a line?

   A. $4! \times 3! \times 2!$

   B. $4 \times 3 \times 1 \times 1$

   C. $9 \times 8 \times 7 \times 6 \times 5 \times 4 \times 3 \times 2 \times 1$

   D. $9! \times 8! \times 7! \times 6! \times 5! \times 4! \times 3! \times 2! \times 1!$

Use the following information to answer the next question.

For the boys' relay race at the local school's track meet, 8 runners take turns (called "legs") to run the race. The coach, Mr. Smith, must decide the order for the 8 runners. Mr. Smith wants Curt and Adam to run the first 2 legs of the relay race, in either order, and Ben to run the last leg of the relay race.

5. The number of different possible orders for the 8 runners in the relay race, according to Mr. Smith's plan, is

   A. 40 320

   B. 720

   C. 240

   D. 120

6. Five different outfits are to be displayed in a store window. From 5 different winter outfits, 3 must be chosen, and from 4 different fall outfits, 2 must be chosen. These outfits will then be arranged in a row in the store window. The number of displays that can be made by choosing the outfits and then arranging them in the window is

A. 300

B. 3 600

C. 7 200

D. 86 400

7. The number of 6-member teams that can be selected from a group of 8 people is

A. 28

B. 56

C. 720

D. 20 160

Use the following information to answer the next question.

There are 300 ways in which a 2-member committee can be selected from a pool of n students.

8. Which of the following quadratic equations can be solved in order to determine the number of students, n?

A. $n^2 - n - 300 = 0$

B. $n^2 - n - 600 = 0$

C. $n^2 - 2n - 600 = 0$

D. $n^2 - 2n - 300 = 0$

9. If there are 17 terms in the expansion $(2x + 3y)^{3n-5}$, then the value of n is

A. 5

B. 7

C. 17

D. 18

10. What is the constant term in the expansion of $\left(x + \dfrac{2}{x}\right)^{16}$?

A. 25 740

B. 205 920

C. 1 647 360

D. 3 294 720

11. In the expansion of $(3x + 1)^7$, the coefficient of the term that contains x^2 is

A. 21

B. 42

C. 189

D. 378

Copyright Protected

Not for Reproduction

12. What is the value of n in the equation $_{n+1}P_2 = 2$?

13. What is the expanded form of the binomial $\left(\dfrac{x}{3} - 9\right)^5$?

Copyright Protected

Written Response

14. If $90 = {}_{n-2}P_2$, what is the value of n?

Not for Reproduction

ANSWERS AND SOLUTIONS—UNIT TEST

1. B	6. C	11. C
2. A	7. A	12. WR
3. D	8. B	13. WR
4. C	9. B	14. WR
5. C	10. D	

1. B

Step 1
Determine the number of results in which 5 even numbers are rolled.

A standard die has 3 even numbers: 2, 4, and 6.

Applying the fundamental counting principle, the number of results in which 5 even numbers are rolled is $3 \times 3 \times 3 \times 3 \times 3 = 243$.

Step 2
Determine the number of results in which 5 odd numbers are rolled.

A standard die has 3 odd numbers: 1, 3, and 5.

Applying the fundamental counting principle, the number of results in which 5 odd numbers are rolled is $3 \times 3 \times 3 \times 3 \times 3 = 243$.

Step 3
Determine the total number of possible results.

The total number of possible results can be found by adding the number possibilities for each scenario together. Therefore, the total number of results is $243 + 243 = 486$.

2. A

In the digits 1, 2, 3, 4, 5, 6, and 7, there are 4 odd digits and 3 even digits. The 4-digit codes must have the following order: odd, odd, even, even.

Step 1
List the stages of the task.

The task is to make a 4-digit code, so this task has 4 stages:

1. Pick the first digit. There are 4 odd digits between 1 and 7, so there are 4 ways to pick the first digit.

2. Pick the second digit. Since you cannot repeat the digit that was used in stage 1, there are only 3 ways to pick the second digit.

3. Pick the third digit. There are 3 even digits between 1 and 7, so there are 3 ways to pick the third digit.

4. Pick the fourth digit. Since you cannot repeat the digit that was used in stage 3, there are 2 ways to pick the fourth digit.

Step 2
Determine the number of possible combinations.

Apply the fundamental counting principle. Multiply all the ways to select each digit in the combination.
$4 \times 3 \times 3 \times 2 = 72$

Therefore, there are 72 possible combinations.

Copyright Protected

3. **D**

Step 1
Determine the number of arrangements for the 3 groups of books.

There are $3! = 6$ possible arrangements.

Step 2
Determine the number of arrangements for the Mathematics books.

The 3 Mathematics books have $3! = 6$ arrangements.

Step 3
Determine the number of arrangements for the Physics books.

The 4 Physics books have $4! = 24$ arrangements.

Step 4
Determine the number of arrangements for the English books.

The 2 English books have $2! = 2$ arrangements.

Step 5
Calculate the total number of arrangements possible for the books.

Applying the fundamental counting principle, the total number of arrangements is $6 \times 6 \times 24 \times 2 = 1\,728$.

4. **C**

In general, $n! = n \times (n-1) \times (n-2) \times \ldots \times 2 \times 1$ represents the number of permutations of n distinct objects.

Since there are 9 family members and no restrictions, the number of arrangements of the family members when they are standing in a line is $9!$, or $9 \times 8 \times 7 \times 6 \times 5 \times 4 \times 3 \times 2 \times 1$.

5. **C**

Since the order of the runners in the event matters, this is a permutation problem.

Step 1
Determine the number of possible arrangements for the restricted leg positions.

Curt and Adam have to run the first 2 legs of the relay race in either order. Therefore, the first 2 legs can be arranged in $2! = 2 \times 1 = 2$ different ways.

Since Ben has to run the last leg of the relay race, there is only 1 arrangement for the last leg.

Step 2
Determine the number of possible arrangements for the other 5 runners.

The remaining 5 runners must be arranged in the third, fourth, fifth, sixth, and seventh leg positions. Arranging 5 people for 5 distinct positions can be represented as $5! = 5 \times 4 \times 3 \times 2 \times 1$. Therefore, the remaining 5 runners can be arranged in $5 \times 4 \times 3 \times 2 \times 1 = 120$ different ways.

Step 3
Applying the fundamental counting principle, the total number of arrangements for the 8 runners is $2 \times 120 \times 1 = 240$.

6. **C**

Step 1
Determine the number of selections of winter outfits.

Since 3 outfits are to be chosen from 5 different winter outfits, the number of selections of winter outfits is $_5C_3$.

Step 2
Determine the number of selections of fall outfits.

Since 2 outfits are to be chosen from 4 different fall outfits, the number of selections of fall outfits is $_4C_2$.

Step 3
Determine the arrangements for the outfits in the window.

The 5 different outfits can be displayed in $5! = 120$ different arrangements in the store window.

Step 4
Determine the total number of possible arrangements.

Apply the fundamental counting principle.
$$5! \times {}_5C_3 \times {}_4C_2$$
$$= 5! \times \frac{5!}{3!\,2!} \times \frac{4!}{2!\,2!}$$
$$= 120 \times 10 \times 6$$
$$= 7\,200$$

Therefore, the total number of possible arrangements is $7\,200$.

7. A

In general, the number of combinations of n objects taken r at a time is $_nC_r$. The number of 6-member teams that can be selected from a group of 8 is $_8C_6$.

$_8C_6$
$= \dfrac{8!}{(8-6)!\,6!}$
$= 28$

Therefore, there are 28 possible teams.

8. B

A 2-member committee can be selected in 300 different ways from a pool of n students. This can be expressed as $300 = {}_nC_2$.

Step 1

In the equation $300 = {}_nC_2$, let $_nC_2 = \dfrac{n!}{(x-2)!\,2!}$.

$300 = {}_nC_2$
$300 = \dfrac{n!}{(n-2)!\,2!}$

Step 2

Simplify the right-hand side of the equation.

$300 = \dfrac{n!}{(n-2)!\,2!}$
$300 = \dfrac{n(n-1)(n-2)!}{(n-2)!\,2!}$
$300 = \dfrac{n(n-1)}{2!}$
$300 = \dfrac{n^2 - n}{2}$

Step 3

Bring all terms to one side of the equation.

$300 = \dfrac{n^2 - n}{2}$
$600 = n^2 - n$
$0 = n^2 - n - 600$

Therefore, an equation used to determine the value of n is $0 = n^2 - n - 600$.

9. B

There are $(n + 1)$ terms in the binomial expansion of $(x + y)^n$. Thus, there are $(3n - 5) + 1$ terms in the expansion of $(2x + 3y)^{3n-5}$.

Since the number of terms in the expansion $(2x + 3y)^{3n-5}$ is given to be 17, let $(3n - 5) + 1 = 17$, and solve for n.
$(3n - 5) + 1 = 17$
$3n - 5 = 16$
$3n = 21$
$n = 7$

10. D

Step 1
Determine the general term of the expansion.

In the equation $t_{k+1} = {}_nC_k x^{n-k} y^k$, let $n = 16$ and $y = \dfrac{2}{x}$.

$t_{k+1} = {}_nC_k x^{n-k} y^k$
$t_{k+1} = {}_{16}C_k \left(x^{16-k}\right)\left(\dfrac{2}{x}\right)^k$

Step 2
Apply the laws of exponents, and simplify the general term.

$t_{k+1} = {}_{16}C_k \left(x^{16-k}\right)\left(\dfrac{2}{x}\right)^k$
$t_{k+1} = {}_{16}C_k \left(x^{16-k}\right)\left(\dfrac{2^k}{x^k}\right)$
$t_{k+1} = {}_{16}C_k \left(\dfrac{x^{16-k}}{x^k}\right)\left(2^k\right)$
$t_{k+1} = {}_{16}C_k \left(x^{16-2k}\right)\left(2^k\right)$

Step 3
Determine the value of k.

The constant term of an expansion has a degree of 0. Therefore, equate the exponent of x^{16-2k} to 0, and solve for k.
$16 - 2k = 0$
$16 = 2k$
$8 = k$

Step 4

Determine the constant term.

In the equation $t_{k+1} = {}_{16}C_k\left(x^{16-k}\right)\left(\dfrac{2}{x}\right)^k$, substitute 8 for k, and simplify.

$$t_{k+1} = {}_{16}C_k\left(x^{16-k}\right)\left(\dfrac{2}{x}\right)^k$$

$$t_{8+1} = {}_{16}C_8\left(x^{16-8}\right)\left(\dfrac{2}{x}\right)^8$$

$$t_9 = (12\ 870)\left(x^8\right)\left(\dfrac{256}{x^8}\right)$$

$$t_9 = (12\ 870)\left(x^8\right)\left(\dfrac{256}{x^8}\right)$$

$$t_9 = (12\ 870)(256)$$

$$t_9 = 3\ 294\ 720$$

Therefore, the constant term in the expansion of $\left(x+\dfrac{2}{x}\right)^6$ is 3 294 720.

11. C

Step 1

Determine the general term of the expansion of $(3x+1)^7$.

In the formula $t_{k+1} = {}_nC_k x^{n-k} y^k$, let $x = 3x$, $y = 1$, and $n = 7$.

$$t_{k+1} = {}_nC_k x^{n-k} y^k$$

$$t_{k+1} = {}_7C_k (3x)^{7-k}(1)^k$$

Step 2

Determine the value of k.

Since the coefficient of the term that contains x^2 is required, the exponent of $(3x)^{7-k}$ must be 2, which means $k = 5$.

Step 3

In the general term, let $k = 5$, and simplify.

$$t_{k+1} = {}_7C_k (3x)^{7-k}(1)^k$$

$$t_{5+1} = {}_7C_5 (3x)^{7-5}(1)^5$$

$$t_6 = (21)(3x)^2(1)$$

$$t_6 = (21)(9x^2)$$

$$t_6 = 189x^2$$

The coefficient of the term that contains x^2 is 189.

12. WR

Step 1

Apply the formula ${}_nP_r = \dfrac{n!}{(n-r)}$. In the equation ${}_{n+1}P_2 = 2$, rewrite ${}_{n+1}P_2$ as $\dfrac{(n+1)!}{((n+1)-2)!}$.

$${}_{n+1}P_2 = 2$$

$$\dfrac{(n+1)!}{((n+1)-2)!} = 2$$

$$\dfrac{(n+1)!}{(n-1)!} = 2$$

Step 2

Rewrite $(n+1)!$ as $(n+1)(n)(n-1)!$, and divide out common factors.

$$\dfrac{(n+1)!}{(n-1)!} = 2$$

$$\dfrac{(n+1)(n)(n-1)!}{(n-1)!} = 2$$

$$n(n+1) = 2$$

Step 3

Solve for n.

$$n(n+1) = 2$$

$$n^2 + n = 2$$

$$n^2 + n - 2 = 0$$

$$(n-1)(n+2) = 0$$

$$n = 1 \text{ or } n = -2$$

Since n cannot be negative, the value of n is 1.

Copyright Protected

Not for Reproduction

13. WR

Step 1

Apply the binomial theorem, and substitute 5 for n, $\dfrac{x}{3}$ for x, and -9 for y.

$$(x+y)^n = {}_nC_0x^n + {}_nC_1x^{n-1}y + {}_nC_2x^{n-2}y^2 + \ldots + {}_nC_ny^n$$

$$\left(\frac{x}{3}-9\right)^5 = {}_5C_0\left(\frac{x}{3}\right)^5 + {}_5C_1\left(\frac{x}{3}\right)^{5-1}(-9)$$
$$+ {}_5C_2\left(\frac{x}{3}\right)^{5-2}(-9)^2 + {}_5C_3\left(\frac{x}{3}\right)^{5-3}(-9)^3$$
$$+ {}_5C_4\left(\frac{x}{3}\right)^{5-4}(-9)^4 + {}_5C_5(-9)^5$$

Step 2

Simplify the equation.

$$\left(\frac{x}{3}-9\right)^5 = {}_5C_0\left(\frac{x}{3}\right)^5 + {}_5C_1\left(\frac{x}{3}\right)^{5-1}(-9)$$
$$+ {}_5C_2\left(\frac{x}{3}\right)^{5-2}(-9)^2 + {}_5C_3\left(\frac{x}{3}\right)^{5-3}(-9)^3$$
$$+ {}_5C_4\left(\frac{x}{3}\right)^{5-4}(-9)^4 + {}_5C_5(-9)^5$$

$$\left(\frac{x}{3}-9\right)^5 = 1\left(\frac{x}{3}\right)^5 + 5\left(\frac{x}{3}\right)^4(-9)$$
$$+ 10\left(\frac{x}{3}\right)^3(-9)^2 + 10\left(\frac{x}{3}\right)^2(-9)^3$$
$$+ 5\left(\frac{x}{3}\right)^1(-9)^4 + 1(-9)^5$$

$$\left(\frac{x}{3}-9\right)^5 = \frac{x^5}{243} + 5\left(\frac{x^4}{81}\right)(-9)$$
$$+ 10\left(\frac{x^3}{27}\right)(81) + 10\left(\frac{x^2}{9}\right)(-729)$$
$$+ 5\left(\frac{x}{3}\right)(6\,561) - 59\,049$$

$$\left(\frac{x}{3}-9\right)^5 = \frac{x^5}{243} - \frac{5x^4}{9} + 30x^3 - 810x^2$$
$$+ 10\,935x - 59\,049$$

14. WR

Step 1

Apply the formula ${}_nP_r = \dfrac{n!}{(n-r)!}$.

$${}_nP_r = \frac{n!}{(n-r)!}$$
$$90 = \frac{(n-2)!}{((n-2)-2)!}$$
$$90 = \frac{(n-2)!}{(n-4)!}$$

Step 2

Rewrite $(n-2)!$ as $(n-2)(n-3)(n-4)!$, then divide out the common factors in the numerator and denominator.

$$90 = \frac{(n-2)!}{(n-4)!}$$
$$90 = \frac{(n-2)(n-3)(n-4)!}{(n-4)!}$$
$$90 = (n-2)(n-3)$$
$$90 = n^2 - 3n - 2n + 6$$
$$90 = n^2 - 5n + 6$$

Step 3

Solve for n in the equation $n^2 - 5n + 6 = 90$.

$$n^2 - 5n + 6 = 90$$
$$n^2 - 5n - 84 = 0$$

Factor the trinomial $n^2 - 5n - 84$, and apply the zero product property to each factor.

$$(n-12)(n+7) = 0$$
$$n = 12 \text{ or } n = -7$$

Since n cannot be negative, the value of n is 12.

Copyright Protected

NOTES

Key Strategies for Success on Tests

Copyright Protected

KEY STRATEGIES FOR SUCCESS ON TESTS

AN OVERVIEW OF THE TEST

This section is all about the skills and strategies you need to be successful on the Mathematics 30-1 Provincial Diploma Exam. It is designed for you to use together with your classroom learning and assignments.

FINDING OUT ABOUT THE TEST

Here are some questions you may wish to discuss with your teacher to help you prepare for the Mathematics 30-1 Provincial Diploma Exam.

1.	What will this test assess, or cover?	The test assesses the expectations from 3 math units: "Trigonometry," "Relations and Functions," and "Permutations, Combinations and Binomial Theorem." The questions will test your ability to understand and apply the math concepts you have learned throughout the year.
2.	What materials do I need to bring to write the test?	You need a pencil, an eraser, and an approved graphing calculator such as the TI-83.
3.	Are there any materials provided for the test?	A formula sheet is provided.
4.	What kinds of questions are on the test?	The test has 28 multiple-choice questions and 12 numerical response questions.
5.	How much time do I have to write the test?	You will have three hours to complete the test.
6.	How important is this test to my final grade?	Your teacher can answer this question.

Having a good understanding of effective test taking skills can help you do well on the test. Being familiar with the question format may help you to prepare for quizzes, unit tests, and year-end tests.

This section is all about the skills and strategies you need to be successful on tests. It is designed for you to use together with your classroom learning and assignments.

Not for Reproduction

THINGS TO CONSIDER WHEN TAKING A TEST

It is normal to feel anxious before you write a test. You can manage this anxiety by using the following strategies:

- Think positive thoughts. Imagine yourself doing well on the test.

- Make a conscious effort to relax by taking several slow, deep, controlled breaths. Concentrate on the air going in and out of your body.

- Before you begin the test, ask questions if you are unsure of anything.

- Jot down key words or phrases from any instructions your teacher gives you.

- Look over the entire test to find out the number and kinds of questions on the test.

- Read each question closely, and reread if necessary.

- Pay close attention to key vocabulary words. Sometimes, these words are **bolded** or *italicized*, and they are usually important words in the question.

- If you are putting your answers on an answer sheet, mark your answers carefully. Always print clearly. If you wish to change an answer, erase the mark completely, and ensure that your final answer is darker than the one you have erased.

- Use highlighting to note directions, key words, and vocabulary that you find confusing or that are important to answering the question.

- Double-check to make sure you have answered everything before handing in your test.

- When taking tests, students often overlook the easy words. Failure to pay close attention to these words can result in an incorrect answer. One way to avoid this is to be aware of these words and to underline, circle, or highlight them while you are taking the test.

- Even though some words are easy to understand, they can change the meaning of the entire question, so it is important that you pay attention to them. Here are some examples.

all	always	most likely	probably	best	not
difference	usually	except	most	unlikely	likely

Example

1. Which of the following expressions is **incorrect**?

    A. $3 + 2 \geq 5$

    B. $4 - 3 < 2$

    C. $5 \times 4 < 15$

    D. $6 \times 3 \geq 18$

TEST PREPARATION AND TEST-TAKING SKILLS

HELPFUL STRATEGIES FOR ANSWERING MULTIPLE-CHOICE QUESTIONS

A multiple-choice question gives you some information and then asks you to select an answer from four choices. Each question has one correct answer. The other choices are distractors, which are incorrect.

The following strategies can help you when answering multiple-choice questions:

- Quickly skim through the entire test. Find out how many questions there are, and plan your time accordingly.

- Read and reread questions carefully. Underline key words, and try to think of an answer before looking at the choices.

- If there is a graphic, look at the graphic, read the question, and go back to the graphic. Then, you may want to underline the important information from the question.

- Carefully read the choices. Read the question first and then each choice that goes with it.

- When choosing an answer, try to eliminate those choices that are clearly wrong or do not make sense.

- Some questions may ask you to select the best answer. These questions will always include words like *best*, *most appropriate*, or *most likely*. All of the choices will be correct to some degree, but one of the choices will be better than the others in some way. Carefully read all four choices before choosing the answer you think is the best.

- If you do not know the answer, or if the question does not make sense to you, it is better to guess than to leave it blank.

- Do not spend too much time on any one question. Make a mark (*) beside a difficult question, and come back to it later. If you are leaving a question to come back to later, make sure you also leave the space on the answer sheet, if you are using one.

- Remember to go back to the difficult questions at the end of the test; sometimes, clues are given throughout the test that will provide you with answers.

- Note any negative words like *no* or *not*, and be sure your answer fits the question.

- Before changing an answer, be sure you have a very good reason to do so.

- Do not look for patterns on your answer sheet, if you are using one.

HELPFUL STRATEGIES FOR ANSWERING WRITTEN-RESPONSE QUESTIONS

A written response requires you to respond to a question or directive indicated by words such as explain, predict, list, describe, show your work, solve, or calculate. The following strategies can help you when answering written-response questions:

- Read and reread the question carefully.

- Recognize and pay close attention to directing words such as *explain*, *show your work*, and *describe*.

- Underline key words and phrases that indicate what is required in your answer, such as *explain*, *estimate*, *answer*, *calculate*, or *show your work*.

- Write down rough, point-form notes regarding the information you want to include in your answer.

- Think about what you want to say, and organize information and ideas in a coherent and concise manner within the time limit you have for the question.

- Be sure to answer every part of the question that is asked.

- Include as much information as you can when you are asked to explain your thinking.

- Include a picture or diagram if it will help to explain your thinking.

- Try to put your final answer to a problem in a complete sentence to be sure it is reasonable.

- Reread your response to ensure you have answered the question.

- Ask yourself if your answer makes sense.

- Ask yourself if your answer sounds right.

- Use appropriate subject vocabulary and terms in your response.

Copyright Protected

ABOUT MATHEMATICS TESTS

WHAT YOU NEED TO KNOW ABOUT MATHEMATICS TESTS

To do well on a mathematics test, you need to understand and apply your knowledge of mathematical concepts. Reading skills can also make a difference in how well you perform. Reading skills can help you follow instructions and find key words, as well as read graphs, diagrams, and tables. They can also help you solve mathematics problems.

Mathematics tests usually have two types of questions: questions that ask for understanding of mathematics ideas and questions that test how well you can solve mathematics problems.

HOW YOU CAN PREPARE FOR MATHEMATICS TESTS

The following strategies are particular to preparing for and writing mathematics tests:

- Know how to use your calculator, and, if it is allowed, use your own for the test.

- Note taking is a good way to review and study important information from your class notes and textbook.

- Sketch a picture of the problem, procedure, or term. Drawing is helpful for learning and remembering concepts.

- Check your answer to practice questions by working backward to the beginning. You can find the beginning by going step by step in reverse order.

- Use the following steps when answering questions with graphics (pictures, diagrams, tables, or graphs):

  1. Read the title of the graphic and any key words.

  2. Read the test question carefully to figure out what information you need to find in the graphic.

  3. Go back to the graphic to find the information you need.

  4. Decide which operation is needed.

- Always pay close attention when pressing the keys on your calculator. Repeat the procedure a second time to be sure you pressed the correct keys.

Not for Reproduction

TEST PREPARATION COUNTDOWN

If you develop a plan for studying and test preparation, you will perform well on tests.

Here is a general plan to follow seven days before you write a test.

COUNTDOWN: 7 DAYS BEFORE THE TEST

1. Use "Finding Out about the Test" to help you make your own personal test preparation plan.

2. Review the following information:

   – Areas to be included on the test

   – Types of test items

   – General and specific test tips

3. Start preparing for the test at least seven days before the test. Develop your test preparation plan, and set time aside to prepare and study.

COUNTDOWN: 6, 5, 4, 3, 2 DAYS BEFORE THE TEST

1. Review old homework assignments, quizzes, and tests.

2. Rework problems on quizzes and tests to make sure you still know how to solve them.

3. Correct any errors made on quizzes and tests.

4. Review key concepts, processes, formulas, and vocabulary.

5. Create practice test questions for yourself, and answer them. Work out many sample problems.

COUNTDOWN: THE NIGHT BEFORE THE TEST

1. Use the night before the test for final preparation, which includes reviewing and gathering materials needed for the test before going to bed.

2. Most importantly, get a good night's rest, and know you have done everything possible to do well on the test.

TEST DAY

1. Eat a healthy and nutritious breakfast.

2. Ensure you have all the necessary materials.

3. Think positive thoughts, such as "I can do this," "I am ready," and "I know I can do well."

4. Arrive at your school early, so you are not rushing, which can cause you anxiety and stress.

Copyright Protected

SUMMARY OF HOW TO BE SUCCESSFUL DURING A TEST

You may find some of the following strategies useful for writing a test:

- Take two or three deep breaths to help you relax.

- Read the directions carefully, and underline, circle, or highlight any important words.

- Look over the entire test to understand what you will need to do.

- Budget your time.

- Begin with an easy question or a question you know you can answer correctly rather than follow the numerical question order of the test.

- If you cannot remember how to answer a question, try repeating the deep breathing and physical relaxation activities. Then, move on to visualization and positive self-talk to get yourself going.

- When answering questions with graphics (pictures, diagrams, tables, or graphs), look at the question carefully, and use the following steps:

    1. Read the title of the graphic and any key words.

    2. Read the test question carefully to figure out what information you need to find in the graphic.

    3. Go back to the graphic to find the information you need.

- Write down anything you remember about the subject on the reverse side of your test paper. This activity sometimes helps to remind you that you do know something and are capable of writing the test.

- Look over your test when you have finished, and double-check your answers to be sure you did not forget anything.

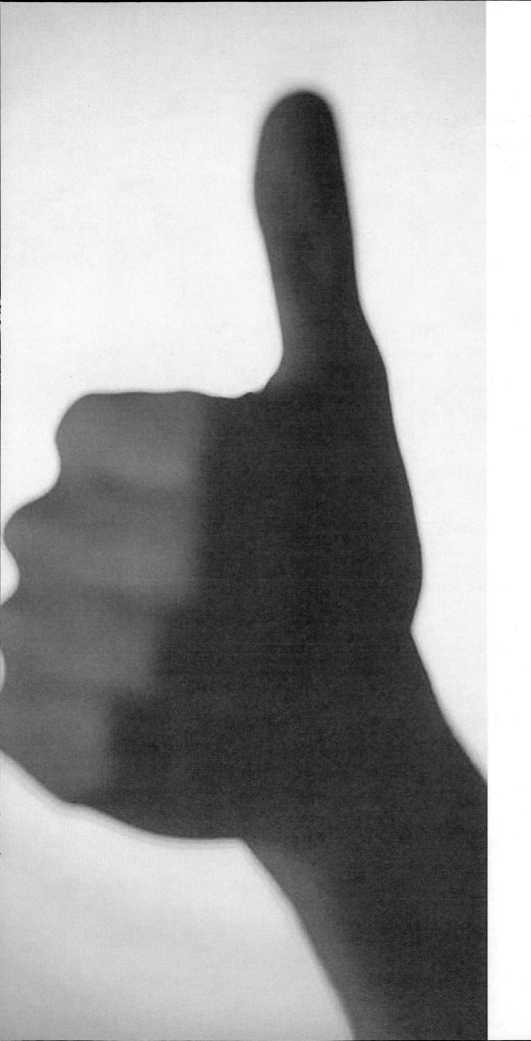

Sample Diploma Examinations

PRACTICE TEST 1

1. Which of the following angles is coterminal with 250°?

   A. $\dfrac{83\pi}{18}$ rad

   B. $\dfrac{11\pi}{18}$ rad

   C. $\dfrac{133\pi}{18}$ rad

   D. $\dfrac{157\pi}{18}$ rad

2. Which of the following procedures would be **most appropriate** to determine the exact value of $\sin\left(\dfrac{4\pi}{3}\right)$?

   A. Determine the sine ratio of the reference angle of $\dfrac{\pi}{6}$ in quadrant II.

   B. Determine the sine ratio of the reference angle of $\dfrac{\pi}{3}$ in quadrant II.

   C. Determine the sine ratio of the reference angle of $\dfrac{\pi}{3}$ in quadrant III.

   D. Determine the sine ratio of the reference angle of $\dfrac{\pi}{4}$ in quadrant III.

3. What is the exact value of $\sec(-330°)$?

   A. $-\dfrac{2}{\sqrt{3}}$

   B. $\dfrac{1}{2}$

   C. $\dfrac{1}{\sqrt{2}}$

   D. $\dfrac{2}{\sqrt{3}}$

4. If $\sin\theta = \dfrac{3}{8}$ and $\dfrac{\pi}{2} \le \theta \le \pi$, then the exact value of $\sec\theta + \tan\theta$ is

   A. $\dfrac{\sqrt{55}}{3}$

   B. $\dfrac{\sqrt{55}}{4}$

   C. $-\dfrac{\sqrt{55}}{5}$

   D. $\dfrac{8\sqrt{55}}{3}$

5. What is the exact value of $\cot\theta$, if $B(-2, -2)$ is on the terminal arm of angle θ in standard position?

   A. -1

   B. 0

   C. $\dfrac{1}{2}$

   D. 1

Use the following information to answer the next question.

The point $\left(\dfrac{\pi}{12}, 4\right)$ is on the graph of $y = 8\sin 2x$.

6. If the graph of $y = 8\sin 2x$ is transformed to the graph of $y = 8\sin 6x$, then the point $\left(\dfrac{\pi}{12}, 4\right)$ will be transformed to the point

   A. $\left(\dfrac{\pi}{36}, \dfrac{4}{3}\right)$

   B. $\left(\dfrac{\pi}{4}, 12\right)$

   C. $\left(\dfrac{\pi}{36}, 4\right)$

   D. $\left(\dfrac{\pi}{4}, 4\right)$

Copyright Protected

Not for Reproduction

Use the following information to answer the next question.

Four sound waves are modelled by the following graphs of trigonometric functions. The portion of each graph on the domain $0° \leq x \leq 360°$ is shown below.

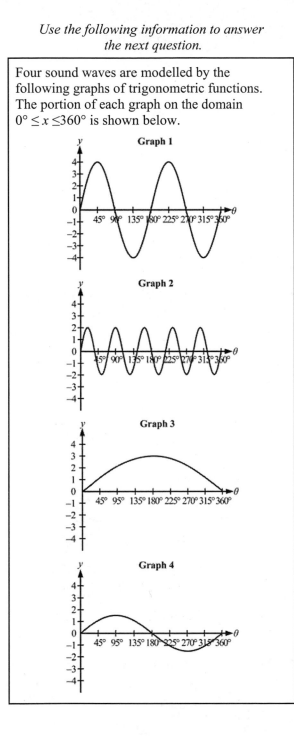

Graph 1

Graph 2

Graph 3

Graph 4

7. The louder a sound is, the greater the amplitude of its sound wave. Therefore, the graph above that corresponds to the loudest sound is

A. graph 1

B. graph 2

C. graph 3

D. graph 4

8. In the equation $5\sin(2x)+2=\cos(x)-1$, the number of solutions for x, where $0 \leq x < 2\pi$, is

A. 2

B. 3

C. 4

D. 5

9. What are the exact solutions to the equation $2\cos^2\theta = \cos\theta$, where $0 \leq \theta < \pi$?

A. $\dfrac{\pi}{6}$ and $\dfrac{\pi}{4}$

B. $\dfrac{\pi}{4}$ and $\dfrac{\pi}{3}$

C. $\dfrac{\pi}{2}$ and $\dfrac{\pi}{3}$

D. 0 and $\dfrac{\pi}{2}$

10. The graphs of $y = a\cos\theta$ and $y = 2$ intersect at $\theta = \dfrac{\pi}{3}$ and $\theta = \dfrac{5\pi}{3}$, where $0 \leq \theta \leq 2\pi$. The value of a in $y = a\cos\theta$ is

A. 0.25

B. 1

C. 2.3

D. 4

Use the following information to answer the next question.

Refraction describes the bending of light rays. Refraction can be calculated using the formula

$$n = \frac{\sin(\theta + \alpha)}{\sin\theta},$$

where n represents refraction.

11. If $\alpha = 30°$, then an equivalent expression for n is

A. $\dfrac{\sqrt{3}}{2} + \cos\theta$

B. $\dfrac{\sqrt{3}}{2} + \dfrac{1}{2}\cot\theta$

C. $\dfrac{\sqrt{3}}{2} + \dfrac{1}{2}\cos\theta$

D. $\dfrac{1}{2} + \dfrac{\sqrt{3}}{2}\cot\theta$

12. An equivalent expression for $\dfrac{(\sin x)(\cos x)}{\tan x}$ is

A. $\sin^2 x$

B. $\sin x$

C. $\cos^2 x$

D. $\cos x$

13. If $f(x) = (x+1)$ and $g(x) = \dfrac{(x+2)}{(x-2)}$, then $g[f(x)]$ equals

A. $\dfrac{x^2 + 3x + 3}{x - 2}$

B. $\dfrac{2x + 3}{2x - 1}$

C. $\dfrac{2x}{x - 2}$

D. $\dfrac{x + 3}{x - 1}$

14. Given $p(x) = \sin x$ and $q(x) = x - 2$, which of the following statements is **true**?

A. The functions $p(x)$ and $q(x)$ have the same range.

B. The functions $p(x)$ and $p(q(x))$ have the same range.

C. The functions $p(x)$ and $q(p(x))$ have the same range.

D. The functions $p(q(x))$ and $q(p(x))$ have the same range.

Use the following information to answer the next question.

The graph of $y = f(x)$ has a domain of $6 \le x \le 11$ and a range of $4 \le y \le 8$.

15. The domain and range of $y = f(x+6)$, respectively, are

A. $0 \le x \le 5$ and $4 \le y \le 8$

B. $6 \le x \le 11$ and $-2 \le y \le 2$

C. $6 \le x \le 11$ and $10 \le y \le 14$

D. $12 \le x \le 17$ and $4 \le y \le 8$

Copyright Protected

Not for Reproduction

Use the following information to answer the next question.

Two graphs are as shown. Graph 2 is a transformation of graph 1.

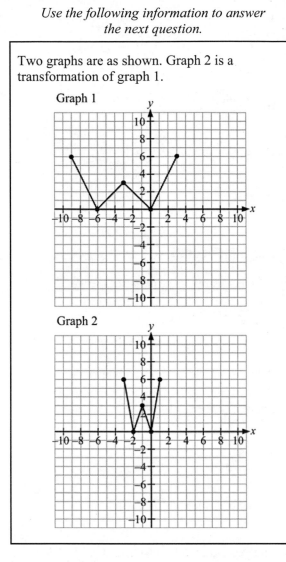

Graph 1

Graph 2

16. If the equation of graph 1 is $y = f(x)$, then the equation of graph 2 could be

   A. $y = f(3x)$

   B. $y = f\left(\dfrac{1}{3}x\right)$

   C. $y = 3f(x)$

   D. $y = \dfrac{1}{3}f(x)$

17. In order to vertically stretch the graph of the function $f(x) = \dfrac{1}{x}$ by a factor of 5 from the x-axis and then translate it 4 units horizontally left, the equation must be transformed into

   A. $g(x) = \dfrac{5}{x-4}$

   B. $g(x) = \dfrac{5}{x+4}$

   C. $g(x) = \dfrac{1}{5(x-4)}$

   D. $g(x) = \dfrac{1}{5(x+4)}$

18. A function $y = f(x)$ is graphed. If $g(x) = -f(x)$, then the graph of $y = g(x)$ is the same as the graph of

   A. $y = f(x)$ reflected in the line $y = x$

   B. $y = f(x)$ reflected in the y-axis

   C. $y = f(x)$ reflected in the x-axis

   D. the reciprocal of $y = f(x)$

Copyright Protected

Use the following information to answer the next question.

A relation, N, is defined by the following set of ordered pairs.

$$N:\{(4, y), (7, 8), (x, 6)\}$$

19. If both N and the inverse of N can be classified as functions, which of the following statements stating the value of an unknown variable is **false**?

A. The x variable cannot equal 4 or 7.

B. The y variable cannot equal 6 or 8.

C. The x variable can never equal the value of y.

D. The y variable can equal 4, and x can equal 6.

Use the following information to answer the next question.

The graph of a quadratic relation is given.

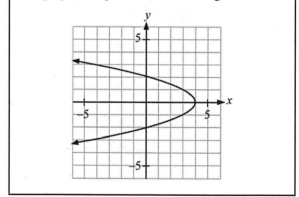

20. What are the domain and range of the inverse of the given quadratic relation?

A. The domain is $x \in R$, and the range is $y \le 4$.

B. The domain is $x \in R$, and the range is $y \ge 4$.

C. The domain is $x \le 4$, and the range is $y \in R$.

D. The domain is $x \ge 4$, and the range is $y \in R$.

21. The equation $y = 4^{3x}$ can also be written in logarithmic form as

A. $y = \dfrac{\log_3 x}{4}$

B. $y = \dfrac{\log_4 x}{3}$

C. $x = \dfrac{\log_3 y}{4}$

D. $x = \dfrac{\log_4 y}{3}$

Numerical Response

22. To the nearest hundredth, the value of $\dfrac{\log_{13} 200}{\log_{13} 6}$ is _____.

(Record your answer to **two** decimal places.)

23. If $\log_b x = l$, $\log_b y = m$, and $\log_b z = n$, the expression $l + m + n$, in terms of $x, y,$ and z, can be expressed as

A. xyz

B. $\log_b xyz$

C. $x + y + z$

D. $(\log_b x)(\log_b y)(\log_b z)$

24. The expression $2\log_a 5 + \log_a 6 - \dfrac{1}{3}\log_a 8$, $a > 0$, equals

A. $\log_a 29$

B. $\log_a 30$

C. $\log_a 75$

D. $\dfrac{8}{3}\log_a 3$

25. Which of the following graphs shows the inverse of the function $y = 3^x$?

A.

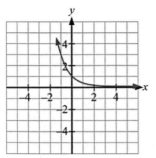

B.

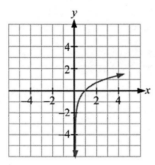

C.

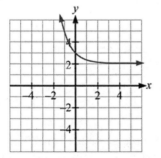

D.

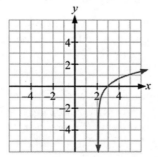

26. In 1996 a particular car was valued at $27500 and its value decreased exponentially each year afterward. For each of the first 7 years the value of the car decreased by 24% of the previous year's value. If t is the number of years and v is the value of the car, then the equation for the car's value when $t \leq 7$ is

A. $v = 27\ 500(1.76)^t$

B. $v = 27\ 500(1.24)^t$

C. $v = 27\ 500(0.76)^t$

D. $v = 27\ 500(0.24)^t$

27. If the factored form of $3x^3 - 2x^2 - 17x - 12$ is $(x-3)(x+1)(ax+b)$, then $(ax+b)$ is

A. $3x - 4$

B. $3x + 4$

C. $-3x + 4$

D. $-3x - 4$

28. A third-degree polynomial function is given by $P(x) = (x-2)(x+3)(x+4)$. If another polynomial function $Q(x) = kP(x)$, $k > 1$, then the graph of $y = Q(x)$ must have

A. a y-intercept that is less than -24

B. a y-intercept that is greater than -24

C. k more x-intercepts than the graph of $P(x)$

D. x-intercepts different from those of the graph of $P(x)$

Copyright Protected

Use the following information to answer the next question.

Lilia is designing a new chocolate-coated ice cream confection. She dips a cylindrical block of ice cream that has a radius of 3.3 cm and a height of 8.6 cm into chocolate to create an even coating surrounding the entire block of ice cream. The volume of the finished confection is 110.25π cm^3.

29. If the volume of a cylinder is calculated using the formula $V = \pi r^2 h$, what is the thickness of the chocolate used to coat the ice cream?

    A. 0.12 cm

    B. 0.20 cm

    C. 0.23 cm

    D. 0.30 cm

30. If the function $y = \sqrt{7x - 1}$ is written in the form $y = a\sqrt{x - c}$, what is the vertical stretch factor?

    A. $\sqrt{\dfrac{1}{7}}$

    B. $\sqrt{7}$

    C. $\dfrac{1}{7}$

    D. 7

31. The equation of the horizontal asymptote for the graph of $y = \dfrac{6x^2}{4 - 2x^2}$ is

    A. $y = 3$

    B. $y = \dfrac{3}{2}$

    C. $y = -\dfrac{3}{2}$

    D. $y = -3$

32. The number of 4-digit codes that either end with an even digit or consist of only odd digits is

    A. 1 250

    B. 3 125

    C. 5 625

    D. 9 000

Use the following information to answer the next question.

There are 6 friends running in a 5 km race. Terry finished first, Lee was second, and Clark was third. Steve, Jay, and Vince are still running

33. In how many different orders can the race finish?

    A. $6! \times 5! \times 4! \times 3! \times 2! \times 1!$

    B. $6 \times 5 \times 4 \times 3 \times 2 \times 1$

    C. $3 \times 2 \times 1$

    D. $3! \times 2! \times 1!$

34. Which of the following problems can **best** be classified as a combination problem?

    A. Determining the number of different bouquets of 12 flowers that can be made using up to 5 types of flowers

    B. Calculating the number of different assignments of gold, silver, and bronze medalists from 9 competitors

    C. Determining the number of different school committees of 1 vice-principal, 2 teachers, and 3 students from 2 vice-principals, 6 teachers, and 8 students

    D. Calculating the number of different 2-topping pizzas that can be created from 12 toppings if the first topping is a type of sauce and the second is a vegetable

35. The students in a music department have practised 6 contemporary and 5 traditional choruses. For their concert, they will choose a program in which they present 4 of the contemporary and 3 of the traditional choruses. How many different programs can be presented, if the order of the choruses does **not** matter?

   A. 25

   B. 35

   C. 150

   D. 330

36. The sum of the terms in the sixth row of Pascal's triangle is

   A. 16

   B. 32

   C. 64

   D. 96

37. In the expansion of $(a+b)^{10}$, the numerical coefficient of a^7b^3 is _____.
   (Record your answer as a **whole** number.)

Copyright Protected

ANSWERS AND SOLUTIONS—PRACTICE TEST 1

1. C	9. C	17. B	25. B	33. C
2. C	10. D	18. C	26. C	34. A
3. D	11. B	19. C	27. B	35. C
4. C	12. C	20. A	28. A	36. B
5. D	13. D	21. D	29. B	37. 120
6. C	14. B	22. 2.96	30. B	
7. A	15. A	23. B	31. D	
8. C	16. A	24. C	32. C	

1. C

Step 1
Convert 250° to radians.

Multiply the angle in degrees by $\dfrac{\pi \, \text{rad}}{180°}$.

$$250° \times \frac{\pi \, \text{rad}}{180°}$$
$$= \frac{250\pi}{180} \text{rad}$$
$$= \frac{25\pi}{18} \text{rad}$$

Step 2
Determine which of the given angles is coterminal with angle $\dfrac{25\pi}{18}$ rad .

For any angle, θ, measured in radians, all angles of the form $(\theta + 2\pi n)$ rad, where $n \in I$, will be coterminal with angle θ .

To find an angle coterminal with $\dfrac{25\pi}{18}$ rad , let

$n = 3$ and $\theta = \dfrac{25\pi}{18}$.

$$(\theta + 2\pi n)$$
$$= \frac{25\pi}{18} + 2\pi(3)$$
$$= \frac{25\pi}{18} + 6\pi$$
$$= \frac{25\pi}{18} + \frac{108\pi}{18}$$
$$= \frac{133\pi}{18} \text{ rad}$$

2. C

The angle $\dfrac{4\pi}{3}$ rad terminates in quadrant III and is

$\dfrac{\pi}{3}$ rad greater than π . Thus, $\dfrac{4\pi}{3}$ rad has a

reference angle of $\dfrac{\pi}{3}$. Therefore, the exact value

of $\sin\left(\dfrac{4\pi}{3}\right)$ can be determined by finding the sine

ratio of the reference angle of $\dfrac{\pi}{3}$ in quadrant III.

3. D

The angle –330° terminates in quadrant I, and the reference angle is 30°. On the unit circle,

$\sec\theta = \dfrac{1}{x}$, and the angle 30° corresponds to the

point $\left(\dfrac{\sqrt{3}}{2}, \dfrac{1}{2}\right)$. Therefore, the exact value of

$\sec(-330)°$ is $\dfrac{1}{\dfrac{\sqrt{3}}{2}} = \dfrac{2}{\sqrt{3}}$.

4. C

Since $\sin\theta = \dfrac{y}{r}$, and it is given that $\sin\theta = \dfrac{3}{8}$, possible values of y and r are $y = 3$ and $r = 8$.

The restriction $\dfrac{\pi}{2} \le \theta \le \pi$ implies that θ is in quadrant II.

Step 1
Determine the value of x using the Pythagorean theorem.
$$x^2 + y^2 = r^2$$
$$x^2 + 3^2 = 8^2$$
$$x^2 + 9 = 64$$
$$x^2 = 55$$
$$x^2 = \pm\sqrt{55}$$

Since θ is in quadrant II, the value of x is negative. Thus, $x = -\sqrt{55}$.

Step 2
Determine the exact value of $\sec\theta + \tan\theta$.

Since $\sec\theta = \dfrac{r}{x}$ and $\tan\theta = \dfrac{y}{x}$, the value of $\sec\theta + \tan\theta$ is determined as follows:
$$\sec\theta + \tan\theta$$
$$= \dfrac{r}{x} + \dfrac{y}{x}$$
$$= \dfrac{8}{-\sqrt{55}} + \dfrac{3}{-\sqrt{55}}$$
$$= -\dfrac{11}{\sqrt{55}}$$
$$= -\dfrac{11\sqrt{55}}{55}$$
$$= -\dfrac{\sqrt{55}}{5}$$

5. D

Since $\cot\theta = \dfrac{x}{y}$, and it is given that $B(-2, -2)$ is on the terminal arm of angle θ, $\cot\theta = \dfrac{-2}{-2} = 1$.

6. C

Step 1
Determine the change in the horizontal stretch factor about the y-axis that the graph of $y = 8\sin 2x$ undergoes when it is transformed to the graph of $y = 8\sin 6x$.

The horizontal stretch factor for the graph of the function $y = a\sin\big[b(x-c)\big] + d$ is $\dfrac{1}{|b|}$.

The horizontal stretch factor for the graph of $y = 8\sin 2x$ is $\dfrac{1}{2}$, and for the graph of $y = 8\sin 6x$, it is $\dfrac{1}{6}$.

Therefore, the change is $\dfrac{1}{6} \div \dfrac{1}{2} = \dfrac{1}{3}$.

Step 2
Determine the effect on the point $\left(\dfrac{\pi}{12}, 4\right)$ when it undergoes the transformation.

The horizontal stretch factor affects the x-coordinates of the points of the original graph.

Since the change in the horizontal stretch factor is $\dfrac{1}{3}$, the x-coordinate of the point $\left(\dfrac{\pi}{12}, 4\right)$ will transform to $\dfrac{\pi}{12} \times \dfrac{1}{3} = \dfrac{\pi}{36}$, resulting in the new point $\left(\dfrac{\pi}{36}, 4\right)$.

7. A

Since amplitude is the distance from the maximum or minimum value of the wave to the horizontal midline axis of the wave, the graphs have the following amplitudes:

Graph 1 has an amplitude of 4.

Graph 2 has an amplitude of 2.

Graph 3 has an amplitude of 3.

Graph 4 has an amplitude of about 1.5.

The louder the sound, the greater the amplitude of its sound wave. Therefore, graph 1 corresponds to the loudest sound.

8. C

To determine the solution of an equation in the form $f(x) = g(x)$, graph each side of the function on a TI-83 or similar calculator, and count the number of intersection points within the domain $0 \le \theta < 2\pi$.

Press $\boxed{Y=}$, enter the equation as two separate functions ($Y_1 = 5\sin(2X) + 2$ and $Y_2 = \cos(X) - 1$), and press $\boxed{GRAPH}$.

An appropriate window setting is $x : \left[0, 2\pi, \dfrac{\pi}{3}\right]$ and $y : [-4, 10, 1]$.

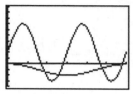

There are 4 points of intersection. Therefore, there are 4 solutions for the equation.

9. C

Step 1
Subtract $\cos\theta$ from both sides.
$$2\cos^2\theta = \cos\theta$$
$$2\cos^2\theta - \cos\theta = 0$$

Step 2
Factor the equation, and apply the zero product property to each factor.
$$2\cos^2\theta - \cos\theta = 0$$
$$\cos\theta(2\cos\theta - 1) = 0$$
$$\cos\theta = 0 \qquad 2\cos\theta - 1 = 0$$
$$2\cos\theta = 1$$
$$\cos\theta = \frac{1}{2}$$

Step 3
Determine the values for θ, where $0 \le \theta < \pi$. Using the unit circle, the value of θ in the equation $\cos\theta = 0$ is $\dfrac{\pi}{2}$. The value of θ in the equation $\cos\theta = \dfrac{1}{2}$ is $\dfrac{\pi}{3}$. Therefore, the solutions are $\theta = \dfrac{\pi}{2}$ and $\dfrac{\pi}{3}$.

10. D

The graph of $y = a\cos\theta$ intersects the graph of $y = 2$ at $\theta = \dfrac{\pi}{3}$ and $\theta = \dfrac{5\pi}{3}$. Therefore, $\theta = \dfrac{\pi}{3}$ and $\theta = \dfrac{5\pi}{3}$ are solutions to the equation $2 = a\cos\theta$.

Substitute $\dfrac{\pi}{3}$ for θ in the equation $2 = a\cos\theta$, and solve for a.
$$y = a\cos\theta$$
$$2 = a\cos\left(\frac{\pi}{3}\right)$$
$$2 = a(0.5)$$
$$\frac{2}{0.5} = a$$
$$4 = a$$

Note: You can use the same method with the values of $\dfrac{5\pi}{3}$ for θ and 2 for y.
$$y = a\cos\theta$$
$$2 = a\cos\left(\frac{5\pi}{3}\right)$$
$$2 = a(0.5)$$
$$\frac{2}{0.5} = a$$
$$4 = a$$

11. B

Step 1
In the equation $n = \dfrac{\sin(\theta + \alpha)}{\sin\theta}$, substitute 30° for α.
$$n = \frac{\sin(\theta + \alpha)}{\sin\theta}$$
$$n = \frac{\sin(\theta + 30°)}{\sin\theta}$$

Step 2
Apply the sum identity, $\sin(A + B) = \sin A\cos B + \cos A\sin B$.
$$n = \frac{\sin(\theta + 30°)}{\sin\theta}$$
$$n = \frac{\sin\theta\cos 30° + \cos\theta\sin 30°}{\sin\theta}$$

Step 3
Divide each term in the numerator by the denominator, and simplify.

$$n = \frac{\sin\theta\cos 30° + \cos\theta\sin 30°}{\sin\theta}$$

$$n = \frac{\sin\theta\cos 30°}{\sin\theta} + \frac{\cos\theta\sin 30°}{\sin\theta}$$

$$n = \cos 30° + \frac{\cos\theta\sin 30°}{\sin\theta}$$

Step 4

Apply the quotient identity, $\cot\theta = \dfrac{\cos\theta}{\sin\theta}$.

$$n = \cos 30° + \frac{\cos\theta\sin 30°}{\sin\theta}$$

$$n = \cos 30° + \cot\theta\sin 30°$$

Step 5
Evaluate cos30° and sin30°.
$$n = \cos 30° + \cot\theta\sin 30°$$

$$n = \frac{\sqrt{3}}{2} + \cot\theta\left(\frac{1}{2}\right)$$

$$n = \frac{\sqrt{3}}{2} + \frac{1}{2}\cot\theta$$

12. C

Step 1

Let $\tan x = \dfrac{\sin x}{\cos x}$ in the given expression.

$$\frac{(\sin x)(\cos x)}{\tan x}$$

$$= \frac{(\sin x)(\cos x)}{\left(\dfrac{\sin x}{\cos x}\right)}$$

Step 2
Simplify the expression.

$$\frac{(\sin x)(\cos x)}{\left(\dfrac{\sin x}{\cos x}\right)}$$

$$= (\sin x)(\cos x)\left(\frac{\cos x}{\sin x}\right)$$

$$= (\cos x)(\cos x)$$

$$= \cos^2 x$$

13. D

Step 1
Replace x in $g(x)$ with the function $f(x)$.

$$g(x) = \frac{(x+2)}{(x-2)}$$

$$g[f(x)] = \frac{((x+1)+2)}{((x+1)-2)}$$

Step 2
Simplify.

$$g[f(x)] = \frac{((x+1)+2)}{((x+1)-2)}$$

$$g[f(x)] = \frac{x+1+2}{x+1-2}$$

$$g[f(x)] = \frac{x+3}{x-1}$$

Therefore, $g[f(x)] = \dfrac{x+3}{x-1}$.

14. B

Step 1
Compare the ranges of $p(x)$ and $q(x)$.

The function $p(x) = \sin x$ is a trigonometric function with a range of $-1 \leq y \leq 1$. The function $q(x) = x - 2$ is a linear function with a range of $y \in R$.

The two functions do not have the same range.

Step 2
Determine $p(q(x))$ and $q(p(x))$.

$$p(q(x))$$
$$= p(x-2)$$
$$= \sin(x-2)$$

$$q(p(x))$$
$$= q(\sin x)$$
$$= \sin x - 2$$

Copyright Protected

Step 3

Compare the ranges of the three functions $p(x)$, $p(q(x))$, and $q(p(x))$.

You can interpret the graph of $p(q(x)) = \sin(x-2)$ as the graph of $y = \sin x$ with a horizontal phase shift of 2 units right. Its range is $-1 \le y \le 1$.

The graph of $q(p(x)) = \sin x - 2$ is the graph of $y = \sin x$ with a vertical translation of 2 units down. Its range is $-3 \le y \le -1$.

The functions $p(x) = \sin x$ and $p(q(x)) = \sin(x-2)$ have the same range.

15. A

The domain of the graph of $y = f(x-h)$ will be $(m+h) \le x \le (n+h)$, where $m \le x \le n$ is the domain of $y = f(x)$. The value of h is -6 because $y = f(x+6)$ is equivalent to $y = f(x-(-6))$.

The domain of $y = f(x+6)$ is $(6-6) \le x \le (11-6)$, or $0 \le x \le 5$.

Since the y-coordinates have not changed, the range of the translated graph will not change. The range is $4 \le y \le 8$.

16. A

Step 1

Identify appropriate points on graph 1.

Possible points on graph 1 include $(-9, 6)$, $(-6, 0)$, $(-3, 3)$, $(0, 0)$, and $(3, 6)$.

Step 2

For each of the points $(-9, 6)$, $(-6, 0)$, $(-3, 3)$, $(0, 0)$, and $(3, 6)$, identify the possible corresponding points on graph 2.

Point $(-9, 6)$ can correspond to point $(-3, 6)$, point $(-6, 0)$ corresponds to point $(-2, 0)$, point $(-3, 3)$ corresponds to point $(-1, 3)$, point $(0, 0)$ corresponds to point $(0, 0)$, and point $(3, 6)$ corresponds to point $(1, 6)$.

Step 3

Determine how each transformed point can be obtained from the corresponding point on graph 1.

Notice that the y-coordinate of any point on graph 2 is the same as the y-coordinate of the corresponding point on graph 1. Also, notice that the x-coordinate of any point on graph 2 is $\frac{1}{3}$ the x-coordinate of the corresponding point. Point (x, y) on graph 1 is transformed to point $\left(\frac{1}{3}x, y\right)$ on graph 2.

Step 4

Determine a possible equation for graph 2.

Since point (x, y) on graph 1 is transformed to point $\left(\frac{1}{3}x, y\right)$ on graph 2, graph 2 is obtained by horizontally stretching graph 1 about the y-axis by a factor of $\frac{1}{3}$. The equation of graph 2 can be arrived at by substituting $3x$ for x (the reciprocal of $\frac{1}{3}$ is 3) in the equation $y = f(x)$. Thus, a possible equation of graph 2 is $y = f(3x)$.

17. B

Step 1

Apply the vertical stretch.

Since the graph of $y = f(x) = \frac{1}{x}$ is vertically stretched by a factor of 5, replace y with $\frac{1}{5}y$ in $y = \frac{1}{x}$.

$$y = \frac{1}{x}$$
$$\frac{1}{5}y = \frac{1}{x}$$

Not for Reproduction

Step 2
Apply the horizontal translation.

Since the graph of $y = \dfrac{1}{x}$ is translated 4 units left,

replace x in $\dfrac{1}{5}y = \dfrac{1}{x}$ with $x + 4$.

$$\frac{1}{5}y = \frac{1}{x}$$
$$\frac{1}{5}y = \frac{1}{x+4}$$

Step 3
Isolate y.
$$\frac{1}{5}y = \frac{1}{x+4}$$
$$y = \frac{5}{x+4}$$

Therefore, the equation of $g(x)$ is $g(x) = \dfrac{5}{x+4}$.

18. C

If $g(x) = -f(x)$, then positive y-values become negative, and negative y-values become positive under the transformation. This happens only when the function is reflected in the x-axis.

19. C

Step 1
Write the inverse of function N.

The inverse of function N is obtained by interchanging the values in the ordered pairs of function N. Therefore, the inverse of function N, N', is $N' : \{(y, 4), (8, 7), (6, x)\}$.

Step 2
Determine whether the statement "The x-variable cannot equal 4 or 7" is true.

In order for N to be classified as a function, the first component of each ordered pair in function N must be different. Therefore, the value of x cannot be 4 or 7. The statement is true.

Step 3
Determine whether the statement "The y-variable cannot equal 6 or 8" is true.

In order for the inverse of function N to be classified as a function, the first component of each of its ordered pairs must be different. Therefore, the value of y cannot be 6 or 8. The statement is true.

Step 4
The statement "The x-variable can never equal the value of y" is false. There are a few values where the value of x cannot equal the value of y. For example, when $x = y = 8$ or $x = y = 4$. However, there are an infinite number of values where the value of x can equal the value of y. For example, when $x = y = 2$ or $x = y = 5$.

Step 5
Determine whether the statement "The y-variable can equal 4, and x can equal 6" is true.

If $x = 6$, and $x = 4$, then N and N' are as follows:
$$N : \{(4, 4), (7, 8), (6, 6)\}$$
$$N' : \{(4, 4), (8, 7), (6, 6)\}$$

For the given values of x and y, both N and N' can be classified as functions. Therefore the statement is true.

20. A

Step 1
Determine the domain of the inverse relation.

The range of the given relation is $y \in R$.
Therefore, the domain of the inverse becomes $x \in R$.

Step 2
Determine the range of the inverse relation.

The domain of the given relation is $x \le 4$.
Therefore, the range of the inverse becomes $y \le 4$.

21. D

Step 1
Write $y = 4^{3x}$ in logarithmic form.

An exponential equation in the form $y = b^x$ is written in logarithmic form as $x = \log_b y$.

Therefore, $y = 4^{3x}$ is written in logarithmic form as $3x = \log_4 y$.

Step 2
Isolate x.
$$3x = \log_4 y$$
$$x = \frac{\log_4 y}{3}$$

Therefore, $y = 4^{3x}$ is written in logarithmic form as $x = \dfrac{\log_4 y}{3}$.

22. 2.96

Step 1

Apply the change of base rule, $\log_b a = \dfrac{\log_c a}{\log_c b}$, in reverse.

$$\dfrac{\log_{13} 200}{\log_{13} 6} = \log_6 200$$

Step 2

Apply the change of base rule again to $\log_6 200$, changing the base to base 10.

$$\log_6 200 = \dfrac{\log 200}{\log 6}$$

Step 3

Use a calculator to evaluate, and round to the nearest hundredth.

$$\dfrac{\log 200}{\log 6} \approx 2.96$$

23. B

Step 1

Substitute $\log_b x$ for l, $\log_b y$ for m, and $\log_b z$ for n in the expression $l + m + n$.

$$l + m + n = \log_b x + \log_b y + \log_b z$$

Step 2

Apply the product law of logarithms.

$$l + m + n = \log_b xyz$$

Therefore, the expression $l + m + n$ can be expressed as $\log_b xyz$.

24. C

Step 1

Apply the power law of logarithms to the first and last terms in the expression.

$$2\log_a 5 + \log_a 6 - \dfrac{1}{3}\log_a 8$$

$$= \log_a 5^2 + \log_a 6 - \log_a 8^{\frac{1}{3}}$$

Step 2

In the expression $\log_a 5^2 + \log_a 6 - \log_a 8^{\frac{1}{3}}$, apply the product law of logarithms to combine the first and second terms.

$$\log_a 5^2 + \log_a 6 - \log_a 8^{\frac{1}{3}}$$

$$= \log_a \left(5^2 \times 6\right) - \log_a 8^{\frac{1}{3}}$$

$$= \log_a \left(25 \times 6\right) - \log_a 8^{\frac{1}{3}}$$

Step 3

Apply the quotient law of logarithms.

$$\log_a \left(25 \times 6\right) - \log_a 8^{\frac{1}{3}} = \log_a \left(\dfrac{25 \times 6}{8^{\frac{1}{3}}}\right)$$

Step 4

Evaluate the terms in the brackets.

$$\log_a \left(\dfrac{25 \times 6}{8^{\frac{1}{3}}}\right)$$

$$= \log_a \left(\dfrac{25 \times 6}{2}\right)$$

$$= \log_a 75$$

25. B

A sketch of the graph of $y = 3^x$ is shown.

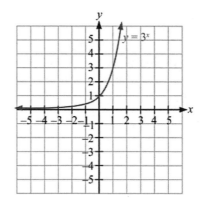

Copyright Protected

Not for Reproduction

The inverse of this function is formed by reflecting the graph of $y = 3^x$ in the line $y = x$, as shown.

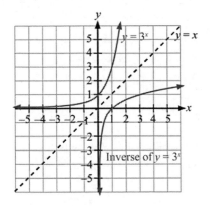

26. C

Use the formula $v_t = a(r)^t$, where v is the value of the car after t years, a is the initial value, and r is the rate of depreciation.

Step 1
Define the variables that have values given in the problem.

The car's value decreases by 24% each year. This means that each year, the car's value decreases by 24%. The value of r is 0.24 less than 1, or $1 - 0.24 = 0.76$.

The initial value of the car was $27 500, so $a = 27\ 500$.

Step 2
Substitute the values $a = 27\ 500$ and $r = 0.76$ into the formula $v_t = a(r)^t$.

$$v_t = a(r)^t$$
$$v_t = 27\ 500(0.76)^t$$

27. B

Fully factor the polynomial $3x^3 - 2x^2 - 17x - 12$.

Step 1
Divide $3x^3 - 2x^2 - 17x - 12$ by one of the given factors.

You can use synthetic division or long division.

$$
\require{enclose}
\begin{array}{r}
3x^2 - 7x + 4 \\
x - 3 \enclose{longdiv}{3x^3 - 2x^2 - 17x - 12} \\
\underline{3x^3 - 9x^2} \\
7x^2 - 17x \\
\underline{7x^2 - 21x} \\
4x - 12 \\
\underline{4x - 12} \\
0
\end{array}
$$

Step 2
Factor the quotient $3x^2 + 7x + 4$.
$$3x^2 + 7x + 4$$
$$= 3x^2 + 3x + 4x + 4$$
$$= 3x(x + 1) + 4(x + 1)$$
$$= (x + 1)(3x + 4)$$

Step 3
Rewrite the given polynomial in factored form.
$$3x^3 - 2x^2 - 17x - 12$$
$$= (x - 3)(x + 1)(3x + 4)$$

From the factored form, it can be seen that $ax + b = 3x + 4$.

28. A

Step 1
Determine how to obtain the graph of $y = kP(x)$ from the graph of $y = P(x)$.

The equation $y = kP(x)$ is in the form $y = af(x)$, where $a = k$. Therefore, the graph of $y = kP(x)$ is formed from $y = P(x)$ by a vertical stretch factor of k.

Step 2
Determine the change to the x-intercepts.

Every point (x, y) on the graph of $P(x)$ will be transformed to the point (x, ky) on the graph of $Q(x)$. This means that the x-intercepts of $Q(x)$ are the same as the x-intercepts of $P(x)$.

Step 3
Determine the change to the *y*-intercept.

The *y*-intercept of $P(x)$ is determined by substituting $x = 0$ into the function.
$$P(x) = (x-2)(x+3)(x+4)$$
$$P(0) = (0-2)(0+3)(0+4)$$
$$P(0) = (-2)(3)(4)$$
$$P(0) = -24$$

The *y*-intercept of $P(x)$ is $(0, -24)$, so the *y*-intercept of $Q(x)$ is $(0, -24k)$. Since $k > 1$, any value of $24k$ must be less than -24.

Therefore, the graph of $y = Q(x)$ must have a *y*-intercept that is less than -24.

29. **B**

Step 1
Identify the variable.

Let *x* equal the thickness of the outer chocolate coating.

Step 2
Draw a diagram.

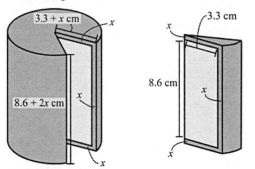

The radius of the entire confection is $3.3 + x$, and the height is $8.6 + 2x$ since there is a layer of chocolate surrounding the outside, top, and bottom of the ice cream.

Step 3
Write an equation for the volume of the confection.
$$V = \pi r^2 h$$
$$110.25\pi = \pi (3.3 + x)^2 (8.6 + 2x)$$

The equation can be simplified by dividing both sides by the factor π.
$$110.25\pi = \pi (3.3 + x)^2 (8.6 + 2x)$$
$$110.25 = (3.3 + x)^2 (8.6 + 2x)$$

Step 4
Graph the related function on a TI-83 or similar calculator.

To identify the related function, subtract 110.25 from both sides of the volume equation.
$$110.25 = (3.3 + x)^2 (8.6 + 2x)$$
$$0 = (3.3 + x)^2 (8.6 + 2x) - 110.25$$

Press $\boxed{\text{Y=}}$, and input the equation as $Y_1 = (3.3 + X)^2(8.6 + 2X) - 110.25$.

You can use the window settings of $x : [-1, 1\ 1]$ and $y : [-10, 10, 1]$. Press $\boxed{\text{GRAPH}}$ to obtain this window.

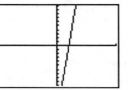

The thickness, *x*, corresponds to the *x*-intercept.

Step 5
Determine the zero of the graph.

Press $\boxed{\text{2nd}}$ $\boxed{\text{TRACE}}$, and select 2:zero.

When asked for a left bound, move the cursor to the left of the *x*-intercept, and press $\boxed{\text{ENTER}}$. When asked for the right bound, move the cursor to the right of the zero, and press $\boxed{\text{ENTER}}$.

Press $\boxed{\text{ENTER}}$ after the "Guess?" prompt.

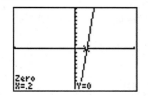

The *x*-intercept occurs at $x = 0.2$.

Therefore, the thickness of the chocolate used to coat the ice cream confection is 0.20 cm.

Not for Reproduction

30. B

Step 1

Factor b out of $bx - c$.

$$y = \sqrt{7x - 1}$$

$$y = \sqrt{7\left(x - \frac{1}{7}\right)}$$

Step 2

Simplify b out of the radicand.

$$y = \sqrt{7\left(x - \frac{1}{7}\right)}$$

$$y = \sqrt{7}\sqrt{x - \frac{1}{7}}$$

The function $y = \sqrt{7x - 1}$ written in the form

$y = a\sqrt{x - c}$ is $y = \sqrt{7}\sqrt{x - \frac{1}{7}}$. The vertical

stretch factor is equal to the value of a, which

is $\sqrt{7}$.

31. D

Step 1

Determine the degree of the numerator and the denominator.

The degree of the numerator, $6x^2$, is 2. The degree of the denominator, $4 - 2x^2$, is 2.

Step 2

Determine the equation for the horizontal asymptote.

Since the degrees of the numerator and the denominator are equal, the horizontal asymptote

occurs at $y = \frac{a}{b}$, where a and b are the leading

coefficients of the numerator and denominator, respectively.

$$y = \frac{a}{b}$$

$$y = \frac{6}{-2}$$

$$y = -3$$

32. C

Step 1

Determine the number of 4-digit codes that end with an even digit.

Since there are 5 even digits (0, 2, 4, 6, and 8), there are 5 ways to pick the last digit.

The other three positions can be any number from 0 to 9. Therefore, there are 10 ways to pick each of the three digits.

By the fundamental counting principle, the number of 4-digit codes that end with an even digit is $10 \times 10 \times 10 \times 5 = 5\,000$.

Step 2

Determine how many 4-digit codes consist of only odd digits.

Since there are 5 odd digits (1, 3, 5, 7, and 9), there are 5 ways to pick each of the four positions.

By the fundamental counting principle, the number of 4-digit codes consisting of odd digits only is $5 \times 5 \times 5 \times 5 = 625$.

Step 3

Determine the total number of possible 4-digit codes.

The total number of 4-digit arrangements that either end with an even digit or consist of only odd digits is determined by adding the two possibilities together. Therefore, the total number of arrangements is $5\,000 + 625 = 5\,625$.

33. C

In general, $n \times (n-1) \times (n-2) \times \ldots \times 2 \times 1 = n!$

represents the number of permutations of n distinct objects. Since the first three positions have already been determined, the solution needs to consider only how the last three runners could finish. Therefore, the race can finish in $3 \times 2 \times 1$, or $3!$, different orders.

Copyright Protected

34. A

Combinations are used when the order in which the objects are selected does not matter.

The order in which 12 flowers are selected for a 5-flower bouquet does not affect the formation of the bouquet. Therefore, this problem can be solved using combinations.

The other three problems are permutation problems. The order in which the members of the committee are selected matters because it will change the group. The assignment of gold, silver, and bronze medalists is a problem in which a different order results in a different outcome. The order in which two toppings are selected matters because the sauce must come before the type of vegetable topping.

35. C

Since the order of the choruses does not matter, this is a combination problem.

Step 1
Calculate the number of combinations of contemporary choruses.

The students must choose 4 contemporary choruses from the 6 they have practised.

$$_6C_4 = \frac{6!}{4!(6-4)!}$$
$$= \frac{6!}{4!2!}$$
$$= 15$$

Step 2
Calculate the number of combinations of traditional choruses.

The students must choose 3 traditional choruses from the 5 they have practised.

$$_5C_3 = \frac{5!}{3!(5-3)!}$$
$$= \frac{5!}{3!2!}$$
$$= 10$$

Step 3
Calculate the total number of programs that can be presented.

There are 15 possible combinations of contemporary choruses and 10 possible combinations of traditional choruses.

Applying the fundamental counting principle, there are $15 \times 10 = 150$ possible programs.

36. B

The terms in the sixth row correspond to the coefficients to the expansion $(x+y)^5$.

These coefficients are $_5C_0$, $_5C_1$, $_5C_2$, $_5C_3$, $_5C_4$, and $_5C_5$. The sum of the coefficients is 32.

37. 120

Step 1
Determine the general term of $(a+b)^{10}$.

In the formula $t_{k+1} = {}_nC_k x^{n-k} y^k$, let $x = a, y = b$, and $n = 10$.
$$t_{k+1} = {}_nC_k x^{n-k} y^k$$
$$t_{k+1} = {}_{10}C_k a^{10-k} b^k$$

Step 2
Determine the value of k.

Since the numerical coefficient of $a^7 b^3$ is required, then the value of k must be 3.

Step 3
In the general term, let $k = 3$, and simplify.
$$t_{3+1} = {}_{10}C_3 x^{10-3} y^3$$
$$t_4 = 120 x^7 y^3$$

The numerical coefficient is 120.

Not for Reproduction

PRACTICE TEST 2

The angle, θ, subtends an arc length of 33.5 units. The measurement of θ is $\dfrac{8\pi}{9}$ rad.

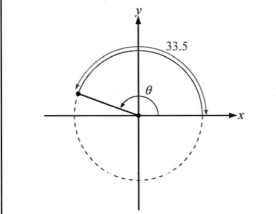

1. If the value of θ is $\dfrac{8\pi}{9}$ rad, what is the length of the terminal arm of angle θ?

A. 4.8 units

B. 12.0 units

C. 29.8 units

D. 32.7 units

2. What is the exact value of $\cot 480°$?

A. $-\dfrac{\sqrt{3}}{2}$

B. $-\dfrac{1}{\sqrt{3}}$

C. $\sqrt{3}$

D. $\dfrac{2}{\sqrt{3}}$

3. If angle θ terminates in quadrant II and has a reference angle of 45°, what is the value of $\cos\theta$?

A. $-\dfrac{\sqrt{3}}{3}$

B. $-\dfrac{\sqrt{2}}{2}$

C. $\dfrac{\sqrt{2}}{2}$

D. $\dfrac{\sqrt{3}}{2}$

4. The exact value of $\tan^{-1}\left(\sqrt{3}\right) - \tan^{-1}\left(\dfrac{1}{\sqrt{3}}\right)$ in radians is

A. $-\dfrac{3\pi}{2}$

B. $-\dfrac{\pi}{6}$

C. $\dfrac{\pi}{6}$

D. $\dfrac{\pi}{2}$

5. The graph of $y = 3\cos\left(\theta + \dfrac{1}{3}\right) + 2$ is the graph of $y = 3\cos\theta$ translated

A. $\dfrac{1}{3}$ radian right and 2 units up

B. $\dfrac{1}{3}$ radian left and 2 units up

C. $\dfrac{\pi}{3}$ radian right and 2 units up

D. $\dfrac{\pi}{3}$ radian left and 2 units down

Use the following information to answer the next question.

The function $h(t) = 14\sin\left(\dfrac{\pi}{20}(t-10)\right) + 15$

describes the height above the ground, h, in metres, of a particular seat on a ferris wheel t seconds after the ride begins.

6. The length of time it takes for the ferris wheel to make one complete revolution is

A. $\dfrac{\pi}{20}$ s

B. 12 s

C. 10π s

D. 40 s

Use the following information to answer the next question.

A stone is stuck in the tread of the back tire of a bicycle. The given graph represents the height, h, in centimetres of the stone relative to the ground with respect to the angle, x, in degrees through which the tire is rotating.

Motion of Stone in Tire Tread

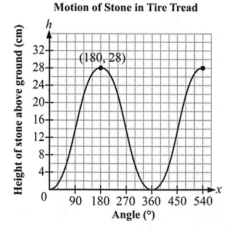

The cosine function that corresponds to the graph of the height of the stone, h, in terms of the angle of rotation, x, is $h = -a\cos x + 14$.

7. The radius of the bicycle tire is

A. 14 cm

B. 16 cm

C. 18 cm

D. 28 cm

8. If $\sin\theta - \cos\theta = 0$, $0 \le \theta \le 2\pi$, then the values of θ are

A. $\dfrac{\pi}{4}$ and $\dfrac{5\pi}{4}$

B. $\dfrac{\pi}{4}$ and $\dfrac{3\pi}{4}$

C. $\dfrac{3\pi}{4}$ and $\dfrac{5\pi}{4}$

D. $\dfrac{5\pi}{4}$ and $\dfrac{7\pi}{4}$

9. If the general solution for $\tan\theta - 1 = 0$ is $\theta = (a + bn)°$, then the value of $a + b$ is

A. 180   B. 210

C. 225   D. 330

10. The vertical asymptotes for the function $y = \tan x$ are given by

A. $x = \pi n$, $n \in I$

B. $x = 2\pi n$, $n \in I$

C. $x = \dfrac{\pi}{2} + \pi n$, $n \in I$

D. $x = \dfrac{\pi}{2} + 2\pi n$, $n \in I$

Numerical Response

11. If $x\cos^2\left(\dfrac{\pi}{8}\right) - x\sin^2\left(\dfrac{\pi}{8}\right) = 5\sqrt{2}$, then the value of x is _____.

(Record your answer as a **whole** number.)

Not for Reproduction

12. If $f(x) = 2x - 15$ and $g(x) = 4x^2 + x - 2$, then $f(x) + g(x)$ is equal to

　　A. $4x - 30$

　　B. $-4x^2 - 13$

　　C. $4x^2 - x + 13$

　　D. $4x^2 + 3x - 17$

13. If $f(x) = x^2 + 2x - 4$, $g(x) = x^2 + 25$, and $h(x) = f(x)g(x)$, what is $h(x)$ in simplified form?

　　A. $x^4 + 2x^3 - 21x^2 + 50x - 100$

　　B. $x^4 - 2x^3 - 29x^2 - 50x + 100$

　　C. $x^4 + 2x^3 + 29x^2 + 50x + 100$

　　D. $x^4 + 2x^3 + 21x^2 + 50x - 100$

Use the following information to answer the next question.

The graph of $y = f(x)$ is shown.

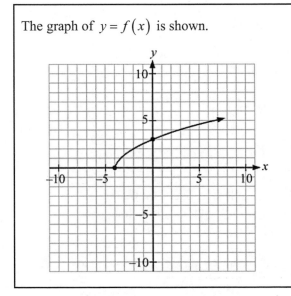

14. The domain of $y = f(x+2)$ is

　　A. $x \in R$

　　B. $x \geq -6$

　　C. $x \geq -2$

　　D. $-3 \leq x \leq 1$

Use the following information to answer the next question.

The partial graph of $y = f(x)$ is shown below.

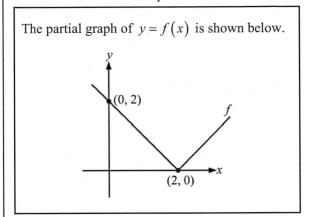

15. Which of the following partial graphs represents the transformed function

$$y = f\left(\frac{1}{2}x\right)?$$

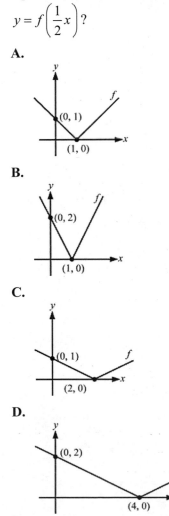

A.

B.

C.

D.

16. If the domain of $f(x) = \sqrt{x-a}$ is $x \geq a$, what is the domain of $g(x) = 2f(x-b)$?

  A. $x \geq (2a + 2b)$

  B. $x \geq (a + b)$

  C. $x \geq (a - b)$

  D. $x \geq b$

17. If $f(x) = 2x^2 - 3$, where $x \geq 0$, then a function g that will have a domain and range that are **both** different from those of function f is

  A. $g(x) = f(-x)$

  B. $g(x) = -f(x)$

  C. $g(x) = f^{-1}(x)$

  D. $g(x) = kf(x), k > 0$

18. Given $f(x) = -x^3 + 9$, the x-intercept for $y = -f(x)$, correct to the nearest **hundredth**, is _____.

19. The restriction on $f(x) = (x-5)^2$ that will make $f^{-1}(x)$ a function is

  A. $x \geq 5$

  B. $x \geq -5$

  C. $f(x) \geq 5$

  D. $f(x) \geq -5$

20. The expression $\dfrac{\log_4 17}{\log_4 21}$ can also be written as

  A. $\log_{21} \dfrac{17}{4}$ B. $\log_{17} 21$

  C. $\log_{21} 17$ D. $\log_{17} \dfrac{4}{21}$

21. If $\log_b a = 0.82$, then the value of $\log_b \left(\dfrac{b}{a} \right)$, correct to the nearest **hundredth**, is _____.

Use the following information to answer the next question.

A student used a graphing calculator to illustrate identities. The student assumed that $\log(x^2) = 2\log x$ because $\log_a(M^n) = n\log_a M$. The student graphed $y = \log(x^2)$ and obtained the graph shown below on the left. The student then graphed $y = 2\log x$ and obtained the graph shown below on the right.

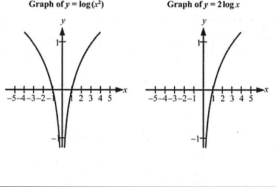

Graph of $y = \log(x^2)$ Graph of $y = 2\log x$

22. The student realized that the reason why the graphs are not identical is that

  A. $\log 0$ is not defined

  B. where $x < 0$, $\log(x^2)$ is defined and $\log x$ is not defined

  C. where $x < 0$, $\log x$ is defined and $\log(x^2)$ is not defined

  D. the range of $y = \log(x^2)$ is different from the range of $y = 2\log x$

Copyright Protected

23. The graph of $y = f(x) = b^x$, where $b > 1$, is translated such that the equation of the new graph is expressed as $y - 2 = f(x-1)$. The range of the new function is

A. $y > 2$

B. $y > 3$

C. $y > -1$

D. $y > -2$

24. What is the value of x in the equation

$$\left(27^{2x+1}\right)^3 = \left(\sqrt[4]{81^{4x+8}}\right)^3 ?$$

A. 1

B. 15

C. $\dfrac{2}{5}$

D. $\dfrac{5}{2}$

Use the following information to answer the next question.

A patient is injected with 10 mg of a radioactive isotope called technetium-99, which is commonly used in various medical diagnoses.

The graph shows the amount of isotope, m, in milligrams remaining in her body over the next 24 hours.

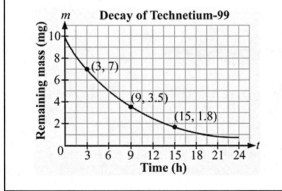

25. How much of the isotope has metabolized after 15 hours?

A. 1.8 mg

B. 8.2 mg

C. 9.2 mg

D. 11.8 mg

26. If $P(x) = x^3 - 7x - 3$ is divided by $(x+1)$, then $P(x)$ may be written as

A. $\left(x^2 - 8\right)(x+1) + 5$

B. $\left(x^2 - x - 6\right)(x+1) + 3$

C. $\left(x^3 - 7x - 3\right)(x+1) + 3$

D. $\left(x^3 - 7x - 3\right)(x+1) + 5$

Use the following information to answer the next question.

The partial graph of a fourth-degree polynomial function $y = P(x)$ is shown below. The graph has x-intercepts of -2 and 1, and a y-intercept of 8.

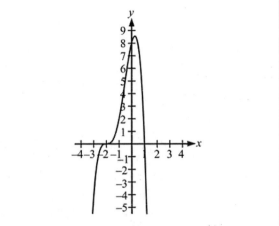

27. The equation of the polynomial function, P, is

A. $P(x) = (x-1)(x+2)^3$

B. $P(x) = (x+1)(x-2)^3$

C. $P(x) = -(x-1)(x+2)^3$

D. $P(x) = -(x+1)(x-2)^3$

Use the following information to answer the next question.

The graph of $y = \sqrt{x}$ is translated 8 units to the right. The equation of the resulting transformed graph is i , and its domain is ii .

28. Which of the following tables contains the information that completes the given statement?

A.
i	ii
$y = \sqrt{x-8}$	$x \geq 8$

B.
i	ii
$y = \sqrt{x-8}$	$x \geq -8$

C.
i	ii
$y = \sqrt{x+8}$	$x \geq 8$

D.
i	ii
$y = \sqrt{x+8}$	$x \geq -8$

29. Which of the following statements about $y = \dfrac{1}{4}\sqrt{x+4} + 4$ is **true**?

A. The domain is $x \leq 4$, and the range is $y \geq 4$.

B. The domain is $x \geq 4$, and the range is $y \leq 4$.

C. The domain is $x \leq -4$, and the range is $y \leq 4$.

D. The domain is $x \geq -4$, and the range is $y \geq 4$.

30. The graph of $f(x) = \dfrac{5x+2}{2x-1}$ is negative in which interval?

A. $x > \dfrac{1}{2}$

B. $-\dfrac{1}{2} < x < \dfrac{2}{5}$

C. $x < -\dfrac{2}{5}$

D. $-\dfrac{2}{5} < x < \dfrac{1}{2}$

31. At one time, a standard licence plate consisted of any 2 consonants followed by any 4 digits. Later, the standard licence plate was changed to consist of any 3 consonants followed by any 3 digits. Given that all 20 consonants can be used, and that any consonant and any digit can be repeated, how many **more** standard licence plates were available after this change?

A. 3 009 600

B. 4 000 000

C. 8 000 000

D. 12 000 000

32. If $10 = \dfrac{{}_nP_2}{2!}$, the value of n is _____.
(Record your answer as a **whole** number.)

33. The number of different arrangements of all the letters in the word **TOOTH** is

A. $5!$

B. $\dfrac{5!}{2!}$

C. $\dfrac{5!}{2!2!}$

D. $\dfrac{5!}{3!2!}$

Not for Reproduction

Use the following information to answer the next question.

The diagram below illustrates all the chords that can be drawn using the 5 points given on the circumference of a circle.

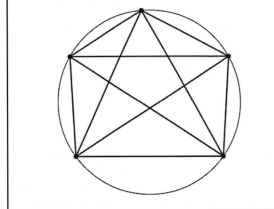

34. The number of chords drawn is the same as the number of

A. arrangements of 5 people in a straight line

B. arrangements of 5 people sitting at a round table

C. selections of 2 people from a group of 5 people

D. selections of 1 person for a certain job and 1 other person for a different job from a group of 5 people

Source: June 2000

Numerical Response

35. A committee of 2 teachers and 3 students is to be randomly chosen from a group of 5 teachers and 6 students. The total number of different committees possible is _____.
(Record your answer as a **whole** number.)

36. In the expansion of $(x + 2y)^8$, the numerical coefficient of the term containing $x^4 y^4$ is

A. 70

B. 140

C. 560

D. 1 120

37. What is the sum of the coefficients of the terms in the expansion of the binomial $(2x - 3)^4$ if the constant is considered to be a coefficient?

A. 0

B. 1

C. 16

D. 625

Copyright Protected

ANSWERS AND SOLUTIONS—PRACTICE TEST 2

1. B	9. C	17. C	25. B	33. C
2. B	10. C	18. 2.08	26. B	34. C
3. B	11. 10	19. A	27. C	35. 200
4. C	12. D	20. C	28. A	36. D
5. B	13. D	21. 0.18	29. D	37. B
6. D	14. B	22. B	30. D	
7. A	15. D	23. A	31. B	
8. A	16. B	24. D	32. 5	

1. B

The length of the terminal arm is the radius. Calculate the length of the terminal arm using the arc length formula, $a = r\theta$.

Let $a = 33.5$, $\theta = \dfrac{8\pi}{9}$, and solve for θ.

$$a = r\theta$$
$$33.5 = r\left(\dfrac{8\pi}{9}\right)$$
$$301.5 = 8\pi r$$
$$\dfrac{301.5}{8\pi} = r$$
$$12.0 \approx r$$

Therefore, the length of the terminal arm is 12.0 units.

2. B

The angle 480° terminates in quadrant II, and the reference angle is 60°. On the unit circle, $\cot\theta = \dfrac{x}{y}$, and the angle 480° corresponds to the point $\left(-\dfrac{1}{2}, \dfrac{\sqrt{3}}{2}\right)$.

Therefore, the exact value of cot480° is
$$\dfrac{-\dfrac{1}{2}}{\dfrac{\sqrt{3}}{2}} = -\dfrac{1}{\sqrt{3}}.$$

3. B

An angle that terminates in quadrant II with a reference angle of 45° corresponds to the point $\left(-\dfrac{\sqrt{2}}{2}, \dfrac{\sqrt{2}}{2}\right)$ on the unit circle. Therefore, the exact value of cosθ is $-\dfrac{\sqrt{2}}{2}$.

4. C

Step 1

Determine the exact value of $\tan^{-1}\left(\sqrt{3}\right)$.

On the unit circle, the terminal arm of the angle $\dfrac{\pi}{3}$ is the point in quadrant I with coordinates $\left(\dfrac{1}{2}, \dfrac{\sqrt{3}}{2}\right)$. Since the ratio $\dfrac{y}{x}$ is equal to the tangent, and $\dfrac{\left(\dfrac{\sqrt{3}}{2}\right)}{\left(\dfrac{1}{2}\right)} = \sqrt{3}$, the exact value of $\tan^{-1}\left(\sqrt{3}\right)$ is $\dfrac{\pi}{3}$.

Step 2

Determine the exact value of $\tan^{-1}\left(\dfrac{1}{\sqrt{3}}\right)$.

The terminal arm of the angle $\dfrac{\pi}{6}$ is the point in

quadrant I with coordinates $\left(\dfrac{\sqrt{3}}{2}, \dfrac{1}{2}\right)$, and

$\dfrac{\left(\dfrac{1}{2}\right)}{\left(\dfrac{\sqrt{3}}{2}\right)} = \dfrac{1}{\sqrt{3}}$. So, the value of $\tan^{-1}\left(\dfrac{1}{\sqrt{3}}\right)$ is $\dfrac{\pi}{6}$.

Step 3

Determine the exact value of

$\tan^{-1}\left(\sqrt{3}\right) - \tan^{-1}\left(\dfrac{1}{\sqrt{3}}\right)$.

$\tan^{-1}\left(\sqrt{3}\right) - \tan^{-1}\left(\dfrac{1}{\sqrt{3}}\right)$

$= \dfrac{\pi}{3} - \dfrac{\pi}{6}$

$= \dfrac{2\pi}{6} - \dfrac{\pi}{6}$

$= \dfrac{\pi}{6}$

5. B

In the general form of the cosine function,
$y = a\cos(b(x-c)) + d$, parameter c represents
the phase shift, and parameter d represents
vertical translation.

In the function $y = 3\cos\left(\theta + \dfrac{1}{3}\right) + 2$, the value

of c is $-\dfrac{1}{3}$, which means there is a phase shift

$\dfrac{1}{3}$ rad left.

The value of c is 2, which means the graph moves
2 units up.

6. D

The time taken to complete one revolution is the
period of the function.

Step 1
Determine the value of b.

Since the function $h(t) = 14\sin\left(\dfrac{\pi}{20}(t-10)\right) + 15$

is of the form $y = a\sin\left[b(x-c)\right] + d$, the value of

b is $\dfrac{\pi}{20}$.

Step 2
Determine the period of the given function using

the formula $\text{period} = \dfrac{2\pi}{|b|}$.

Substitute $\dfrac{\pi}{20}$ for b into the formula.

$\text{period} = \dfrac{2\pi}{|b|}$

$\text{period} = \dfrac{2\pi}{\left|\dfrac{\pi}{20}\right|}$.

$\text{period} = 40$

The time it takes the ferris wheel to complete one
rotation is 40 s.

7. A

The radius of the tire is equal to amplitude of the
graph. Since the maximum height is 28 m, and the

minimum height is 0, the radius is $\dfrac{|28-0|}{2} = 14\,\text{cm}$.

8. A

Step 1
Add $\cos\theta$ to both sides of the equation.
$\sin\theta - \cos\theta = 0$
$\quad\quad \sin\theta = \cos\theta$

Step 2
Divide both sides by $\cos\theta$.
$\quad \sin\theta = \cos\theta$
$\quad \dfrac{\sin\theta}{\cos\theta} = 1$

Step 3
Apply the reciprocal identity.

$$\frac{\sin\theta}{\cos\theta}=1$$
$$\tan\theta=1$$

Step 4
Solve the equation $\tan\theta=1$.

According to the unit circle, the values θ in the equation $\tan\theta=1$, where $0\le\theta\le2\pi$, are $\dfrac{\pi}{4}$ and $\dfrac{5\pi}{4}$.

9. **C**

Step 1
Isolate $\tan\theta$ in the equation.
$$\tan\theta-1=0$$
$$\tan\theta=1$$

Step 2
Determine the values of θ in the equation within the domain $0\le\theta<360°$.

Using unit circle, the values of θ in the equation $\tan\theta=1$ are 45° and 225°.

Step 3
Determine the general solution.

Since $45°+180°=225°$, the general solution is $\theta=(45+180n)°$, where $n\in I$.

Therefore, the value of $a+b$ is $45+180=225$.

10. **C**

Within the domain of $0\le x\le\pi$, $\tan x$ has a vertical asymptote located at $x=\dfrac{\pi}{2}$.

The function $y=\tan x$ has a period of π rad. Therefore, the vertical asymptotes are given by $x=\dfrac{\pi}{2}+\pi n$, where $n\in I$.

11. 10

Step 1
Factor out x from each term on the left side of the equation.

$$x\cos^2\left(\frac{\pi}{8}\right)-x\sin^2\left(\frac{\pi}{8}\right)=5\sqrt{2}$$
$$x\left(\cos^2\left(\frac{\pi}{8}\right)-\sin^2\left(\frac{\pi}{8}\right)\right)=5\sqrt{2}$$

Step 2
Determine an equivalent expression for $\cos^2\left(\dfrac{\pi}{8}\right)-\sin^2\left(\dfrac{\pi}{8}\right)$.

Since $\cos^2\left(\dfrac{\pi}{8}\right)-\sin^2\left(\dfrac{\pi}{8}\right)$ is of the form $\cos^2 A-\sin^2 A$, the double-angle identity, $\cos^2 A-\sin^2 A=\cos(2A)$, can be applied.

Substitute $\dfrac{\pi}{8}$ for A in the double-angle identity.

$$\cos^2 A-\sin^2 A=\cos(2A)$$
$$\cos^2\left(\frac{\pi}{8}\right)-\sin^2\left(\frac{\pi}{8}\right)=\cos\left(2\left(\frac{\pi}{8}\right)\right)$$
$$\cos^2\left(\frac{\pi}{8}\right)-\sin^2\left(\frac{\pi}{8}\right)=\cos\left(\frac{\pi}{4}\right)$$

Step 3
Substitute $\cos\left(\dfrac{\pi}{4}\right)$ for $\cos^2\left(\dfrac{\pi}{8}\right)-\sin^2\left(\dfrac{\pi}{8}\right)$ in the equation $x\left(\cos^2\left(\dfrac{\pi}{8}\right)-\sin^2\left(\dfrac{\pi}{8}\right)\right)=5\sqrt{2}$.

$$x\left(\cos^2\left(\frac{\pi}{8}\right)-\sin^2\left(\frac{\pi}{8}\right)\right)=5\sqrt{2}$$
$$x\cos\left(\frac{\pi}{4}\right)=5\sqrt{2}$$

Step 4
Solve for x.

$$x\cos\left(\frac{\pi}{4}\right)=5\sqrt{2}$$
$$x\left(\frac{\sqrt{2}}{2}\right)=5\sqrt{2}$$
$$x\left(\sqrt{2}\right)=10\sqrt{2}$$
$$x=10$$

Copyright Protected

12. D

Step 1

Substitute $2x-15$ for $f(x)$ and $4x^2+x-2$ for $g(x)$.

$$f(x)+g(x)=(2x-15)+(4x^2+x-2)$$

Step 2

Combine like terms, and simplify.

$$\begin{aligned}f(x)+g(x)&=(2x-15)+(4x^2+x-2)\\&=4x^2+2x+x-15-2\\&=4x^2+3x-17\end{aligned}$$

13. D

Step 1

Substitute x^2+2x-4 for $f(x)$ and x^2+25 for $g(x)$ into the equation $h(x)=f(x)g(x)$.

$$\begin{aligned}h(x)&=f(x)g(x)\\h(x)&=(x^2+2x-4)(x^2+25)\end{aligned}$$

Step 2

Expand using the distributive property, and simplify by combining like terms.

$$\begin{aligned}h(x)&=(x^2+2x-4)(x^2+25)\\h(x)&=x^4+2x^3-4x^2+25x^2+50x-100\\h(x)&=x^4+2x^3+21x^2+50x-100\end{aligned}$$

14. B

Step 1

Determine how to obtain the graph of $y=f(x+2)$ from the graph of $y=f(x)$.

The equation $y=f(x+2)$ is in the form $y=f(x-h)$, where $h=-2$. Therefore, the graph of $y=f(x+2)$ is formed from $y=f(x)$ by translating it 2 units to the left.

Step 2

Determine the domain of $y=f(x+2)$.

The domain of the graph of $y=f(x)$ is $x\ge-4$. The graph of $y=f(x+2)$ is translated 2 units to the left, so the domain of $y=f(x+2)$ will also shift 2 points to the left.

The domain of $y=f(x+2)$ is $x\ge(-4-2)$, or $x\ge-6$.

15. D

Step 1

Determine how to obtain the graph of $y=f\left(\dfrac{1}{2}x\right)$ from the graph of $y=f(x)$.

The equation $y=f\left(\dfrac{1}{2}x\right)$ is in the form $y=f(bx)$, where $b=\dfrac{1}{2}$. Therefore, the graph of $y=f\left(\dfrac{1}{2}x\right)$ is formed from $y=f(x)$ by a horizontal stretch about the y-axis by a factor of 2.

Step 2

Identify points on the graph of $y=f(x)$.

Points on the graph of $y=f(x)$ are $(0, 2)$ and $(2, 0)$.

Step 3

Transform points on the graph of $y=f(x)$ to obtain points on the graph of $y=f\left(\dfrac{1}{2}x\right)$.

Multiply the x-coordinates of $y=f(x)$ by 2.
$(0, 2) \rightarrow (2 \times 0, 2) \rightarrow (0, 2)$
$(2, 0) \rightarrow (2 \times 2, 0) \rightarrow (4, 0)$

The graph of $y=f\left(\dfrac{1}{2}x\right)$ must contain the points $(0, 2)$ and $(4, 0)$.

16. B

Step 1

Determine the necessary transformations to produce the graph of $g(x)$ from the graph of $f(x)$.

The equation $g(x)=2f(x-b)$ can be rewritten as

$$\frac{1}{2}g(x)=f(x-b).$$

The graph of $g(x)$ is obtained by vertically stretching the graph of $f(x)$ about the x-axis by a factor of 2 (since $g(x)$ is replaced with $\dfrac{1}{2}g(x)$) and then translating the resulting graph b units to the right (since x is replaced with $x-b$).

Step 2

State the domain of $g(x)$.

A vertical stretch about the x-axis will not affect the domain of the transformed graph.

Since the domain of $f(x) = \sqrt{x-a}$ is $x \geq a$ and the graph of $f(x)$ is translated b units to the right, the domain of $g(x)$ is $x \geq (a + b)$.

17. C

The graph of $y = f(x), x \geq 0$ is a half parabola opening upward with a vertex at $(0, -3)$.
The domain of $f(x)$ is $x \geq 0$, and the range is $y \geq -3$.

The function $g(x) = f^{-1}(x)$ is the inverse function of $y = f(x)$. The graph of $g(x)$ is a parabola opening to the right with a vertex at $(-3, 0)$. The domain of $g(x) = f^{-1}(x)$ is $x \geq -3$, and the range is $y \geq 0$. Thus, both the domain and the range have changed.

The transformation $g(x) = f(-x)$ will produce the same graph as $f(x)$, so neither the domain nor the range are changed.

The transformation $g(x) = -f(x)$ creates half a parabola opening downward with a vertex at $(0, 3)$. The domain is still $x \geq 0$.

The transformation $g(x) = kf(x), k > 0$, produces a vertical stretch of $f(x)$. The domain is still $x \geq 0$.

18. 2.08

Substitute $f(x) = -x^3 + 9$ into $y = -f(x)$, and simplify.
$$y = f(x)$$
$$y = -\left(-x^3 + 9\right)$$
$$y = x^3 - 9$$

Substitute $y = 0$, and solve for x.
$$y = x^3 - 9$$
$$0 = x^3 - 9$$
$$x^3 = 9$$
$$x = \sqrt[3]{9}$$
$$x \approx 2.08$$

19. A

Step 1
Replace $f(x)$ with y.
$$f(x) = (x-5)^2$$
$$y = (x-5)^2$$

Step 2
Interchange x and y, and solve for y.
$$y = (x-5)^2$$
$$x = (y-5)^2$$
$$\pm\sqrt{x} = y - 5$$
$$y = 5 \pm \sqrt{x}$$

Step 3
Determine the restriction on x in $f(x)$.

This inverse is not a function unless restricted to $y \geq 5$ or $y \leq 5$, which is equivalent to a restriction of $x \geq 5$ or $x \leq 5$ in the original function.

20. C

Apply the base conversion identity,
$$\log_b a = \frac{\log_c a}{\log_c b}.$$

$$\frac{\log_4 17}{\log_4 21} = \log_{21} 17$$

21. 0.18

Step 1
Apply the quotient rule of logarithms to the equation $\log_b\left(\dfrac{b}{a}\right)$.

$$\log_b\left(\frac{b}{a}\right)$$
$$= \log_b b - \log_b a$$
$$= 1 - \log_b a$$

Step 2
Substitute $\log_b a = 0.82$ into the equation $1 - \log_b a$.
$$1 - \log_b a$$
$$= 1 - 0.82$$
$$= 0.18$$

Copyright Protected

Not for Reproduction

22. B

By definition, $\log_a x$ is defined only when $x > 0$.

So, $y = 2\log x$ has a domain of $x > 0$.

But, $y = \log\left(x^2\right)$ has a domain of $x \neq 0$, since

$x^2 > 0$ for all $x > 0$ and all $x < 0$, but not for $x = 0$.

23. A

The graph is shifted to the right when x is replaced by $(x-1)$, and it is shifted up when y is replaced by $y-2$.

$$y - 2 = f(x-1)$$
$$y = f(x-1) + 2$$

The range of $y = f(x) = b^x$, where $b > 1$,

is $y > 0$. If the graph is shifted up 2 units, the range becomes $y > 2$.

24. D

Step 1

Rewrite $\left(\sqrt[4]{81^{4x+8}}\right)^3$ using the rational exponent

property of radicals.

$$\left(27^{2x+1}\right)^3 = \left(\sqrt[4]{81^{4x+8}}\right)^3$$
$$\left(27^{2x+1}\right)^3 = \left(81^{4x+8}\right)^{\frac{3}{4}}$$

Step 2

Apply the power of a power rule for exponents.

$$\left(27^{2x+1}\right)^3 = \left(81^{4x+8}\right)^{\frac{3}{4}}$$
$$27^{(3)(2x+1)} = 81^{\left(\frac{3}{4}\right)(4x+8)}$$
$$27^{6x+3} = 81^{3x+6}$$

Step 3

Express 27 and 81 with a base of 3.

$$27^{6x+3} = 81^{3x+6}$$
$$\left(3^3\right)^{6x+3} = \left(3^4\right)^{3x+6}$$

Step 4

Apply the power of a power rule for exponents.

$$\left(3^3\right)^{6x+3} = \left(3^4\right)^{3x+6}$$
$$3^{(3)(6x+3)} = 3^{(4)(3x+6)}$$
$$3^{18x+9} = 3^{12x+24}$$

Step 5

Since the bases are equal, equate the exponents, and solve for x.

$$18x + 9 = 12x + 24$$
$$6x = 15$$
$$x = \frac{15}{6}$$
$$x = \frac{5}{2}$$

25. B

According to the graph, after 15 hours, there is approximately 1.8 mg of isotope left in the patient's body. Therefore, the amount of isotope that has been metabolized after 15 hours is
$10 - 1.8 = 8.2$ mg.

26. B

Use long division or synthetic division to divide $x^3 - 7x - 3$ by $x + 1$.

Step 1
Rewrite $P(x)$ to include all powers of x.
$$P(x) = x^3 - 7x - 3$$
$$P(x) = x^3 + 0x^2 - 7x - 3$$

Step 2
Divide.

$$
\begin{array}{r}
x^2 - x - 6 \\
x+1\overline{\smash{)}x^3 + 0x^2 - 7x - 3} \\
\underline{x^3 + x^2} \\
-x^2 - 7x \\
\underline{-x^2 - x} \\
-6x - 3 \\
\underline{-6x - 6} \\
3
\end{array}
$$

Step 3
Rewrite the equation in the form
$P(x) = Q(x)d(x) + R$, where $Q(x)$ is the quotient, $d(x)$ is the divisor, and R is the remainder.
$$P(x) = Q(x)d(x) + R$$
$$P(x) = \left(x^2 - x - 6\right)(x+1) + 3$$

27. C

Step 1
Determine the multiplicity of each root.

The graph crosses and is tangent to the x-axis at $x = -2$. Therefore, the multiplicity of this root is an odd number greater than 1. Since $P(x)$ has a degree of 4, the multiplicity of this root must be 3.

The graph passes straight through the x-axis at $x + 1$. Therefore, the multiplicity of this root is 1.

Step 2
Determine the orientation of the graph of $y = P(x)$.

The end behaviour of the graph is away from the x-axis toward $-\infty$ in both quadrants III and IV. Therefore, the leading coefficient of the equation of $P(x)$ will be negative.

Step 3
Write the equation of the function $P(x)$.

The graph of $y = P(x)$ has a root of multiplicity 1 at $x = 1$. Therefore, $(x - 1)$ is a factor of the function.

The graph also has a root of multiplicity 3 at $x = -2$, so $(x + 2)^3$ will be part of the factored form of $P(x)$.

The equation must also have a negative coefficient.

Hence, the factored form of the equation is $P(x) = -(x - 1)(x + 2)^3$.

28. A

Step 1
Apply the horizontal translation.

Since the graph of $y = \sqrt{x}$ is translated 8 units to the right, replace x in $y = \sqrt{x}$ with $x - 8$.
$y = \sqrt{x - 8}$

Step 2
Determine the domain of $y = \sqrt{x - 8}$.

The domain of the graph of $y = \sqrt{x}$ is $x \geq 0$.

The graph of $y = \sqrt{x - 8}$ is translated 8 units to the right, so the domain of $y = \sqrt{x - 8}$ is also 8 units to the right.

The domain of $y = \sqrt{x - 8}$ is $x \geq (0 + 8)$, or $x \geq 8$.

Therefore, the equation of the resulting transformation is $y = \sqrt{x - 8}$, and its domain is $x \geq 8$.

29. D

The function $y = \sqrt{x}$ has a domain of $x \geq 0$ and a range of $y \geq 0$. The function $y = a\sqrt{x - c} + d$ is a transformation of the basic square root function $y = \sqrt{x}$, where the parameters a, c, and d represent specific transformations.

Step 1
Determine the transformation caused by parameter a.

A change in a causes a vertical stretch by a factor of a and reflects the graph in the x-axis if a is negative.

Since $a = \frac{1}{4}$, the graph of the function is stretched by a factor of $\frac{1}{4}$. The value is positive, so it has no effect on the domain or range of the function.

Step 2
Determine the transformation caused by parameter c.

A change in c causes a horizontal translation c units to the right when c is positive and c units to the left when c is negative.

Since $c = -4$, the graph of the function is translated 4 units to the left. The domain changes from $x \geq 0$ to $x \geq -4$.

Step 3
Determine the transformation caused by parameter d.

A change in d causes a vertical translation d units up when d is positive and d units down when d is negative.

Since $d = 4$, the graph of the function is translated 4 units up. The range changes from $y \geq 0$ to $y \geq 4$.

The domain of the function is $x \geq -4$, and the range is $y \geq 4$.

Not for Reproduction

30. D

Step 1

Determine the vertical asymptote.

Since the function $f(x) = \dfrac{5x+2}{2x-1}$ is in the form

$f(x) = \dfrac{ax+c}{mx+b}$, the vertical asymptote occurs when $mx + b = 0$.

Substitute 2 for m and -1 for b in the equation $mx + b = 0$, and solve for x.

$2x - 1 = 0$

$2x = 1$

$x = \dfrac{1}{2}$

The vertical asymptote occurs at $x = \dfrac{1}{2}$.

Step 2

Determine the x-intercept.

Substitute 0 for $f(x)$, and solve for x.

$0 = \dfrac{5x+2}{2x-1}$

$0 = 5x + 2$

$-2 = 5x$

$-\dfrac{2}{5} = x$

The x-intercept is at $\left(-\dfrac{2}{5}, 0\right)$.

Step 3

Determine the intervals where the graph is positive or negative.

The function is positive when $\dfrac{5x+2}{2x-1} > 0$ and

negative when $\dfrac{5x+2}{2x-1} < 0$.

Build a table to determine when each component of

the expression $\dfrac{5x+2}{2x-1}$ is positive or negative, then

use the vertical asymptote and the x-intercept as intervals.

Interval	$x < -\dfrac{2}{5}$	$-\dfrac{2}{5} < x < \dfrac{1}{2}$	$x > \dfrac{1}{2}$
$5x+2$	$-$	$+$	$+$
$2x-1$	$-$	$-$	$+$
$\dfrac{5x+2}{2x-1}$	$+$	$-$	$+$

The graph of $f(x) = \dfrac{5x+2}{2x-1}$ is negative in the

interval $-\dfrac{2}{5} < x < \dfrac{1}{2}$ and positive in the intervals

$x < -\dfrac{2}{5}$ and $x > \dfrac{1}{2}$.

31. B

Step 1

Determine the number of possible old licence plates.

An old licence plate had 2 consonants followed by 4 digits. Since there are 20 consonants and 10 digits to pick from, the number of possible plates is given by
$20 \times 20 \times 10 \times 10 \times 10 \times 10 = 4\ 000\ 000$.

Step 2

Determine the number of possible new licence plates.

A new licence plate has 2 consonants followed by 3 digits. Therefore, the number of possible plates is $20 \times 20 \times 20 \times 10 \times 10 \times 10 = 8\ 000\ 000$.

Step 3

Determine how many more standard plates were available after the change.

The increase is $8\ 000\ 000 - 4\ 000\ 000 = 4\ 000\ 000$.

Copyright Protected

32. 5

Step 1

Let $_nP_2 = \dfrac{n!}{(n-2)!}$.

$$10 = \frac{_nP_2}{2!}$$

$$10 = \frac{\left(\dfrac{n!}{(n-2)!}\right)}{2!}$$

$$20 = \frac{n!}{(n-2)!}$$

Step 2

Expand the factorials, and divide out common terms.

$$20 = \frac{n!}{(n-2)!}$$

$$20 = \frac{n(n-1)(n-2)!}{(n-2)!}$$

$$20 = n(n-1)$$

Step 3

Solve for n.

$$20 = n(n-1)$$
$$20 = n^2 - n$$
$$0 = n^2 - n - 20$$
$$0 = (n-5)(n+4)$$
$$n = 5 \text{ or } n = -4$$

Since n cannot be negative, $n = 5$.

33. C

The number of different arrangements of the letters in the word TOOTH is a permutation problem with two sets of identical elements. Of the 5 letters in the word, there are 2 Ts and 2 Os. Therefore, the total number of arrangements is given by $\dfrac{5!}{2!\,2!}$.

34. C

Step 1
Determine the total number of chords drawn.

The number of chords drawn is a combination problem. Therefore, the chords that join 2 of 5 points on a circle is $_5C_2 = 10$.

Step 2
Determine which alternative is equal to the number of chords drawn on the circle.

Selecting 2 people from a group of 5 is a combination problem. The number of selections of 2 people from a group of 5 people is $_5C_2 = 10$, which is the same number as the chords drawn.

The other alternatives are permutation problems, not combination problems.

35. 200

Step 1
Determine the number of possible choices of teachers.

The number of possible choices for teachers is $_5C_2 = 10$.

Step 2
Determine the number of possible choices of students.

The number of possible choices for students is $_6C_3 = 20$.

Step 3
Determine the total number of possible committees.

Applying the fundamental counting principle, the total number of possible committees is $10 \times 20 = 200$.

36. D

Step 1

Determine the general term of the expansion of $(x+2y)^8$.

In the formula $t_{k+1} = {}_nC_k x^{n-k} y^k$, replace y with $2y$, and let $n = 8$.

$$t_{k+1} = {}_nC_k x^{n-k} y^k$$
$$t_{k+1} = {}_8C_k x^{8-k} (2y)^k$$

Step 2

Determine the value of k.

Since the coefficient of the term containing $x^4 y^4$ is required, then $k = 4$.

Step 3

In the general term formula, let $k = 4$, and simplify.

$$t_{k+1} = {}_8C_k x^{8-k} (2y)^k$$
$$t_{4+1} = {}_8C_4 x^{8-4} (2y)^4$$
$$t_5 = (70) x^4 (16y^4)$$
$$t_5 = 1120 x^4 y^4$$

The numerical coefficient of the term containing $x^4 y^4$ is 1 120.

37. B

Step 1

Apply the binomial theorem, and write the expansion for $(x+y)^4$.

$$(x+y)^4$$
$$= {}_4C_0 x^4 + {}_4C_1 x^3 y + {}_4C_2 x^2 y^2 + {}_4C_3 xy^3 + {}_4C_4 y^4$$

Step 2

In the expansion of $(x+y)^4$, replace x with $2x$ and y with -3, and simplify.

$${}_4C_0 x^4 + {}_4C_1 x^3 y + {}_4C_2 x^2 y^2 + {}_4C_3 xy^3 + {}_4C_4 y^4$$
$$= {}_4C_0 (2x)^4 + {}_4C_1 (2x)^3 (-3) + {}_4C_2 (2x)^2 (-3)^2$$
$$\quad + {}_4C_3 (2x)(-3)^3 + {}_4C_4 (-3)^4$$
$$= (1)(16x^4) + (4)(8x^3)(-3) + (6)(4x^2)(9)$$
$$\quad + (4)(2x)(-27) + (1)(81)$$
$$= 16x^4 - 96x^3 + 216x^2 - 216x + 81$$

Step 3

Determine the sum of the coefficients.
$$16 + (-96) + 216 + (-216) + 81 = 1$$

Copyright Protected

NOTES

0211.00
0212.00
0213.00
0214.00
0215.00
0216.00
0217.00
0218.00
0219.00
0220.00
0221.00
0222.00
0223.00
0224.00

Copyright Protected

NOTES

Not for Reproduction

FORMULAS

RELATIONS AND FUNCTIONS

For $0 = ax^2 + bx + c$, $x = \dfrac{-b \pm \sqrt{b^2 - 4ac}}{2a}$.

Graphing Calculator Window Format

$x : [x_{\min}, x_{\max}, x_{\text{scl}}]$

$y : [y_{\min}, y_{\max}, y_{\text{scl}}]$

Laws of Logarithms

$\log_b (M \times N) = \log_b M + \log_b N$

$\log_b \left(\dfrac{M}{N} \right) = \log_b M - \log_b N$

$\log_b (M^n) = n \log_b M$

$\log_b c = \dfrac{\log_a c}{\log_a b}$

Growth/Decay Formula

$y = ab^{\frac{t}{p}}$

General Function

$y = af\left[b(x - h) \right] + k$

PERMUTATIONS, COMBINATIONS, AND THE BINOMIAL THEOREM

$n! = n(n-1)(n-2)...3 \times 2 \times 1$, where $n \in N$ and $0! = 1$

$_nP_r = \dfrac{n!}{(n-r)!}$

$_nC_r = \dfrac{n!}{(n-r)!\,r!}$

$_nC_r = \dbinom{n}{r}$

In the expansion of $(x + y)^n$, the general term is

$t_{k+1} = {_nC_k}\, x^{n-k} y^k$

TRIGONOMETRY

$\theta = \dfrac{a}{r}$

$\tan \theta = \dfrac{\sin \theta}{\cos \theta}$

$\cot \theta = \dfrac{\cos \theta}{\sin \theta}$

$\csc \theta = \dfrac{1}{\sin \theta}$

$\sec \theta = \dfrac{1}{\cos \theta}$

$\cot \theta = \dfrac{1}{\tan \theta}$

$\sin^2 \theta + \cos^2 \theta = 1$

$1 + \tan^2 \theta = \sec^2 \theta$

$1 + \cot^2 \theta = \csc^2 \theta$

$\sin(A + B) = \sin A \cos B + \cos A \sin B$

$\sin(A - B) = \sin A \cos B - \cos A \sin B$

$\cos(A + B) = \cos A \cos B - \sin A \sin B$

$\cos(A - B) = \cos A \cos B + \sin A \sin B$

$\tan(A + B) = \dfrac{\tan A + \tan B}{1 - \tan A \tan B}$

$\tan(A - B) = \dfrac{\tan A - \tan B}{1 + \tan A \tan B}$

$\sin(2A) = 2 \sin A \cos A$

$\cos(2A) = \cos^2 A - \sin^2 A$

$\cos(2A) = 2 \cos^2 A - 1$

$\cos(2A) = 1 - 2 \sin^2 A$

$\tan(2A) = \dfrac{2 \tan A}{1 - \tan^2 A}$

$y = a \sin\left[b(x - c) \right] + d$

$y = a \cos\left[b(x - c) \right] + d$

Copyright Protected

CREDITS

Every effort has been made to provide proper acknowledgement of the original source and to comply with copyright law. However, some attempts to establish original copyright ownership may have been unsuccessful. If copyright ownership can be identified, please notify Castle Rock Research Corp so that appropriate corrective action can be taken.

Some images in this document are from www.clipart.com, © 2012 Clipart.com, a division of Getty Images.

BOOK ORDERING INFORMATION

SENIOR HIGH SCHOOL TITLES

Castle Rock Research offers the following resources to support Alberta students. You can order any of these materials online at:

www.castlerockresearch.com/store

SOLARO.com - Study Online		The KEY		SNAP	Prob Solved	Class Notes
$29.95 ea.*		**$29.95 ea.***		**$29.95 ea.***	**$19.95 ea.***	**$19.95 ea.***
Biology 30	Mathematics 30-1	Biology 30	Mathematics 30-1	Biology 20	Biology 20	Biology 20
Biology 20	Mathematics 30-2	Biology 20	Mathematics 30-2	Chemistry 30	Chemistry 30	Chemistry 30
Chemistry 30	Mathematics 30-3	Chemistry 30	Mathematics 20-1	Chemistry 20	Chemistry 20	Chemistry 20
Chemistry 20	Mathematics 20-1	Chemistry 20	Mathematics 10 C	Mathematics 30-1	Mathematics 30-1	Mathematics 30-1
Physics 30	Mathematics 20-2	English 30-1	Social Studies 30-1	Mathematics 30-2	Mathematics 30-2	Mathematics 30-2
Physics 20	Mathematics 20-3	English 30-2	Social Studies 30-2	Mathematics 31	Mathematics 31	Mathematics 31
Science 30	Mathematics 20-4	English 20-1	Social Studies 20-1	Mathematics 20-1	Mathematics 20-1	Mathematics 20-1
Science 20	Mathematics 10 C	English 10-1	Social Studies 10-1	Mathematics 10 C	Mathematics 10 C	Mathematics 10 C
Science 10	Mathematics 10-3	Physics 30		Physics 30	Physics 30	Physics 30
English 30-1	Mathematics 10-4	Physics 20		Physics 20	Physics 20	Physics 20
English 30-2	Social Studies 30-1	Science 10		Science 10	Science 10	Science 10
English 20-1	Social Studies 30-2					
English 20-2	Social Studies 20-1					
English 10-1	Social Studies 10-1					
English 10-2						

Prices do not include taxes or shipping.

Study online using **SOLARO,** with access to multiple courses available by either a monthly or an annual subscription.

The KEY Study Guide is specifically designed to assist students in preparing for unit tests, final exams, and provincial examinations.

The **Student Notes and Problems (SNAP) Workbook** contains complete explanations of curriculum concepts, examples, and exercise questions.

The **Problem Solved** contains exercise questions and complete solutions.

The **Class Notes** contains complete explanations of curriculum concepts.

If you would like to order Castle Rock resources for your school, please visit our school ordering page:

www.castlerockresearch.com/school-orders/

solaro